The Ultimate CST Study Guide

For Surgical Technologists

Monique De Ville B.S., CST

THE ULTIMATE CST STUDY GUIDE FOR SURGICAL TECHNOLOGISTS

ISBN:13: 978-0-9853765-5-0
ISBN:10: 0985376554

The instrument images in this book were provided courtesy of Miltex. Permission granted by Integra Miltex, a business of Integra Life Sciences Corporation, Plainsboro, New Jersey, USA.

DISCLAIMER

Care has been taken to confirm the accuracy of the information present and to describe generally accepted practices. However, the author, editor, and publisher are not responsible for errors or omissions or for any consequences from application of the information in this book and make no warranty, expressed or implied with respect to the currency, completeness, or accuracy of the contents of the publication. Application of this information in a particular situation remains the professional responsibility of the practitioner, the clinical treatments described and recommended may not be considered absolute and universal recommendations.

The author, editor, and publisher have exerted every effort to ensure that drug selection and dosage set forth in this text are in accordance with the current recommendations and practice at the time of publication. However, in view of the ongoing research, changes in government regulations, and the constant flow of information relating to drug therapy and drug reactions, the reader is urged to check the package insert for each drug for any change in indications and dosage and for added warnings and precautions. This is particularly important when the recommended agent is a new or infrequently employed drug.

Some drugs and medical devices presented in this publication have Food and Drug Administration (FDA) clearance for limited use in restricted research settings. It is the responsibility of the health care provider to ascertain the FDA status of each drug or device planned for use in their clinical practice.

I dedicate this book to my parents,
Colonel E. J. De Ville and Della J. De Ville.
Without their guidance and love over my lifetime,
I would have never learned the discipline it took
to complete the endeavor of this book.

ACKNOWLEDGEMENTS

Dr. Kenneth S. Meacham,
thank you for suggesting I write this book
and supporting me every step of the way, from the
first two questions all the way to the last night of writing.

CONTENTS

SECTION 1 - BASIC SCIENCE (395 Questions)

Anatomy & Physiology (182 Questions) 9
Anatomy & Physiology Answers 31

Microbiology (29 Questions) 45
Microbiology Answers 50

Pharmacology (73 Questions) 53
Pharmacology Answers 63

Pathophysiology (111 Questions) 69
Phathophysiology Answers 83

SECTION 2 - PERIOPERATIVE CARE (557 Questions)

Preoperative Preparation & Management (112 Questions) 95
Aseptic Technique / Preference card / Time Out
Instruments and supplies
Operating room set up
Surgical scrub / Gown / Glove
Patient transportation / Positioning / Preparation
Draping
Preoperative Preperation & Management Answers 110

Intraoperative Procedures & Management (413 Questions) 121
Supplies
Diagnostics
Procedures
Instruments
Intraoperative Procedures & Management Answers 180

Postoperative Procedures & Management (32 Questions) 213
Patient care
Operating room clean terminal cleaning
Postoperative Procedures & Management Answers 218

SECTION 3 - ADDITIONAL RESPONSIBILITIES & DUTIES (52 Questions)

Sterilization & Maintenance (26 Questions) 225
Sterilization & Maintenance Answers 229
Administrative & Personnel (26 Questions) 233
Administrative & Personnel Answers 238

REFERENCES 242

SECTION 1

BASIC SCIENCE

Anatomy & Physiology

Microbiology

Pharmacology

Pathophysiology

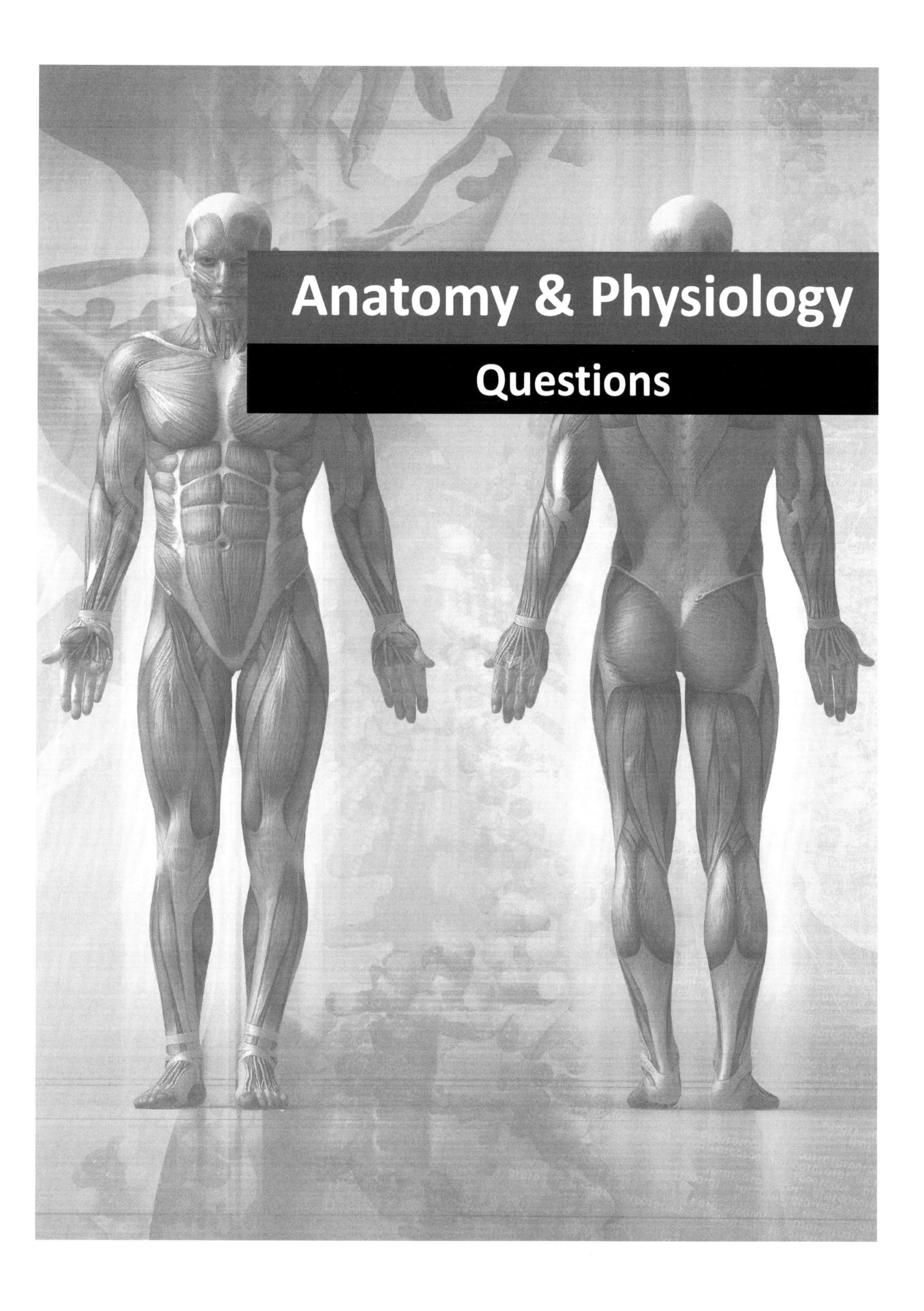
Anatomy & Physiology
Questions

1. Which of the following defines the term 'anatomical position'?
A. Standing erect, arms at sides, toes and palms forward, and facing forward
B. Facing forward palms at sides
C. Standing erect, toes forward, palms at sides and facing forward
D. None of the above

2. Which system is made of the heart and the blood vessels?
A. Nervous system
B. Skeletal system
C. Endocrine system
D. Circulatory system

3. Which system regulates water balance, metabolism, reproduction, and growth in the body?
A. Lymphatic system
B. Endocrine system
C. Muscular system
D. Circulatory system

4. Which of the following is the correct listing of the components of the nervous system?
A. Brain, nerves, and sense organs
B. Brain, spinal cord, sense organs
C. Brain, spinal cord, nerves, and sense organs
D. Brain and spinal cord

5. What is the basic unit of life?
A. Tissues
B. Cell
C. Organelles
D. Organs

6. What organ would be found in the right upper quadrant of the abdomen?
A Gallbladder
B. Spleen
C. Appendix
D. Heart

7. The appendix is located in which abdominal quadrant?
A. Right upper quadrant
B. Left lower quadrant
C. Right lower quadrant
D. Left upper quadrant

8. Which cavities are located in the abdominopelvic cavity?
A. Abdominal cavity and Pelvic cavity
B. Thoracic cavity and the abdominal cavity
C. Pelvic cavity and the spinal cavity
D. Ventral cavity and the thoracic cavity

9. What organ would be located in the mediastinal cavity?
A. Liver
B. Spleen
C. Gallbladder
D. Thymus gland

10. Which cavity does the cranial and spinal cavities make up?
A. Thoracic cavity
B. Ventral cavity
C. Dorsal cavity
D. Pelvic cavity

11. Which tissue cushions and stores fat?
A. Areolar tissue
B. Adipose tissue
C. Reticular tissue
D. Elastic cartilage

12. Which of the following is the structure that surrounds bone and is the attachment surface for muscle?
A. Periosteum
B. Medullary cavity
C. Epiphyseal disc
D. Epiphysis

13. What part of the bone is where longitudinal bone growth takes place?
A. Epiphyseal disc
B. Periosteum
C. Medullary cavity
D. Shaft

14. What makes up the sternum?
A. Body, sternum, xiphoid
B. Manubrium, sternum, coccyx
C. Manubrium, body, xiphoid process
D. Manubrium, body, coccyx

15. Which of the following make up the axial anatomy?
A. Cranium, mandible, thoracic vertebra, sacrum, rib cage
B. Cranium, mandible, vertebral column, sacrum, coccyx, rib cage, costal cartilage, hyoid, sternum
C. Cranium, lumbar vertebra, sacrum, coccyx, rib cage, costal cartilage, sternum
D. Cranium, rib cage, vertebral column, pelvis, rib cage, sacrum

16. Which part of the nervous system works unconsciously and automatically?
A. Autonomic nervous system
B. Parasympathetic nervous system
C. Sympathetic nervous system
D. Nervous System

17. Which of the following is **NOT** part of the alimentary canal?
A.Gallbladder
B. Esophagus
C. Stomach
D. Colon

18. Which of the following is **NOT** part of the biliary tract?
A. Gallbladder
B. Cystic duct
C. Common hepatic duct
D. Small intestine

19. Which of the following is a list of the sternum from superior to inferior?
A. Manubrium, xiphoid process, body
B. Xiphoid process, body, manubrium
C. Xiphoid process, manubrium, body
D. Body, xiphoid process, manubrium
E. Manubrium, body, xiphoid process

20. How many lobes do the lungs have?
A. 5 lobes
B. 2 lobes
C. 3 lobes
D. 4 lobes

21. What does the parietal pleura line?
A. The surface of the lungs
B. Inner surface of ribs, the superior surface of the diaphragm, and the pericardium of the heart
C. The space between the parietal pleura and the visceral pleura
D. The abdominal cavity

22. Which of the following is not found in the mediastinum?
A. Esophagus
B. Thymus
C. Stomach
D. Heart

23. What muscles are used for inspiration?
A. Diaphragm and the external intercostal muscles
B. Diaphragm and the internal intercostals
C. Abdominal muscles and the internal intercostals
D. Abdominal muscles and the diaphragm
E. None of the above

24. Where does respiratory gas exchange take place?
A. Bronchioles
B. Alveoli
C. Hilum
D. Pulmonary veins
E. All of the above

25. Where do the bronchus and other structures enter the lung?
A. Base
B. Apex
C. Cardiac sphincter
D. Hilum

26. Which of the following lists the heart layers from the outer layer to the inner layer?
A. Epicardium, myocardium, endocardium
B. Endocardium, myocardium, epicardium
C. Epicardium, endocardium, myocardium
D. Endocardium, epicardium, myocardium
E. None of the above

27. Which part of the heart pumps blood into the lungs?
A. Right atrium
B. Right ventricle
C. Left ventricle
D. Left atrium

28. Which valve allows blood to move from the left atrium to the left ventricle?
A. Tricuspid valve
B. Pulmonary semilunar valve
C. Aortic semilunar valve
D. Mitral valve

29. The rhythmic contraction of the heart is controlled by:
A. Atrioventricular node
B. Sinoatrial node
C. Purkinje fibers
D. Bundle of His
E. None of the above

30. When the electric impulse leaves the Bundle of His where does it travel next?
A. Purkinje fibers
B. Sinoatrial node
C. Atrioventricular node
D. None of the above

31. What structures are affected by thoracic outlet syndrome?
A. Median nerve and vessels
B. Cervical plexus and subclavian vessels
C. Brachial plexus nerve complex and subclavian vessels
D. Cervical and brachial plexus

32. What comprises the outer ear?
A. Malleus and incus
B. Semicircular canal and the cochlea
C. Auricle and the meatus
D. Tympanic membrane

33. What structure separates the outer ear from the middle ear?
A. Tympanic membrane
B. Lobule
C. Tragus
D. Ceruminous gland

34. What cranial bone houses the middle ear?
A. Frontal Bone
B. Temporal bone
C. Maxilla
D. Occiput
E. All of the above

35. What structure connects the nasopharynx to the middle ear?
A. Mastoid sinus
B. Cristae
C. Lobule
D. Eustachian tube

36. What structures are located in the tympanic cavity?
A. Malleus, incus, stapes
B. Cristae, ampulla, semicircular canals
C. Malleus, ampulla, stapes
D. Semicircular canals, cristae, incus

37. What is located in the nasal cavity?
A. Nares
B. Turbinates
C. Ostia
D. Epistaxis
E. All of the above

38. Which of the following are the paranasal sinuses?
A. Frontal, ethmoid, sphenoid, and maxillary
B. Frontal, coronal, sphenoid, and maxillary
C. Ethmoid, rostrum, sphenoid, and maxillary
D. Frontal, rostrum, coronal, maxillary

39. What do the nasopharynx, oropharynx, and laryngopharynx combine to make?
A. Larynx
B. Trachea
C. Pharynx
D. None of the above

40. What is the functioning tissue of the lung?
A. Bronchioles
B. Bronchi
C. Alveolar sacs
D. Carina

41. How many lobes is the right lung divided into?
A. 1
B. 2
C. 3
D. 4

42. How many lobes is the left lung divided into?
A. 1
B. 2
C. 3
D. 4

43. Which of the following structures carries food to the stomach?
A. Esophagus
B. Pharynx
C. Epiglottis
D. Oropharynx

44. Where are the suprarenal glands located?
A. Kidneys
B. Bladder
C. Thyroid gland
D. Uterus

45. What are the functional part of the kidney called?
A. Cortex
B. Nephrons
C. Corpuscles
D. Hilum

46. Where are the kidneys located?
A. Pelvis space
B. Peritoneal space
C. Retroperitoneal space
D. Thoracic space

47. Which landmarks make up the vesical trigone?
A. Urethral openings and the urethral aperture
B. Internal sphincter and the rugae
C. Rugae and urethral openings
D. Urethral aperture and serosa

48. What structure in the kidney stores urine?
A. Renal medulla
B. Renal cortex
C. Renal pyramid
D. Renal pelvis

49. What supplies blood to the kidney?
A. Aorta
B. Phrenic artery
C. Renal artery
D. Gastric artery

50. Which of the following is **NOT** a part of the urinary system?
A. Bartholin's gland
B. Kidney
C. Ureters
D. Urethra

51. Which of the following is **NOT** a process of urine formation?
A. Tubular reabsorption
B. Emulsification
C. Glomerular filtration
D. Tubular secretion

52. What structure connects the kidney to the bladder?
A. Urethra
B. Bladder
C. Ureter
D. Kidney

53. Which of the following makes up the Peripheral nervous system?
A. Somatic nervous system and autonomic nervous system
B. Sympathetic nervous system and parasympathetic nervous system
C. Somatic nervous system and the sympathetic nervous system
D. Autonomic nervous system and the parasympathetic nervous system

54. Which system maintains homeostatic balance and conserves energy.
A. Autonomic nervous system
B. Sympathetic nervous system
C. Parasympathetic nervous system
D. Somatic nervous system

55. What is the outer most layer the meninges called?
A. Arachnoid matter
B. Dura lmatter
C. Pia matter
D. Cortex

56. Which part of the brain is the largest?
A. Cerebrum
B. Cortex
C. Basal ganglia
D. Cerebellum

57. How many ventricles are located in the brain?
A. 2
B. 3
C. 4
D. 5

58. What structure produces cerebral spinal fluid?
A. Lateral ventricles
B. Third ventricle
C. Fourth ventricle
D. All ventricles

59. Which structure in the brain maintains the balance in humans?
A. Cortex
B. Basal ganglia
C. Cerebellum
D. Sulci

60. Which nerve controls hearing?
A. II
B. V
C. VIII
D. IX

61. What part of the vertebrae does the spinal cord pass through?
A. Body of the vertebrae
B. Vertebral foramen
C. The laminal groove
D. None of the above

62. What does the brachial plexus innervate?
A. The genitals and leg
B. The shoulder and arm
C. Face and head
D. Abdomen
E. None of the above

63. Which of the following is a complete list of bones that make up the orbit of the eye?
A. Frontal, sphenoid, ethmoid, superior maxillary, zygomatic, lacrimal, and palate bones
B. Frontal, sphenoid, ethmoid, superior maxillary and lacrimal
C. Frontal, ethmoid, superior maxillary, zygomatic, and palate
D. Frontal, sphenoid, ethmoid, zygomatic, and palate

64. Which muscle moves the eyeball toward the midline and upward?
A. Inferior rectus
B. Medial rectus
C. Superior rectus
D. Inferior oblique

65. What is the action of the Inferior rectus muscle?
A. Moves the eyeball upward
B. Moves the eyeball laterally
C. None of the above
D. Moves the eyeball downward and to the midline
E. All of the above

66. How many extrinsic muscles are there in the eye?
A. 4
B. 6
C. 7
D. 8

67. What mucous membrane covers the eye?
A. Sclera
B. Vitreous humor
C. Conjunctiva
D. Aqueous humor

68. Where are images received in the eye?
A. Retina
B. Sclera
C. Lens
D. Pupil

69. What is located posterior to the cornea and anterior to the iris?
A. Posterior chamber
B. Posterior cavity
C. Fovea centralis
D. Anterior chamber

70. What structure of the eye constricts and dilates?
A. Cornea
B. Iris
C. Lens
D. Retina

71. Which of the following is **NOT** a function of the skeletal system?
A. Transmits electric impulses
B. Source of red blood cells
C. Stores calcium
D. Attachment points for muscles

72. Which of the following is the bone that is around the marrow cavity and is dense tissue.
A. Cancellous
B. Collagen
C. Cortical
D. Spongy

73. What is the name of the fibrous layer that surrounds the bone?
A. Epiphyses
B. Synovial membrane
C. Cartilage
D. Periosteum

74. Where does active bone growth take place?
A. Articular surface
B. Spongy bone
C. Epiphyseal plate
D. Cancellous bone

75. Which of the following is a synarthrosis joint?
A. Saggital suture
B. Shoulder joint
C. Interphalangeal joint
D. Wrist joint

76. Which of the following minerals are stored in bone?
A. Potassium
B. Magnesium
C. Calcium
D. All of the above

77. What is the correct order of osteogenesis?
A. Inflammation, callus formation, cellular proliferation, ossification, remodeling
B. Inflammation, cellular proliferation, callus formation, ossification, remodeling
C. Callus formation, inflammation, cellular proliferation, remodeling, ossification
D. Cellular proliferation, inflammation, remodeling, callus formation, ossification

78. What needs to take place to make a stable union in a bone fracture?
A. Distraction
B. Delayed union
C. Malunion
D. Immobilization

79. What part of the body does compartment syndrome take place?
A. Femur and pelvis
B. Tibia and forearm
C. Femur and forearm
D. Humerus and tibia

80. Which of the following can be used to immobilize fractured bones?
A. Casts and splints
B. Casts and ace wraps
C. Splints and ace wraps
D. None of the above

81. What is the main purpose of the rotator cuff muscles?
A. Hip joint stability
B. Knee joint stability
C. Shoulder joint stability
D. Elbow joint stability

82. Which of the following comprise the lower leg?
A. Fibula and femur
B. Tibia and ulna
C. Fibula and tibia
D. Femur, fibula, tibia

83. Where would the lateral malleolus be found?
A. Distal end of the fibula
B. Proximal end of the humerus
C. Distal end of the tibia
D. Proximal end of the fibula

84. What term is defined as a fracture to a bone where one side is bent and the opposite side is broken?
A. Pott's fracture
B. Greenstick fracture
C. Spiral fracture
D. Comminuted fracture

85. What fracture spirals around the bone?
A. Transcervical fracture
B. Spiral fracture
C. Transverse fracture
D. Compound fracture

86. Choose the best definition of a transcervical fracture.
A. A horizontal fracture of the bone
B. A fracture that is bent on one side and broken on the other
C. A fracture in the neck of the femur
D. The bone has been shattered or crushed

87. Choose the best definition of stellate fracture.
A. A break that radiates out from a break at a central point
B. A fracture that is bent on one side and broken on the other
C. Two bone ends that have been forced into each other
D. The broken bone pushes through the skin

88. When a bone is broken horizontally what type of fracture is it considered to be?
A. Compound fracture
B. Transcervical fracture
C. Transverse fracture
D. None of the above
E. All of the above

89. The bone has been broken into many pieces. What type of fracture is this?
A. Comminuted fracture
B. Compound fracture
C. Colles' fracture
D. B and C
E. A and B

90. When a bone has been broken into many pieces due to two bone ends being compressed into each other. What type of fracture is this?
A. Comminuted fracture
B. Impacted fracture
C. Tracscervical fracture
D. Colles's fracture

91. Which of the following defines a compound fracture?
A. A fracture in the neck of the femur
B. A bimalleolar ankle fracture
C. The distal radius is broken
D. A fracture in which the bone penetrates the skin

92. Which of the following terms refers to a structure that is close to the origin of the limb?
A. Distal
B. Proximal
C. Medial
D. Lateral

93. Which of the following is a large rounded process on the end of a long bone that forms a joint?
A. Condyle
B. Fossa
C. Shaft
D. Crest

94. Which of the following branch off of the aortic arch?
A. Brachiocephalic artery, right common carotid artery, left subclavian artery
B. Left coronary artery, right common carotid artery, right subclavian artery
C. Right coronary artery, left common carotid artery, left subclavian artery
D. Brachiocephalic artery, left common carotid artery, left subclavian artery

95. Which of the following is the correct order from superior to inferior?
A. Left ventricle of the heart, ascending aorta, aortic arch, thoracic aorta, abdominal aorta, common iliac arteries, femoral arteries, popliteal artery
B. Left ventricle of the heart, aortic, arch ascending aorta, thoracic aorta, abdominal aorta, common iliac arteries, femoral arteries, popliteal artery
C. Left ventricle of the heart, ascending aorta, aortic arch, abdominal aorta, thoracic aorta, common iliac arteries, femoral arteries, popliteal artery
D. Left ventricle of the heart, ascending aorta, aortic arch, thoracic aorta, abdominal aorta, femoral arteries, common iliac arteries, popliteal artery
E. None of the above

96. Which vein carries the blood from the brain back toward the heart?
A. External jugular
B. Common Carotid artery
C. Internal jugular vein
D. Saphenous vein

97. Which of the following lists the layers of the blood vessel wall from exterior to interior.
A. Tunica media, tunica intima, tunica adventitia
B. Tunica adventitia, tunica media, tunica intima
C. Tunica intima, tunica media, tunica adventitia
D. Tunica media, tunica adventitia, tunica intima

98. Which section of blood vessel has the thinnest walls?
A. Veins
B. Arteries
C. Capillaries
D. Arterioles

99. Which of the following branch off of the aortic arch?
A. Brachiocephalic artery, left common carotid artery, subclavian artery
B. Brachiocephalic artery, right common carotid artery, axillary artery
C. Subclavian artery, vertebral artery, carotid artery
D. Subclavian artery, left common carotid artery, right common carotid artery, brachiocephalic artery

100. What major vein does the head, shoulder, and upper extremities drain into?
A. Superior vena cava
B. Inferior vena cava
C. Subclavian artery
D. Coronary artery
E. None of the above

101. The common iliac artery branches off of which of the following?
A. Thoracic aorta
B. Vena cava
C. Lumbar artery
D. Distal abdominal aorta

102.What organs are located in the "lesser pelvis"?
A. Duodenum, ovaries, uterus, vagina
B. Cecum, ovaries, fallopian tubes, cervix
C. Ovaries, uterus, vagina
D. Ovaries, fallopian tubes, uterus, vagina, cervix

103. Which of the following is the list of female external genitalia?
A. Mons pubis, labia majora, labia minora, clitoris, perineum
B. Mons pubis, labia majora, labia minora, clitoris, Bartholin's glands, forchette, perineum
C. Mons pubis, labia minora, Bartholin's gland, clitoris, forchette
D. Mons pubis, labia majora, clitoris, perineum

104. The fallopian tube is located in which of the following ligaments?
A. Cardinal ligament
B. Pubic ligament
C. Broad ligament
D. Sacral ligament

105. Which of the following is **NOT** a part of the fallopian tube?
A. Fundus
B. Fimbria
C. Ampulla
D. Adnexa

106. What structures compose the penis?
A. Corpus spongiosum and testis
B. Corpora cavernosa and corpus spongiosum
C. Testis and Tunica vaginalis
D. Tunica albuginea and corpora cavernosa

107. In what structure do the sperm mature?
A. Seminiferous tubules
B. Vas Deferens
C. Epididymis
D. Prostate gland

108. Which of the following is **NOT** an accessory gland of the male reproductive system?
A. Epididymis
B. Seminal vesicles
C. Prostate gland
D. Bulbourethral glands

109. Which of the following terms means to move away from midline or turn outward?
A. Adduction
B. Rotation
C. Supination
D. Abduction

110. Which of the following terms means to move toward the midline or turn inward?
A. Adduction
B. Abduction
C. Circumduction
D. Prone

111. Which of the following refers to a condition where body tissues that are normally separate, adhere to one another?
A. Fistula
B. Adhesion
C. Adhesive
D. Dehiscence

112. Which of the following terms refers to the appendages or accessory structures of an organ?
A. Appendix
B. Prepuce
C. Adnexa
D. Axillary

113. Which of the following refers to the tissues of the respiratory and upper digestive tract?
A. Nasopharynx
B. Esophagus
C. Aerodigestive tract
D. None of the above

114. Which of the following refers to a joint whose opposing surfaces are connected by fibrocartilage and permit slight or limited motion?
A. Arthrodial
B. Amphiarthrosis
C. Synarthrodial
D. None of the above

115. Which of the following is the term used to describe a human body positioned upright, facing forward, arms slightly outward from the body, palms, and feet facing forward?
A. Anatomic position
B. Supine position
C. Prone position
D. Lateral position

116. Which of the following refers to the front of the body?
A. Medial
B. Anterior
C. Posterior
D. Prone

117. What is another name for compact bone?
A. Cancellous bone
B. Spongy bone
C. Cortical bone
D. None of the above

118. The Circle of Willis is located:
A. Base of the brain
B. Deep in the kidney
C. Within the spleen
D. Distal end of the colon

119. What organ is the ciliary muscle found?
A. Bladder
B. Eyeball
C. Uterus
D. Testicle

120. Chyme is a semifluid substance located in which of the following organ?
A. Spleen
B. Liver
C. Lung
D. Stomach

121. What is located within the medullary marrow cavity and bone ends?
A. Cortical bone
B. Cartilage
C. Cancellous bone
D. None of the above

122. Which of the following terms is defined as a freely movable joint:
A. Diarthrosis
B. Synarthrosis
C. Amphiarthrosis
D. None of the above

123. Which of the following does not assist in respiration?
A. Digastric muscle
B. Diaphragm
C. Internal intercostal muscles
D. Scalenes

124. What structure separates the larynx from the trachea?
A. Palatine tonsils
B. Epiglottis
C. Thyroid cartilage
D. Hyoid bone

125. What is the outer layer of heart tissue called?
A. Cardium
B. Epicardium
C. Endocardium
D. Exocardium

126. What is the name of the lining covering the inside of the heart chambers?
A. Cardium
B. Epicardium
C. Endocardium
D. Exocardium

127. When a vessel crumbles or tears easily, it is :
A. Friable
B. Pliable
C. Flexible
D. Rigid

128. What bone is the glenoid fossa located?
A. Humerus
B. Pelvis
C. Femur
D. Scapula

129. What fibrous tissue holds the kidney in anatomical position and encapsulates the kidney?
A. Periosteum
B. Peritonitis
C. Gerota's fascia
D. External tunica

130. When referring to grafting, which of the following terms means the graft is taken from the same species?
A. Homologous
B. Xenograft
C. Autologous
D. Synthetic

131. What term refers to the lack of oxygen?
A. Eschimia
B. Halitosis
C. Ischemia
D. None of the above

132. The iris is located in which of the following organs?
A. Eye
B. Colon
C. Uterus
D. Testicle

133. Which of the following terms means 'on the same side'?
A. Bilateral
B. Ipsilateral
C. Unilateral
D. None of the above

134. Where is the mitral valve located?
A. Between the right atrium and the right ventricle
B. Between the left atrium and the left ventricle
C. Between the right atrium and left atrium
D. Between the right ventricle and the left ventricle

135. Where are meninges located?
A. Muscle
B. Bone
C. Colon
D. Brain and spinal cord

136. Where is the median nerve located?
A. Leg
B. Pelvis
C. Wrist
D. Cranium

137. Which term directs you toward the middle of a structure?
A. Medial
B. Lateral
C. Ventral
D. Superior

138. What term is used in reference to elevated body temperature?
A. Thermal
B. Pyrex
C. Cryo
D. None of the above

139. Which of the following receive impulse from Bundle of His and spread it to the left ventricular apex and onto the myocardium of the ventricle?
A. Purkinje fibers
B. AV node
C. Bundle of His
D. SA node

140. When an organ slips out of anatomical position.
A. Prophylaxis
B. Prolapse
C. Prevention
D. None of the above

141. Which of the following is a cleft palate?
A. Phimosis
B. Palatoplasty
C. Buccal
D. Palatoschisis

142. What is the space called between the posterior abdominal wall and the peritoneum?
A. Retroperitoneal
B. Peritoneal
C. Thoracic
D. Pelvic

143. What is the contraction phase of the cardiac cycle called?
A. Diastole
B. Contractile
C. Relaxation
D. Systole

144. Where would the suprarenal glands be located?
A. Bladder
B. Thyroid
C. Kidney
D. Ovary

145. Supine is defined as:
A. Patient is lying on her back, arms at sides, face and palms up
B. Patient is lying on her stomach with arms at her sides
C. Patient is lying on her back, arms at sides, ankles crossed
D. Patient is lying on her stomach with ankles crossed

146. When moisture penetrates a sterile drape it is called:
A. Contamination
B. Strike-through
C. Wet drape
D. Strike-through contamination

147. The definition of systole:
A. Relaxation phase of the cardiac cycle
B. Contraction phase of the cardiac cycle
C. Contraction phase of the respiratory cycle
D. Relaxation phase of the respiratory cycle

148. Which of the following line the articular capsule within a freely movable joint and lubricate the joint?
A. Bursa
B. Cartilage
C. Ligaments
D. Synovial membrane

149. What part of the nervous system is responsible for the "fight or flight" mechanism?
A. Sympathetic nervous system
B. Autonomic nervous system
C. Somatic nervous system
D. Parasympathetic nervous system

150. Which of the following is the best definition of the term *superior*?
A. A directional term meaning toward the top of the torso
B. A directional term meaning below a structure
C. A directional term meaning toward the head or toward the top of a structure
D. A directional term meaning above a structure

151. What anatomical structure is made up of the manubrium, body, and xiphoid process?
A. Pelvis
B. Wrist
C. Vertebra
D. Sternum

152. What joint is made up of the glenoid fossa and the head of the humerus?
A. Hip Joint
B. Shoulder Joint
C. Elbow Joint
D. Knee Joint

153. What type of healing will take place when a wound heals from the inside out due to granulation:
A. First intention healing
B. Second intention healing
C. Third intention healing
D. Fourth intention healing

154. Where are sebaceous glands located?
A. Skin
B. Colon
C. Esophagus
D. None of the above

155. When a structure becomes stiff and hardens it is?
A. Stenotic
B. Stent
C. Septic
D. Sclerotic

156. Which of the following is the white portion of the eyeball?
A. Sclera
B. Cornea
C. Retina
D. Iris

157. What is the name of the structure that lies between the larynx and the primary bronchi.
A. Bronchiole
B. Trachea
C. Esophagus
D. Uvula

158. When a patient at rest has a heart rate higher than 100 beats per minute, what is it labeled?
A. Bradycardia
B. Hypertension
C. Tachycardia
D. Hypotension

159. Which of the following is harvested from a different species than its recipient?
A. Xenograft
B. Autologous
C. Homologous
D. None of the above

160. Damage to tissue of the body:
A. Wound
B. Trauma
C. Injury
D. All of the above

161. The definition of the term *Leukocyte* is:
A. White blood cell
B. White cell
C. Red blood cell
D. Blood cell

162. What are the vital bodily function measurements called ?
A. Blood pressure
B. Pulse
C. Temperature
D. Vital Signs

163. What are the ureter openings and the urethra opening called in the bladder?
A. Trigone
B. Vesical trigone
C. Vesical
D. Bladder triangle

164. When the ventricle contracts abnormally fast, it is called:
A. Atrial tachycardia
B. Ventricular bradycardia
C. Ventricular tachycardia
D. Atrial bradycardia

165. When the ventricles of the heart have abnormal opening between them.
A. Atrial septal defect
B. Ventricular septal defect
C. Cardiac defect
D. Septal defect

166. Uncoordinated, fast contractions of the heart ventricles.
A. Fibrillation
B. Ventricular fibrillation
C. Tachycardia
D. Atrial fibrillation

167. The caudal chambers of the heart.
A. Atrium
B. Ventricle
C. Ventricles
D. Atria

168. What is the tube that connects the bladder to the body's exterior?
A. Urethra
B. Ureter
C. Urethral
D. Urethral meatus

169. Which of the following is the tube that urine travels through between the kidney and the bladder?
A. Urethra
B. Ureters
C. Urethral meatus
D. None of the above

170. When something affects only one side.
A. Lateral
B. Unilateral
C. Bilateral
D. Medial

171. What position is the patient in when he is laying on his back with arms and hands at his side?
A. Supine
B. Prone
C. Lateral
D. Lithotomy

172. Which of the following is affected by Carpal Tunnel Syndrome?
A. Brachial plexus
B. Femoral nerve
C. Radial nerve
D. Median nerve

173. What anatomical structure is affected by Colle's fracture?
A. Distal fibula
B. Distal radius
C. Proximal ulna
D. Carpal bones

174. Where does gas and nutrient exchange take place in the blood?
A. Arterioles
B. Cilia in the colon
C. Golgi apparatus
D. Capillaries

175. When blood returns to the heart from the extremities, what part of the heart does it enter?
A. Left atrium
B. Right atrium
C. Left ventricle
D. Right ventricle

176. What causes a decrease in blood pressure?
A. Vasodilation
B. Vasoconstriction
C. Arteriole dilation
D. Arteriole constriction

177. Which layer of the artery is in contact with the blood?
A. Tunica adventitia
B. Tunica media
C. Tunica intima
D. All of the above

178. Arterial blood pressure is affected by:
A. Strength of heart's ventricular contraction
B. The body's level of water retention
C. Cardiac output
D. All of the above

179. Choose the organ from the list below that has sensory input, protects against disease, and assists in homeostasis?
A. Skin
B. Colon
C. Spinal cord
D. Lymph nodes

180. Which layer of the skin has no blood vessels or nerves?
A. Dermis
B. Epidermis
C. Subcutaneous layer
D. None of the above

181. Which layer anchors the skin?
A. Reticular layer
B. Papillary layer
C. Subcutaneous layer
D. Stratum layer

182. What produces cerumen?
A. Ceruminous gland
B. Sebaceous gland
C. Sudoriferous gland
D. Apocrine gland

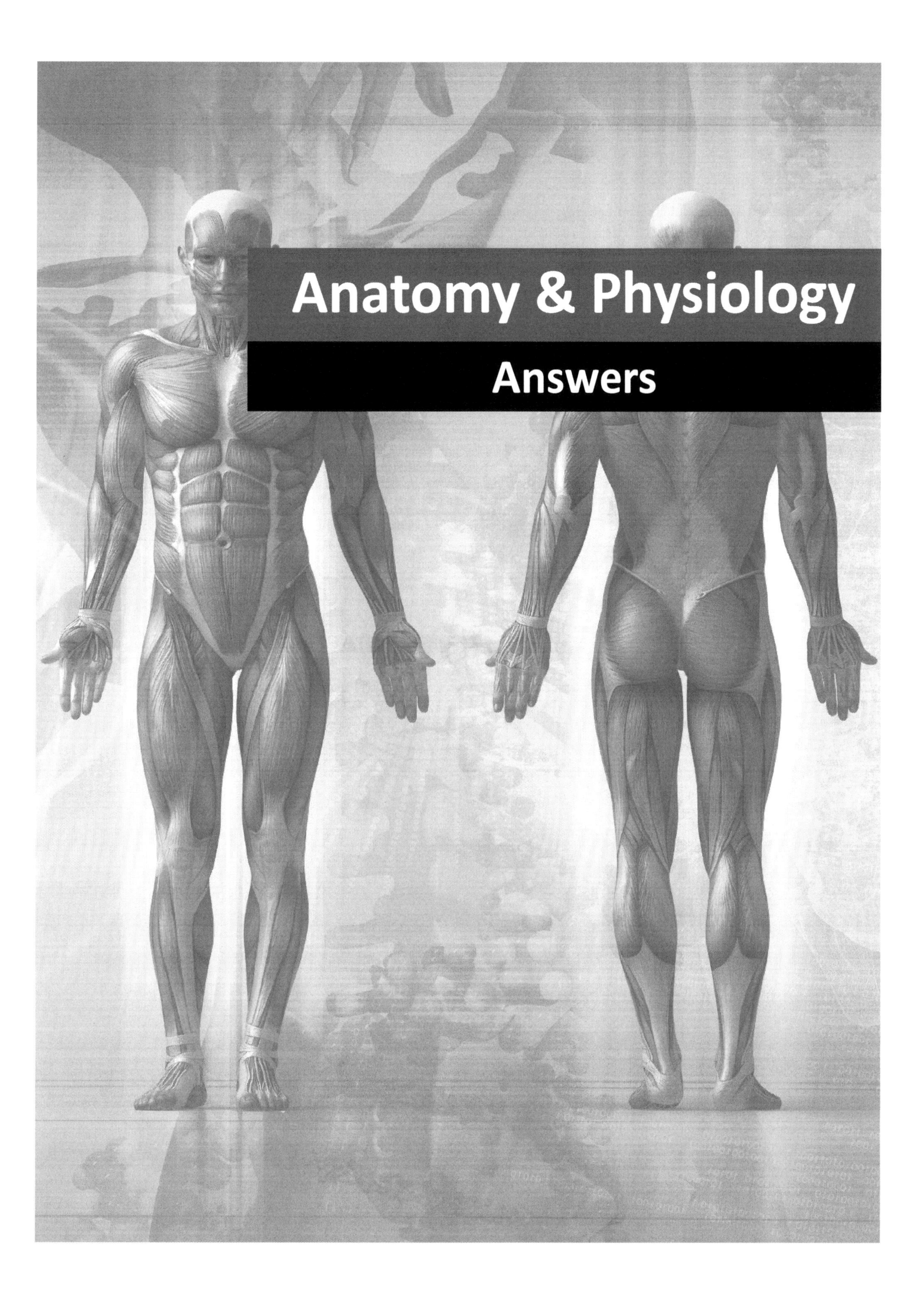
Anatomy & Physiology
Answers

1. Which of the following defines the term 'anatomical position'?
A. Standing erect, arms at sides, toes and palms forward, and facing forward - Anatomical position is when a person stands erect, facing forward, arms at the sides of the body, toes and palms are forward.

2. Which system is made of the heart and the blood vessels?
D. Circulatory system - The circulatory system consists of the heart and all the blood vessels (aorta, veins, arteries, capillaries).

3. Which system regulates water balance, metabolism, reproduction, and growth in the body?
B. Endocrine system - The endocrine system takes care of the body's reproduction, metabolism, and growth. It also regulates water balance in the body.

4. Which of the following is the correct listing of the components of the nervous system?
C. Brain, spinal cord, nerves, and sense organs - There are four components of the nervous system: brain, spinal cord, nerves, and sense organs.

5. What is the basic unit of life?
B. Cell - The basic unit of life is the cell.

6. What organ would be found in the right upper quadrant of the abdomen?
A. Gallbladder - The gallbladder, a large portion of the liver, and a portion of the intestines are located in the right upper quadrant of the abdominal cavity.

7. The appendix is located in which abdominal quadrant?
C. Right lower quadrant - The Right lower quadrant is where the appendix is located.

8. Which cavities are located in the abdominopelvic cavity?
A. Abdominal cavity and Pelvic cavity - The abdominopelvic cavity is made up of the abdominal and pelvic cavities. The ventral cavity is made up of the thoracic cavity and the abdominopelvic cavity.

9. What organ would be located in the mediastinal cavity?
D. Thymus gland -The thymus gland, heart, esophagus, and trachea are located in the mediastinal cavity.

10. Which cavity does the cranial and spinal cavities make up?
C. Dorsal cavity - The dorsal cavity is made up of the cranial cavity and the spinal cavity.

11. Which tissue cushions and stores fat?
B. Adipose tissue - Adipose tissue is a loose connective tissue that stores fat, is a cushion and provides insulation.

12. Which of the following is the structure that surrounds bone and is the attachment surface for muscle?
A. Periosteum - The periosteum is a tough fibrous tissue that surrounds bone. It is the tissue membrane the muscle adjoins on the bone.

13. What part of the bone is where longitudinal bone growth takes place?
A. Epiphyseal disc - The epiphyseal disc is located in the end of the long bones and it is in this area the bone grows longitudinally.

14. What makes up the sternum?
C. Manubrium, body, xiphoid process - The sternum is made up of the manubrium, body, and xiphoid process.

15. Which of the following make up the axial anatomy?
B. Cranium, mandible, vertebral column, sacrum, coccyx, rib cage, costal cartilage, hyoid, sternum - The axial skeleton is made up of the cranium, mandible, vertebral column, sacrum, coccyx, rib cage, costal cartilage, hyoid, and sternum.

16. Which part of the nervous system works unconsciously and automatically?
A. Autonomic nervous system - The autonomic nervous system allows the body to function without thought, automatically, unconsciously.

17. Which of the following is **NOT** part of the alimentary canal?
A. Gallbladder - The mouth, pharynx, esophagus, stomach, small intestine, large intestine (colon), rectum, and anus make up the alimentary canal.

18. Which of the following is **NOT** part of the biliary tract?
D. Small intestine -The gallbladder, cystic duct, common hepatic duct, and the common bile duct make up the biliary tract which joins the liver to the duodenum.

19. Which of the following is a list of the sternum from superior to inferior?
E. Manubrium, body, xiphoid process - The sternum is made up of the manubrium, body, and xiphoid process - superior to inferiorly.

20. How many lobes do the lungs have?
A. 5 lobes - The right lung has 3 lobes and the left lung has 2 lobes so the lungs have 5 lobes.

21. What does the parietal pleura line?
B. Inner surface of ribs, the superior surface of the diaphragm, and the pericardium of the heart - The parietal pleura is the lining in the thoracic cavity. It covers the pericardium of the heart, the inner surface of the ribs, and the superior surface of the diaphragm.

22. Which of the following is not found in the mediastinum?
C. Stomach - The esophagus, trachea, thymus, lymph nodes and heart are located in the mediastinum. The stomach is located in the abdomen.

23. What muscles are used for inspiration?
A. Diaphragm and the external intercostal muscles - The diaphragm and the external intercostals are the primary muscles used for inhalation.

24. Where does respiratory gas exchange take place?
B. Alveoli - The respiratory gas exchange takes place at the alveoli.

25. Where do the bronchus and other structures enter the lung?
D. Hilum -The bronchus enters the lung at the hilum. The cardiac sphincter is located at the distal end of the esophagus.

26. Which of the following lists the heart layers from the outer layer to the inner layer?
A. Epicardium, myocardium, endocardium -The layers of the heart from outside to inside: epicardium, myocardium, endocardium. Epi- (upon), cardi- (heart), myo- (muscle), endo- (within)

27. Which part of the heart pumps blood into the lungs?
B. Right ventricle - The atria are filled with blood that comes from the veins of the body. The left ventricle pumps blood toward the body and the right ventricle pumps blood to the lungs.

28. Which valve allows blood to move from the left atrium to the left ventricle?
D. Mitral valve - The mitral valve allows blood to flow from the left atrium to the left ventricle.

29. The rhythmic contraction of the heart is controlled by:
B. Sinoatrial node - The SA node (sinoatrial node) is found in the right atrial wall and emits an electric impulse to regulate the rhythmic contraction of the heart.

30. When the electric impulse leaves the Bundle of His where does it travel next?
A. Purkinje fibers - The electric impulse moves from the SA node to the AV node to the Bundle of His and then to the Purkinje fibers.

31. What structures are affected by thoracic outlet syndrome?
C. Brachial plexus nerve complex and subclavian vessels - The brachial plexus nerve complex (musculocutaneus, axillary, median, radial, and ulnar nerves) and the subclavian vessels are compressed causing thoracic outlet syndrome.

32. What comprises the outer ear?
C. Auricle and the meatus - The outer ear is comprised of the auricle (pinna), meatus (external auditory canal), helix, lobule, and tragus.

33. What structure separates the outer ear from the middle ear?
A. Tympanic membrane - The tympanic membrane separates the outer ear from the middle ear.

34. What cranial bone houses the middle ear?
B. Temporal bone - The temporal bone houses the air filled chamber called the middle ear or tympanic cavity.

35. What structure connects the nasopharynx to the middle ear?
D. Eustachian tube - The eustachian tube connects the middle ear to the nasopharynx.

36. What structures are located in the tympanic cavity?
A. Malleus, incus, stapes - The malleus (hammer), incus (anvil), and the stapes (stirrup) are located in the tympanic cavity within the middle ear.

37. What is located in the nasal cavity?
B. Turbinates - The turbinates are bony projections that are located in the nasal cavity. Turbinates are also known as conchae.

38. Which of the following are the paranasal sinuses?
A. Frontal, ethmoid, sphenoid, and maxillary - The four pair of paranasal sinuses are the frontal, ethmoid, sphenoid, and maxillary sinuses.

39. What do the nasopharynx, oropharynx, and laryngopharynx combine to make?
C. Pharynx - The pharynx is made up of the nasopharynx, oropharynx, and the laryngopharynx.

40. What is the functioning tissue of the lung?
C. Alveolar sacs - Gas exchange takes place at the alveolar sacs

41. How many lobes is the right lung divided into?
C. 3 - The right lung is divided into 3 lobes and the left lung is divided into 2 lobes.

42. How many lobes is the left lung divided into?
B. 2 - The right lung is divided into 3 lobes and the left lung is divided into 2 lobes.

43. Which of the following structures carries food to the stomach?
A. Esophagus - The esophagus is the passage for food to reach the stomach

44. Where are the suprarenal glands located?
A. Kidneys -The superior medial aspect of the kidney is where the suprarenal glands are located.

45. What are the functional part of the kidney called?
B. Nephrons - The kidneys functional unit is the nephron. It is made up of the glomerulus and Bowman's capsule.

46. Where are the kidneys located?
C. Retroperitoneal space - The retroperitoneal space, between the posterior abdominal wall and the peritoneum, is where the kidneys are located.

47. Which landmarks make up the vesical trigone?
A. Urethral openings and the urethral aperture - The vesical trigone is made up of the urethral openings and the urethral aperture.

48. What structure in the kidney stores urine?
D. Renal pelvis - The renal pelvis is the area that stores the urine within the kidney.

49. What supplies blood to the kidney?
C. Renal artery - The renal artery supplies the kidney with blood.

50. Which of the following is **NOT** a part of the urinary system?
A. Bartholin's gland - The Bartholin's gland is located in the vaginal wall and secretes fluid for lubricating the vagina.

51. Which of the following is **NOT** a process of urine formation?
B. Emulsification - Urine is processed through tubular reabsorption, glomerular filtration, and tubular reabsorption. Emulsification is the process of breaking fat down in the intestine.

52. What structure connects the kidney to the bladder?
C. Ureter - The ureters connect the kidney to the bladder.

53. Which of the following makes up the Peripheral nervous system?
A. Somatic nervous system and autonomic nervous system - The Peripheral nervous system includes the somatic and autonomic nervous system and the sympathetic and parasympathetic nervous system makes up the Autonomic nervous system.

54. Which system maintains homeostatic balance and conserves energy.
C. Parasympathetic nervous system - Parasympathetic nervous system response conserves energy and maintains homeostasis.

55. What is the outer most layer the meninges called?
B. Dura matter - The dura matter is the outer layer.

56. Which part of the brain is the largest?
A. Cerebrum - The cerebrum is the largest part of the brain.

57. How many ventricles are located in the brain?
C. 4 - The brain has 4 ventricles.

58. What structure produces cerebral spinal fluid?
D. All ventricles - All four ventricles produce cerebral spinal fluid. The lateral ventricles produce the largest amount out of the four.

59. Which structure in the brain maintains the balance in humans?
C. Cerebellum - The cerebellum is the part of the brain that maintains human balance.

60. Which nerve controls hearing?
C. VIII - The vestibulocochlear nerve (VIII) controls hearing.

61. What part of the vertebrae does the spinal cord pass through?
B. Vertebral foramen - The spinal cord passes through the vertebral foramen.

62. What does the brachial plexus innervate?
B. The shoulder and arm - The brachial plexus intervates the shoulder and arm.

63. Which of the following is a complete list of bones that make up the orbit of the eye?
A. Frontal, sphenoid, ethmoid, superior maxillary, zygomatic, lacrimal, and palate bones - The seven bones that make up the eye orbit include: frontal, sphenoid, ethmoid, superior maxillary, zygomatic, lacrimal, and palate bones.

64. Which muscle moves the eyeball toward the midline and upward?
C. Superior rectus - The superior rectus muscle of the eyeball moves the eye to toward the nose (midline) and upward toward the forehead.

65. What is the action of the Inferior rectus muscle?
D. Moves the eyeball downward and to the midline - The inferior rectus muscle moves the eye so it can see the floor, downward, and toward the midline.

66. How many extrinsic muscles are there in the eye?
B. 6 - There are 6 extrinsic eye muscles: superior rectus, inferior rectus, medial rectus, lateral rectus, superior oblique and inferior oblique muscles.

67. What mucous membrane covers the eye?
C. Conjunctiva - The conjunctiva is the mucous membrane that covers the eye.

68. Where are images received in the eye?
A. Retina - The retina is the nervous membrane in the eye that receives images.

69. What is located posterior to the cornea and anterior to the iris?
D. Anterior chamber - The anterior chamber is located behind the cornea and in front of the iris.

70. What structure of the eye constricts and dilates?
B. Iris - The iris is the structure in the eye that constricts and dilates. The external tunic or covering of the eye is formed by the cornea and the sclera. The lens is a biconvex structure of the eye that is transparent. The retina is the nervous membrane that receives images and lines the inner eye.

71. Which of the following is NOT a function of the skeletal system?
A. Transmits electric impulses - The skeletal system is the base structure of the human body it is where red blood cells are formed, calcium is stored, and is the attachment site for muscles. It also protects the internal organs from injury. The electric impulses are transmitted through the nervous system.

72. Which of the following is the bone that is around the marrow cavity and is dense tissue.
C. Cortical - Cortical bone is the dense bone that is around the marrow cavity and in shafts of long bone

73. What is the name of the fibrous layer that surrounds the bone?
D. Periosteum - The periosteum is a fibrous tissue that surrounds the bone and has blood vessels and nerves within it.

74. Where does active bone growth take place?
C. Epiphyseal plate - The epiphyseal plate is where the bone grows.

75. Which of the following is a synarthrosis joint?
A. Saggital suture - The sutures located in the cranium are synarthritic joints. These joints are immovable.

76. Which of the following minerals are stored in bone?
D. All of the above - Potassium, magnesium, calcium, sodium, and phosphorus are stored in bone.

77. What is the correct order of osteogenesis?
B. Inflammation, cellular proliferation, callus formation, ossification, remodeling - Osteogenesis: inflammation, cellular proliferation, callus formation, ossification, remodeling

78. What needs to take place to make a stable union in a bone fracture?
D. Immobilization - For a bone fracture to heal in a stable way the bone needs to be immobilized correctly.

79. What part of the body does compartment syndrome take place?
B. Tibia and forearm - Compartment syndrome is when pressure increases in a space that cannot expand; tibia and forearm.

80. Which of the following can be used to immobilize fractured bones?
A. Casts and splints - Immobilization of broken bones can be accomplished with fiberglass casts, plaster casts, and splints.

81. What is the main purpose of the rotator cuff muscles?
C. Shoulder joint stability - The rotator cuff muscles (supraspinatus, infraspinatus, teres minor, subscapularis) provide shoulder joint stability.

82. Which of the following comprise the lower leg?
C. Fibula and tibia - The fibula and the tibia make up the lower leg.

83. Where would the lateral malleolus be found?
A. Distal end of the fibula -The lateral malleolus is located on the distal end of the fibula.

84. What term is defined as a fracture to a bone where one side is bent and the opposite side is broken?
B. Greenstick fracture - Greenstick fracture is where the bone is not broken through and through. It is bent on one side and broken on the other.

85. What fracture spirals around the bone?
B. Spiral fracture - A spiral fracture is where the bone is fractured from a twisting motion and the fracture spirals around the bone.

86. Choose the best definition of a transcervical fracture.
C. A fracture in the neck of the femur - A transcervical fracture is a fracture in the neck of the femur.

87. Choose the best definition of stellate fracture.
A. A break that radiates out from a break at a central point - A stellate fracture is a facture that occurs at a central point and has more factures that radiate away from that central point.

88. When a bone is broken horizontally what type of fracture is it considered to be?
C. Transverse fracture - A transverse fracture is a horizontal fracture of the bone.

89. The bone has been broken into many pieces. What type of fracture is this?
A. Comminuted fracture - Comminuted fracture is where the bone has been shattered or crushed. It is broken into many pieces.

90. When a bone has been broken into many pieces due to two bone ends being compressed into each other. What type of fracture is this?
B. Impacted fracture -An impacted fracture occurs when two bone ends are compressed into each other producing many broken bone pieces.

91. Which of the following defines a compound fracture?
D. A fracture in which the bone penetrates the skin - A compound fracture is when the broken bone pushes through the skin.

92. Which of the following terms refers to a structure that is close to the origin of the limb?
B. Proximal -Proximal is the directional term used when referring to a structure closer to the origin of the limb.

93. Which of the following is a large rounded process on the end of a long bone that forms a joint?
A. Condyle - The condyle is found on the end of a long bone. It is a large rounded projection that articulates with another bone. It is also an attachment site for muscle and ligaments.

94. Which of the following branch off of the aortic arch?
D. Brachiocephalic artery, left common carotid artery, left subclavian artery -The brachiocephalic artery, left common carotid artery, and left subclavian artery branch off from the aortic arch.

95. Which of the following is the correct order from superior to inferior?
A. Left ventricle of the heart, ascending aorta, aortic arch, thoracic aorta, abdominal aorta, common -The correct order of the arterial system : Left ventricle of the heart, ascending aorta, aortic arch, thoracic aorta, abdominal aorta, common iliac arteries, femoral arteries, popliteal artery.

96. Which vein carries the blood from the brain back toward the heart?
C. Internal jugular vein - The internal jugular vein empties the brain and the meninges into the right and left subclavian veins.

97. Which of the following lists the layers of the blood vessel wall from exterior to interior.
B. Tunica adventitia, tunica media, tunica intima - The layers of the blood vessels from exterior to interior: tunica adventitia, tunica media, tunica intima.

98. Which section of blood vessel has the thinnest walls?
C. Capillaries - Capillaries have a single layer of endothelium and are the thinnest of the vessels.

99. Which of the following branch off of the aortic arch?
A. Brachiocephalic artery, left common carotid artery, subclavian artery - The brachiocephalic artery, left common carotid artery, and subclavian artery all branch off of the aortic arch.

100. What major vein does the head, shoulder, and upper extremities drain into?
A. Superior vena cava - The head, shoulder, and upper extremities drain into the superior vena cava.

101. The common iliac artery branches off of which of the following?
D. Distal abdominal aorta - The aortic arch comes off of the heart and turns into the thoracic aorta then turns into the descending aorta (distal abdominal aorta) where it bifurcates into the common iliac arteries.

102. What organs are located in the "lesser pelvis"?
D. Ovaries, fallopian tubes, uterus, vagina, cervix -The lesser pelvis holds the ovaries, fallopian tubes, uterus, vagina, and cervix.

103. Which of the following is the list of female external genitalia?
B. Mons pubis, labia majora, labia minora, clitoris, Bartholin's glands, forchette, perineum -The external female genitalia: mons pubis, labia majora, labia minora, clitoris, Bartholin's glands, fourchette, and perineum.

104. The fallopian tube is located in which of the following ligaments?
C. Broad ligament -The broad ligament houses the fallopian tubes, the round ligaments, the ovarian ligaments, lymphatic structures, nerves, and blood vessels.

105. Which of the following is **NOT** a part of the fallopian tube?
A. Fundus -The fallopian tube consists of the fimbria, infundibulum, adnexa, ampulla, fallopian tube.

106. What structures compose the penis?
B. Corpora cavernosa and corpus spongiosum - The penis is made of three cylindrical masses: two corpora cavernosa and one corpus spongiosum.

107. In what structure do the sperm mature?
C. Epididymis -The epididymis is where the sperm become motile and fertile, mature. The sperm pass through the seminiferous tubules on their way to the epididymis. The Vas Deferens turns into the ejaculatory duct. The prostate gland is the structure that secretes substances that increase the sperm mobility.

108. Which of the following is **NOT** an accessory gland of the male reproductive system?
A. Epididymis -The accessory glands of the male reproductive system include the seminal vesicles, prostate gland, and Bulbourethral glands. The epididymis is a portion of the duct system where the sperm mature and become fertile and mobile.

109. Which of the following terms means to move away from midline or turn outward?
D. Abduction - Abduction means to move away from the midline or turn outward.

110. Which of the following terms means to move toward the midline or turn inward?
A. Adduction - Adduction means to move toward the midline or turn inward.

111. Which of the following refers to a condition where body tissues that are normally separate, adhere to one another?
B. Adhesion - Adhesion is a condition where bodily tissues that are normally separate, adhere to one another.

112. Which of the following terms refers to the appendages or accessory structures of an organ?
C. Adnexa - The term adnexa refers to the appendages or accessory structures of an organ.

113. Which of the following refers to the tissues of the respiratory and upper digestive tract?
C. Aerodigestive tract - The aerodigestive tract refers to the tissues of the respiratory and upper digestive tract. These tissues include the lips, mouth, tongue, nose, throat, vocal cords, and part of the esophagus and windpipe.

114. Which of the following refers to a joint whose opposing surfaces are connected by fibrocartilage and permit slight or limited motion?
B. Amphiarthrosis - Amphiarthrosis is a term used to describe a joint whose opposing surfaces are connected by fibrocartilage and permit slight or limited motion. The joints between the vertebrae are considered amphiarthrosis joints.

115. Which of the following is the term used to describe a human body positioned upright, facing forward, arms slightly outward from the body, palms, and feet facing forward?
A. Anatomic position - The term anatomic position is described as a human body positioned upright, facing forward, arms slightly outward from the body, palms, and feet facing forward.

116. Which of the following refers to the front of the body?
B. Anterior - When referring to the front of the body medical personnel use the term anterior.

117. What is another name for compact bone?
C. Cortical bone - Cortical bone or compact bone surrounds the cavity where the marrow is located and it is dense.

118. The Circle of Willis is located:
A. Base of the brain - The Circle of Willis is a vascular network of arteries located in the base of the brain.

119. What organ is the ciliary muscle found?
B. Eyeball - The ciliary muscle is located in the eyeball. It helps the eye focus on objects that are close.

120. Chyme is a semifluid substance located in which of the following organ?
D. Stomach - The stomach produces Chyme during the digestive process.

121. What is located within the medullary marrow cavity and bone ends?
C. Cancellous bone - Cancellous bone is found within the bone ends and the medullary marrow cavity.

122. Which of the following terms is defined as a freely movable joint:
A. Diarthrosis - Diarthrosis is a freely movable joint.

123. Which of the following does not assist in respiration?
A. Digastric muscle - The digastric muscle is located in the anterior neck and retracts and depresses the mandible.

124. What structure separates the larynx from the trachea?
B. Epiglottis - The larynx is separated from the trachea by the epiglottis.

125. What is the outer layer of heart tissue called?
B. Epicardium - The epicardium is a layer of tissue that is on the outside of the heart and protects the heart.

126. What is the name of the lining covering the inside of the heart chambers?
C. Endocardium - The endocardium is the lining on the inside of the heart chambers and valves.

127. When a vessel crumbles or tears easily, it is :
A. Friable - Friable is the term used when a vessel is delicate and tears easily.

128. What bone is the glenoid fossa located?
D. Scapula - The glenoid fossa is a depression in the scapula that articulates with the head of the humerus to form the shoulder joint.

129. What fibrous tissue holds the kidney in anatomical position and encapsulates the kidney?
C. Gerota's fascia - The Gerota's fascia is the fibrous tissue that keeps the kidney in anatomical position as well as encapsulates it.

130. When referring to grafting, which of the following terms means the graft is taken from the same species?
A. Homologous - A homologous graft is one that is taken from the same species.

131. What term refers to the lack of oxygen?
C. Ischemia - Ischemia is the term used for lack of oxygen.

132. The iris is located in which of the following organs?
A. Eye - The iris is the part of the eye that contracts and dilates to allow light to enter the eye. It is located in the center of the colored portion of the eye.

133. Which of the following terms means 'on the same side'?
B. Ipsilateral - Ipsilateral is a term used when referring to structures on the same side.

134. Where is the mitral valve located?
B. Between the left atrium and the left ventricle - The Mitral Valve is located between the left atrium and the left ventricle. The Tricuspid valve is located between the right atrium and the right ventricle.

135. Where are meninges located?
D. Brain and spinal cord - The meninges are membranes located in the brain and spinal cord.

136. Where is the median nerve located?
C. Wrist - The median nerve is located in the wrist.

137. Which term directs you toward the middle of a structure?
A. Medial - Medial is a term that refers to the middle of a structure, body, or bone.

138. What term is used in reference to elevated body temperature?
B. Pyrex - Pyrex is the term used to reference elevated body temperature or fever.

139. Which of the following receive impulse from Bundle of His and spread it to the left ventricular apex and onto the myocardium of the ventricle?
A. Purkinje fibers - The Purkinje fibers take the impulse from the Bundle of His and send it to the left ventricle apex and on to the ventricular myocardium.

140. When an organ slips out of anatomical position.
B. Prolapse - Prolapse is when an organ moves out of proper anatomical position.

141. Which of the following is a cleft palate?
D. Palatoschisis - Palatoschisis is a genetic condition where the palate is cleft.

142. What is the space called between the posterior abdominal wall and the peritoneum?
A. Retroperitoneal - Retroperitoneal is the term used when referencing the space between the posterior abdominal wall and the peritoneum.

143. What is the contraction phase of the cardiac cycle called?
D. Systole - The systole phase of the cardiac cycle is when the heart contracts.

144. Where would the suprarenal glands be located?
C. Kidney - The superior aspect of the kidney is where the suprarenal glands are located.

145. Supine is defined as:
A. Patient is lying on her back, arms at sides, face and palms up -The term anatomic position is described as a human body positioned upright, facing forward, arms slightly outward from the body, palms, and feet facing forward. The term supine is defined as a patient laying on her back, arms at sides with face and palms up.

146. When moisture penetrates a sterile drape it is called:
D. Strike-through contamination - When moisture penetrates a sterile drape it is called strike-through contamination.

147. The definition of systole:
B. Contraction phase of the cardiac cycle - Systole is the contraction phase of the cardiac cycle.

148. Which of the following line the articular capsule within a freely movable joint and lubricate the joint?
D. Synovial membrane - The synovial membrane lines and lubricates the articular capsule within freely movable joints.

149. What part of the nervous system is responsible for the "fight or flight" mechanism?
A. Sympathetic nervous system - The sympathetic system is responsible for the 'Fight or Flight' mechanism and the parasympathetic system works on homeostasis.
The autonomic nervous system connects the central nervous system to the organs and has two parts: sympathetic system and the parasympathetic system.

150. Which of the following is the best definition of the term *superior*?
C. A directional term meaning toward the head or toward the top of a structure - Superior is a directional term that meanings toward the top of a structure/organ.

151. What anatomical structure is made up of the manubrium, body, and xiphoid process?
D. Sternum - The manubrium, body, and xiphoid process together form the sternum.

152. What joint is made up of the glenoid fossa and the head of the humerus?
B. Shoulder Joint - The shoulder joint is made up of the glenoid fossa and the head of the humerus. The hip joint is made up of the acetabulum and the head of the femur. The elbow joint is made up of the distal end of the humerus and the proximal end of the ulna. The knee joint is made up of the distal end of the femur and the proximal end of the tibia.

153. What type of healing will take place when a wound heals from the inside out due to granulation:
B. Second intention healing - Second intention healing occurs when granulation takes place and the wound heals from the inside out.

154. Where are sebaceous glands located?
A. Skin - The skin is the organ that sebaceous glands are located.

155. When a structure becomes stiff and hardens it is?
D. Sclerotic - Sclerosis (sclerotic) is the hardening or stiffening of a structure.

156. Which of the following is the white portion of the eyeball?
A. Sclera - The sclera is the white fibrous part of the eyeball.

157. What is the name of the structure that lies between the larynx and the primary bronchi.
B. Trachea - The trachea lies between the larynx and the primary bronchi and allows air to pass into the lungs.

158. When a patient at rest has a heart rate higher than 100 beats per minute, what is it labeled?
C. Tachycardia - Tachycardia is a heart rate faster than 100 beats per minute.

159. Which of the following is harvested from a different species than its recipient?
A. Xenograft - When a graft is taken from a species that is different than the recipient it is a xenograft.

160. Damage to tissue of the body:
D. All of the above - Wound, trauma, and injury are all terms used when referring to damage to the body, whether intentional, traumatic, or chronic.

161. The definition of the term *Leukocyte* is:
A. White blood cell - Leuko means white and cyte means cell. Leukocyte is the term used for white blood cells.

162. What are the vital bodily function measurements called ?
D. Vital Signs - Vital signs include blood pressure, pulse, respiration, and temperature.

163. What are the ureter openings and the urethra opening called in the bladder?
B. Vesical trigone - The vesical trigone is the anatomical landmark in the bladder marked by the two ureteral openings and the urethra opening.

164. When the ventricle contracts abnormally fast, it is called:
C. Ventricular tachycardia - When the ventricle contracts quickly, three or more times in succession, 140-250/minute, it is called ventricular tachycardia.

165. When the ventricles of the heart have abnormal opening between them.
B. Ventricular septal defect - Ventricular septal defect is when there is an opening between the left and right ventricle of the heart that does not allow proper blood flow through the heart.

166. Uncoordinated, fast contractions of the heart ventricles.
B. Ventricular fibrillation - Ventricular fibrillation is when the heart ventricles contract rapidly and in an uncoordinated fashion.

167. The caudal chambers of the heart.
C. Ventricles - The ventricles receive blood from the atria and are located on the lower half of the heart.

168. What is the tube that connects the bladder to the body's exterior?
A. Urethra - The urethra is the path urine takes from the bladder to the outside of the body.

169. Which of the following is the tube that urine travels through between the kidney and the bladder?
B. Ureters - The Ureters connect the kidneys to the bladder and allows urine to flow from the kidneys to the bladder. The urethra is the passage urine takes from the bladder to the outside of the body.

170. When something affects only one side.
B. Unilateral - Unilateral refers to only one side (uni- means one. Lateral means side).

171. What position is the patient in when he is laying on his back with arms and hands at his side?
A. Supine - Supine is when a person lies on her back with her arms at her side palms and face upward.

172. Which of the following is affected by Carpal Tunnel Syndrome?
D. Median nerve - The median nerve is entrapped by the transverse carpal ligament causing pain, tingling, and numbness in the fingers.

173. What anatomical structure is affected by Colle's fracture?
B. Distal radius - The epiphysis at the distal radius will have an angled fracture called Colle's fracture.

174. Where does gas and nutrient exchange take place in the blood?
D. Capillaries - Capillary beds are the microscopic area where gas and nutrient exchange take place in the blood.

175. When blood returns to the heart from the extremities, what part of the heart does it enter?
B. Right atrium - The blood enters the right atrium when it returns to the heart from the body.

176. What causes a decrease in blood pressure?
A. Vasodilation - Blood pressure is increased during vasoconstriction and decreased during vasodilation.

177. Which layer of the artery is in contact with the blood?
C. Tunica intima - Tunica intima is the innermost layer and is in contact with the blood. The tunica adventitia is the outer layer and has connective tissue that attaches the artery to the tissues around it. The tunica media is the smooth muscle fiber of the artery and is found in the middle.

178. Arterial blood pressure is affected by:
D. All of the above - Arterial blood pressure is affected by the amount of water/fluid in the body, cardiac output, and the ventricular contraction strength.

179. Choose the organ from the list below that has sensory input, protects against disease, and assists in homeostasis?
A. Skin - The skin is the organ that has sensors for temperature, pain, and pressure as well as assisting in homeostasis.

180. Which layer of the skin has no blood vessels or nerves?
B. Epidermis - The epidermis is the layer of the skin that has no blood vessels or nerves in it. The blood vessels and nerves are located in the dermal layer.

181. Which layer anchors the skin?
C. Subcutaneous layer - The subcutaneous layer of the skin is the anchor for the skin.

182. What produces cerumen?
A. Ceruminous gland - Ceruminous gland produces cerumen, ear wax.

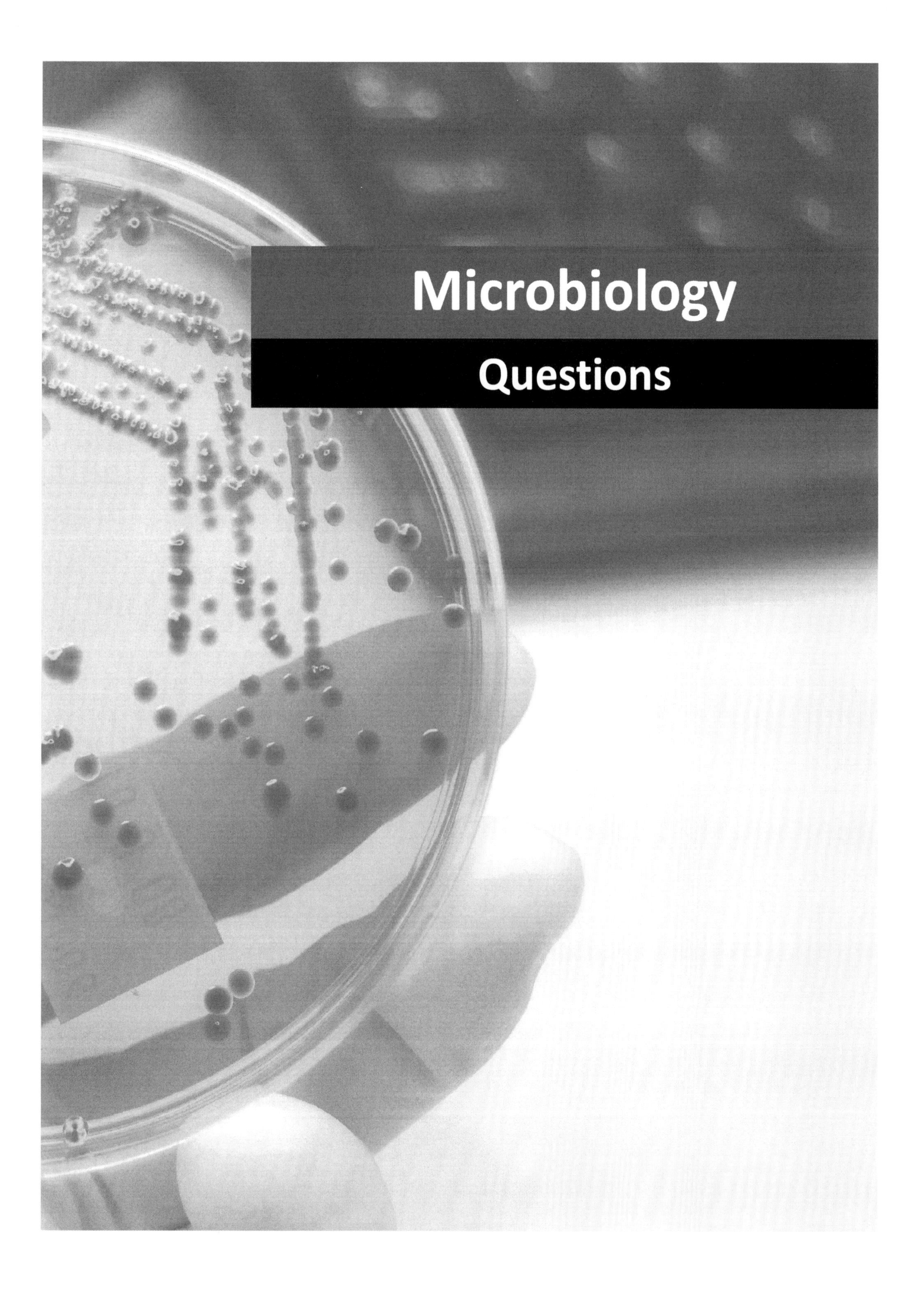

Microbiology

Questions

1. Which of the following can cause tonsillitis?
A. Staphylococcus
B. Haemophilus influenzae
C. Streptococcus
D. All of the above

2. Which of the following is associated with streptococcus pyogenes?
A. Hansen's disease
B. Gangrene
C. Anthrax
D. Necrotizing fasciitis

3. An aerobe organism is one that will grow best in the presence of:
A. Oxygen
B. Light
C. Water
D. Carbon dioxide

4. Which of the following grows in the absence of oxygen?
A. Aerobe
B. Anaerobe
C. Analgesic
D. Anergy

5. When a child produces her own immunoglobulins because she has been ill and recovered, it is referred to as:
A. Naturally acquired active immunity
B. Naturally acquired passive immunity
C. Artificially acquired active immunity
D. Artificially acquired passive immunity

6. When an immunity is passed from mother to fetus it is referred to as:
A. Naturally acquired active immunity
B. Artificially acquired active immunity
C. Artificially acquired passive immunity
D. Naturally acquired passive immunity

7. Which of the following is the probable cause for peptic ulcers?
A. Treponema pallidum
B. Helicobacter pylori
C. Bordetella pertussis
D. Neisseria gonorrhoeae

8. When gram staining what color will the bacteria turn if it is gram-positive?
A. Red
B. Blue
C. Violet
D. Green

9. What color will the bacteria stain if it is gram-negative?
A. Red
B. Violet
C. Green
D. Blue

10. Which of the following are classifications of bacteria?
A. Cocci
B. Spirilla
C. Bacilli
D. All of the above
E. None of the above

11. When a population is infected with a disease and the disease is studied within that group it is referred to as:
A. Epidemiologist
B. Epidemiology
C. Incidence
D. Prevalence

12. Which of the following is short duration and can be life-threatening?
A. Acute disease
B. Chronic disease
C. Morbidity
D. Opportunistic disease

13. Which of the following is **NOT** an immediate threat to its host, has milder signs and symptoms, and is long in duration?
A. Subacute disease
B. Chronic disease
C. Opportunistic disease
D. Latent disease

14. Which of the following could be considered portals of entry for pathogens?
A. Catheterization
B. Intubation
C. Wounds
D. All of the above
E. None of the above

15. Which of the following is the degree that a pathogen will cause disease?
A. Infection
B. Invasiveness
C. Disease
D. Virulence

16. Which of the following is found on the feet?
A. Tinea pedis
B. Tinea capitis
C. Tinea cruris
D. Tinea manis

17. Which of the following cause fever blisters?
A. Varicella-Zoster virus
B. Herpes simplex virus
C. Staphylococcus aureus
D. Candida albicans

18. Which of the following is a bacteria?
A. Candida albicans
B. Herpes simplex
C. Staphylococcus aureus
D. Microsporum

19. Which of the following is not a sexually transmitted disease?
A. Neisseria meningitis
B. Chlamydia trachomatis
C. Treponema pallidum
D. Human papilloma virus

20. What organ does encephalitis affect?
A. Kidney
B. Brain
C. Liver
D. Pancreas

21. Which of the following are tick born diseases?
A. Rocky mountain spotted fever
B. Lyme disease
C. Ehrlichiosis
D. All of the above

22. Which of the following is used on living tissue to inhibit or stop the growth of a microorganism?
A. Disinfectant
B. Sterilization
C. Antiseptic
D. Insecticide

23. Which of the following is a method used to prevent microorganisms from contaminating objects in the operating room?
A. Sanitize
B. Asepsis
C. Antiseptic
D. Disinfectant

24. Which of the following refers to a microorganism that can live and grow in the absence of oxygen?
A. Anaerobe
B. Aerobe
C. Aero
D. None of the above

25. Which of the following refers to a protein produced by the body's immune system when harmful substances known as antigens are detected?
A. Antigen
B. Antibody
C. Microorganism
D. None of the above

26. What does the term leukocyte mean?
A. Plasma
B. Red blood cell
C. Nerve cell
D. White blood cell

27. These are the microorganisms that benefit the body and live on/within the body.
A. Organisms
B. Transient organisms
C. Resident organisms
D. All of the above

28. What is the organism that is easy to remove through washing and lives on the surface of the skin?
A. Resident organisms
B. Transient organisms
C. Microorganisms
D. Parasite

29. A *leukocyte* is defined as a:
A. White cell
B. Red blood cell
C. Blood cell
D. White blood cell

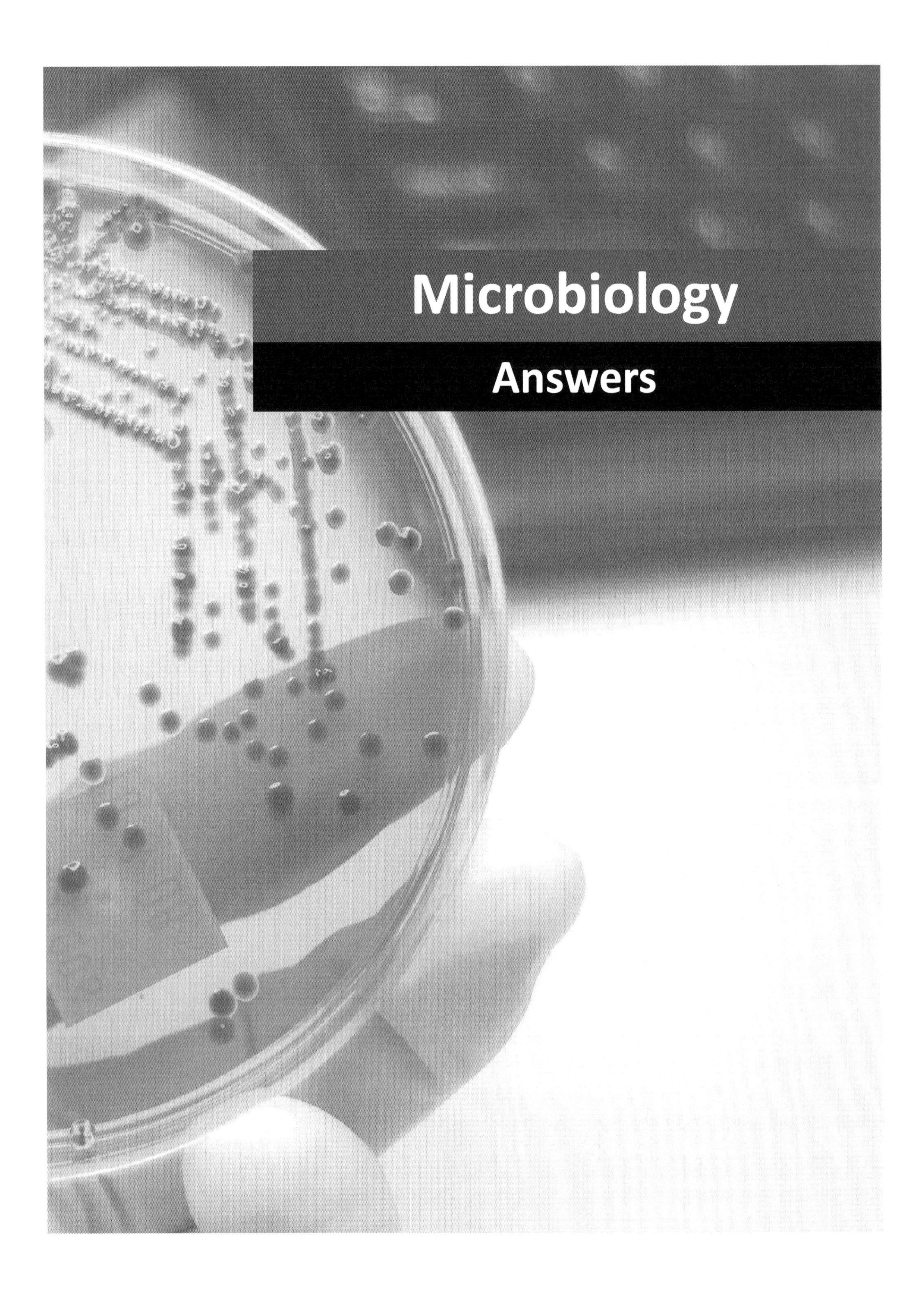
Microbiology
Answers

1. Which of the following can cause tonsillitis?
C. Streptococcus - Streptococcus is the infecting agent for tonsillitis.

2. Which of the following is associated with streptococcus pyogenes?
D. Necrotizing fasciitis - Necrotizing fasciitis is caused by streptococcus pyogenes.

3. An aerobe organism is one that will grow best in the presence of:
A. Oxygen - An organism that grows best in the presence of oxygen is called an aerobe.

4. Which of the following grows in the absence of oxygen?
B. Anaerobe - Anaerobe is an organism that does not need oxygen to grow.

5. When a child produces her own immunoglobulins because she has been ill and recovered, it is referred to as:
A. Naturally acquired active immunity - A naturally acquired active immunity is one where the person has the illness and recovers. While sick the body develops the immunoglobulins to prevent a reoccurring infection.

6. When an immunity is passed from mother to fetus it is referred to as:
D. Naturally acquired passive immunity - When the IgG molecules are transferred to the baby via the placenta it is called naturally acquired passive immunity.

7. Which of the following is the probable cause for peptic ulcers?
B. Helicobacter pylori - Duodenal and peptic ulcers are caused by the pathogen Helicobacter pylori.

8. When gram staining what color will the bacteria turn if it is gram-positive?
C. Violet - The gram-positive bacteria will stain a violet color.

9. What color will the bacteria stain if it is gram-negative?
A. Red - The gram-negative will stain red.

10. Which of the following are classifications of bacteria?
D. All of the above - Bacteria are classified as spirilla, bacilli, or cocci.

11. When a population is infected with a disease and the disease is studied within that group it is referred to as:
B. Epidemiology - Epidemiology is the study of a disease within the population it is infecting.

12. Which of the following is short duration and can be life-threatening?
A. Acute disease - An acute disease can be life-threatening and is usually short in duration. Chronic disease is one that is not as severe and has a long duration. Opportunistic disease is one that develops because the host has a weakened immune system. Morbidity is another term for illness.

13. Which of the following is **NOT** an immediate threat to its host, has milder signs and symptoms, and is long in duration?
B. Chronic disease - Chronic disease is one that is not as severe and has a long duration.

14. Which of the following could be considered portals of entry for pathogens?
D. All of the above - Catheterization and intubation are procedures where something foreign is entering the body and therefore are considered a portal of entry.
Wounds are openings in the body and are portals of entry for pathogens.

15. Which of the following is the degree that a pathogen will cause disease?
D. Virulence - Virulence is the degree that a pathogen will cause disease

16. Which of the following is found on the feet?
A. Tinea pedis - Tinea pedis is a fungal infection of the feet. Usually starting between the toes

17. Which of the following cause fever blisters?
B. Herpes simplex virus - Herpes simplex virus is commonly called fever blisters.

18. Which of the following is a bacteria?
C. Staphylococcus aureus - Staphylococcus aureus is bacteria.

19. Which of the following is not a sexually transmitted disease?
A. Neisseria meningitis - Chlamydia trachomatis is chlamydia a sexually transmitted disease. Treponema pallidum is the causative agent for syphilis. Human papilloma virus is the cause of genital warts. Neisseria meningitis affects the nervous system.

20. What organ does encephalitis affect?
B. Brain - Encephalitis affects the brain.

21. Which of the following are tick born diseases?
D. All of the above - Rickettsia rickettsii is transmitted by the wood tick and causes Rocky Mountain Fever. Lyme disease is caused by ticks that carry Borrelia burgdorferi. Deer ticks are the vectors that carry ehrlichiosis.

22. Which of the following is used on living tissue to inhibit or stop the growth of a microorganism?
C. Antiseptic - Antiseptics are used on living tissue to stop the growth or inhibit the growth of a microorganism(s).

23. Which of the following is a method used to prevent microorganisms from contaminating objects in the operating room?
B. Asepsis - Asepsis is a method to prevent microorganisms from contaminating things.

24. Which of the following refers to a microorganism that can live and grow in the absence of oxygen?
A. Anaerobe - The term anaerobe refers to a microorganism that can live and grow in the absence of oxygen.
The term aerobe refers to a microorganism that lives and grows in the presence of oxygen.
Aero is a word part that means air or gas.

25. Which of the following refers to a protein produced by the body's immune system when harmful substances known as antigens are detected?
B. Antibody - An antibody is a protein produced by the body's immune system when harmful substances known as antigens are detected.

26. What does the term leukocyte mean?
D. White blood cell - A leukocyte is a white blood cell.

27. These are the microorganisms that benefit the body and live on/within the body.
C. Resident organisms - Resident organisms are located in and on the body and are beneficial to the wellbeing of the human.

28. What is the organism that is easy to remove through washing and lives on the surface of the skin?
B. Transient organisms - A transient organism lives on the surface of the skin and is easy to remove by washing .

29. A *leukocyte* is defined as a:
D. White blood cell - Leuko means white and cyte means cell. Leukocyte is the term used for white blood cells.

Pharmacology

Questions

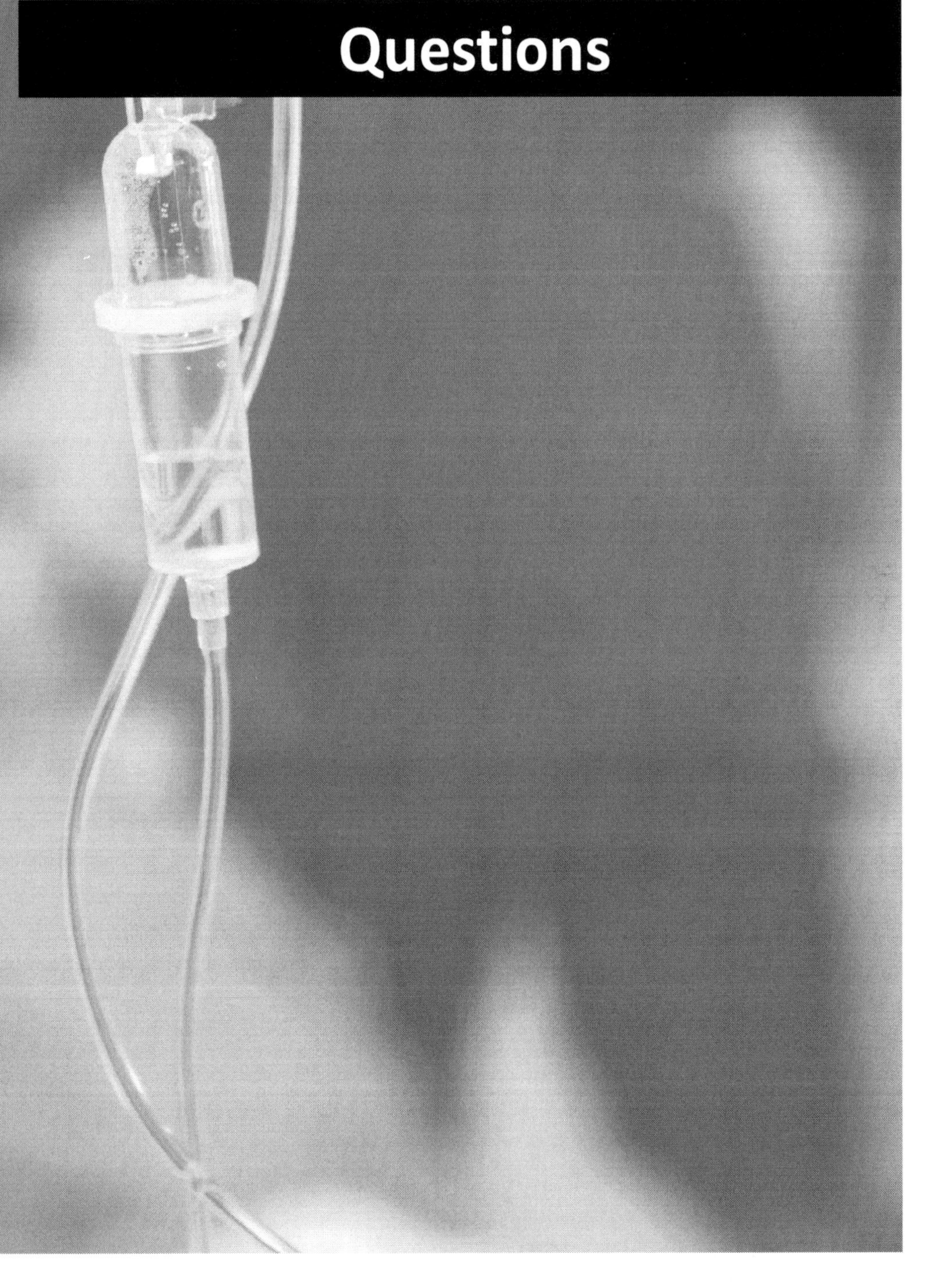

1. Which stage of anesthesia causes loss of consciousness and eyelid reflex?
A. Stage I
B. Stage II
C. Stage III
D. Stage IV

2. Which of the following is referred to as the overdose stage of anesthesia?
A. Stage I
B. Stage II
C. Stage III
D. Sage IV

3. Which stage is referred to as the excitement stage of anesthesia?
A. Stage I
B. Stage II
C. Stage III
D. Stage IV

4. Stage I of anesthesia is considered the ____ stage.
A. Amnesia
B. Excitement
C. Overdose
D. Preinduction

5. In which stage of anesthesia does surgery take place?
A. Stage I (amnesia stage)
B. Stage II (delirium stage)
C. Stage III (surgical anesthesia stage)
D. Stage IV (overdose stage)

6. Which of the following is the correct order for general anesthesia phases?
A. Induction, maintenance, recovery, emergence
B. Induction, maintenance, emergence, and recovery
C. Induction, recovery, maintenance, emergence
D. Maintenance, induction, emergence, recovery

7. What is the purpose of the Sellick's maneuver?
A. Increases the risk of aspiration
B. Reduces the risk of choking
C. Reduces bronchospasm
D. Reduce the chance of aspiration

8. Which of the following is **NOT** a regional anesthesia?
A. Nerve plexus block
B. Bier block
C. Spinal block
D. MAC block

9. To administer a Bier block what supply would be needed?
A. Tourniquet
B. Allen stirrup
C. Mayo-Hegar needle holder
D. Scalpel

10. Where is a spinal block administered?
A. Muscle
B. Vertebrae column
C. Subarachnoid space
D. Nerve

11. Where is the epidural anesthesia administered?
A. Dural space of the vertebrae
B. Subarachnoid space
C. Muscle
D. Epidural space of the vertebrae

12. Which of the following is **NOT** an anesthetic agent?
A. Nitrous oxide
B. Oxygen
C. Sevoflurane
D. Desflurane

13. Which of the following is **NOT** an induction agent?
A. Ketamine hydrochloride
B. Propofol
C. Etomidate
D. Pentothal sodium

14. Which of the following is the most commonly used dissociative agent for surgery?
A. Pentothal sodium
B. Desflurane (Suprane)
C. Enflurane
D. Ketamine hydrochloride (Ketalar)

15. Which of the following anesthesia medications produce hypnosis and depress the CNS?
A. Pentothal and Marcaine
B. Pentothal and Sodium
C. Sodium and Xylocaine
D. Marcaine and Xylocaine

16. Which of the following are nerve conduction blockers?
A. Succinylcholine and Ethrane
B. Xylocaine and Succinylcholine
C. Xylocaine and Marcaine
D. Ethrane and Marcaine

17. Which of the following cause pupil dilation?
A. Cycloplegic drugs
B. Viscoelastic drugs
C. Mydriatic drugs
D. Both B and D

18. Which of the following solutions is similar to plasma?
A. Dextrose solution
B. Ringer's solution
C. Saline solution
D. Plasma solution

19. Which of the following are used to correct acidosis, electrolyte, and fluid imbalance?
A. Dextrose solution and saline solution
B. Ringer's solution and lactated ringer's solution
C. Ringer's solution and dextrose solution
D. Lactated ringer's solution and saline solution

20. When a patient has metabolic alkalosis what solution should be administered?
A. 0.9% saline solution
B. 5% Dextrose solution
C. Lactated ringer's solution
D. None of the above

21. Which of the following can be used when a patient has large blood loss?
A. Whole blood
B. Packed red blood cells and plasma
C. Plasma
D. Whole blood and packed red blood cells

22. What condition would the blood expander, Hespan, be used to correct?
A. Hypervolemia
B. Hypovolemia
C. Hypotension
D. Hypertension

23. During surgery the patient begins having the following signs and symptoms: tachycardia, increased levels of carbon dioxide, and unstable blood pressure, and muscular contracture. What condition is the patient more than likely presenting?
A. Malignant hyperthermia
B. Malignant hypothermia
C. Shock
D. Allergic reaction

24. Which of the following is a medication for Malignant Hyperthermia?
A. Lidocaine Hydrochloride
B. Mazicon
C. Keflex
D. Dantrolene

25. What treatment should be followed during surgery when a patient goes into malignant hyperthermia?
A. Stop anesthesia, administer Dantrolene
B. Stop anesthesia, administer 100% oxygen, Dantrolene, chilled IV fluids, and use chilled saline lavage
C. Increase anesthesia and oxygen and administer chilled saline lavage
D. Increase anesthesia and oxygen, administer chilled IV fluids and saline lavage

26. What fluid needs to be mixed with Dantrolene prior to administering the Dantrolene?
A. Injectable water
B. Sterile injectable saline
C. Sterile injectable water
D. Saline

27. What is the loading dose of Dantrolene?
A. 1 mg/kg
B. 2.0 mg/kg
C. 2.5 mg/kg
D. 3.5 mg/kg

28. What class of drug are opiates?
A. Class I
B. Class II
C. Class III
D. Class IV

29. Which of the following is used in the OR setting for pain management?
A. Xylocaine
B. Versed
C. Codeine
D. Keflex

30. Heparin and Coumadin are found in which of the following category?
A. Antiemetics
B. Analgesics
C. Anti-arrhythmias
D. Anticoagulants

31. What do Gelfoam, Avitene, and Surgicel do?
A. Stimulate clot breakdown
B. Decreases edema
C. Identifies lymph vessels
D. Stimulate clot formation

32. What solution is used to stain the cervical mucosa during a conization?
A. Ringer's solution
B. Lugol's solution
C. Dextrose solution
D. Lactated ringer's solution

33. Schiller's solution is used in which of the following procedures?
A. Conization
B. Colposcopy
C. Vulvectomy
D. Marsupialization

34. Which of the following anesthetic agents is called 'milk of amnesia'?
A. Etomidate
B. Thiopental sodium
C. Propofol
D. Morphine sulfate

35. Which of the following is **NOT** a parenteral application of medication?
A. Intramuscular
B. Intrathecal
C. Buccal
D. Intracardiac

36. What is a solution prepared with water called?
A. Tincture solution
B. Aqueous solution
C. Emulsion
D. Elixir

37. Which drug causes pupil dilation?
A. Mydriatic drugs
B. Cycloplegic drugs
C. Both A and B
D. None of the above

38. When the pupil needs to be constricted what drug would be used?
A. Mydriatic drugs
B. Miotic drugs
C. Cycloplegic drugs
D. Anti-inflammatory drugs

39. When sensations of sensory and motor eye function need to be blocked, what would the surgeon use?
A. Retrobulbar anesthesia
B. Halogenated anesthesia
C. Propofol
D. Thiopental sodium

40. Which of the following is **NOT** an eye lubricant?
A. BSS (Balanced Salt Solution)
B. Lacri-lube
C. Carbachol
D. Dura tears

41. What can be used to facilitate hemostasis at the surgical site?
A. Epinephrine
B. Lidocaine with saline
C. Lidocaine with epinephrine
D. Lidocaine

42. This is when a substance is enhanced by a chemical/drug.
A. Synergist
B. Agonist
C. Antagonist
D. Prophylaxis

43. This is used to prevent the agonist from working.
A. Agonist
B. Antagonist
C. Prophylaxis
D. Synergist

44. This is the time it takes a medication to take effect.
A. On set
B. Peak effect
C. Indication
D. Contraindication

45. This is the term used for the duration a medication is effective within the patient.
A. Indication
B. Peak effect
C. On set
D. Duration

46. This is an effect that is expected as a result of a drug.
A. Toxic effect
B. Side effect
C. Adverse effect
D. Therapeutic effect

47. This is the amount of a drug needed to produce the desired effect.
A. Side effect
B. Toxic effect
C. Addictive effect
D. Therapeutic effect

48. This is when a medication produces a harmful effect to the patient.
A. Adverse effect
B. Side effect
C. Therapeutic effect
D. Indicated effect

49. This is a term used when a patient needs a higher dose of medication to produce the desired effect.
A. Side effect
B. Therapeutic effect
C. Tolerance
D. Addictive effect

50. This is when a patient has a physiological or psychological dependency for a medication.
A. Tolerance
B. Addiction
C. Need
D. Adversity

51. What is the meaning of NPO?
A. Note patients orders
B. Not per operation
C. Nothing by mouth
D. None of the above

52. This is when a substance is enhanced by a chemical/drug.
A. Agonist
B. Synergist
C. Antagonist
D. Prophylaxis

53. This is when a medication produces a harmful effect to the patient.
A. Adverse effect
B. Side effect
C. Therapeutic effect
D. Indicated effect

54. This is when a patient has a physiological or psychological dependency for a medication.
A. Tolerance
B. Addiction
C. Need
D. Adversity

55. Which of the following word suffixes is synonymous with the word pain?
A. -al
B. -itis
C. -osis
D.-algia

56. Which of the following is an air tight glass vessel commonly used to hold medications for hypodermic injection?
A. Ampule
B. Vial
C. Syringe
D. None of the above

57. Which of the following refers to a medication that reduces or eliminates pain?
A. Antibiotic
B. Anticoagulant
C. Analgesic
D. Antihistamine

58. Which of the following refers to a drug that neutralizes the effects of another drug?
A. Agonist
B. Antagonist
C. Analgesic
D. None of the above

59. Which of the following refers to a medication used to kill microorganisms?
A. Antibiotic
B. Antihistamine
C. Analgesic
D. Anticoagulant

60. Which of the following refers to an agent used to prevent the formation of blood clots?
A. Coagulant
B. Insulin
C. Miotic
D. Anticoagulant

61. When two liquids are put together but will not mix it is called:
A. Semisolid
B. Aqueous
C. Emulsion
D. None of the above

62. What term is defined as an accumulation of fluid in the intercellular space.
A. Swelling
B. Edema
C. Inflammation
D. All of the above

63. When the doctor hands off a tissue to be sent to pathology and it needs to be preserved, it is placed:
A. In formalin
B. In a non sterile medicine cup
C. In a sterile bowl
D. On a raytec

64. A mydriatic is a drug that:
A. Causes the arteries to dilate
B. Causes the pupil to constrict
C. Causes the arteries to constrict
D. Causes the pupil to dilate

65. Miotic drugs make
A. The pupil dilate
B. The veins constrict
C. The veins dilate
D. The pupil constrict

66. The study of how drugs move, how they are absorbed, and excreted from the body.
A. Pharmacokinetics
B. Pharmacologist
C. Pharmacodynamics
D. All of the above

67. Which of the following is **NOT** a parenteral route of drug administration?
A. Intramuscular
B. Intra-articular
C. Buccal
D. Intravenous

68. What term is defined as a sweetened aqueous solution?
A. Syrup
B. Tincture
C. Elixir
D. Emulsion

69. Which is prepared with alcohol?
A. Emulsion
B. Tincture
C. Aqueous
D. Syrup

70. What term is used for anesthesia vapors escaping the tubing and anesthesia machine?
A. Waste gas
B. Waste vapors
C. Waste anesthetic gases
D. None of the above

71. Which medication is used to prevent vasospasms?
A. Papaverine
B. Sodium heparin
C. Lidocaine
D. Epinephrine

72. What does tumescent liposuction involve?
A. A mixture of epinephrine, saline, and anesthetic
B. A mixture of local anesthetic, midazolam, and saline
C. A mixture of epinephrine, saline, midazolam, and Wydase
D. A mixture of local anesthetic, epinephrine, saline, and Wydase

73. How should Gelfoam be prepared for a craniotomy?
A. Placed in saline
B. Placed in epinephrine
C. Placed in cocaine
D. Placed in thrombin

Pharmacology

Answers

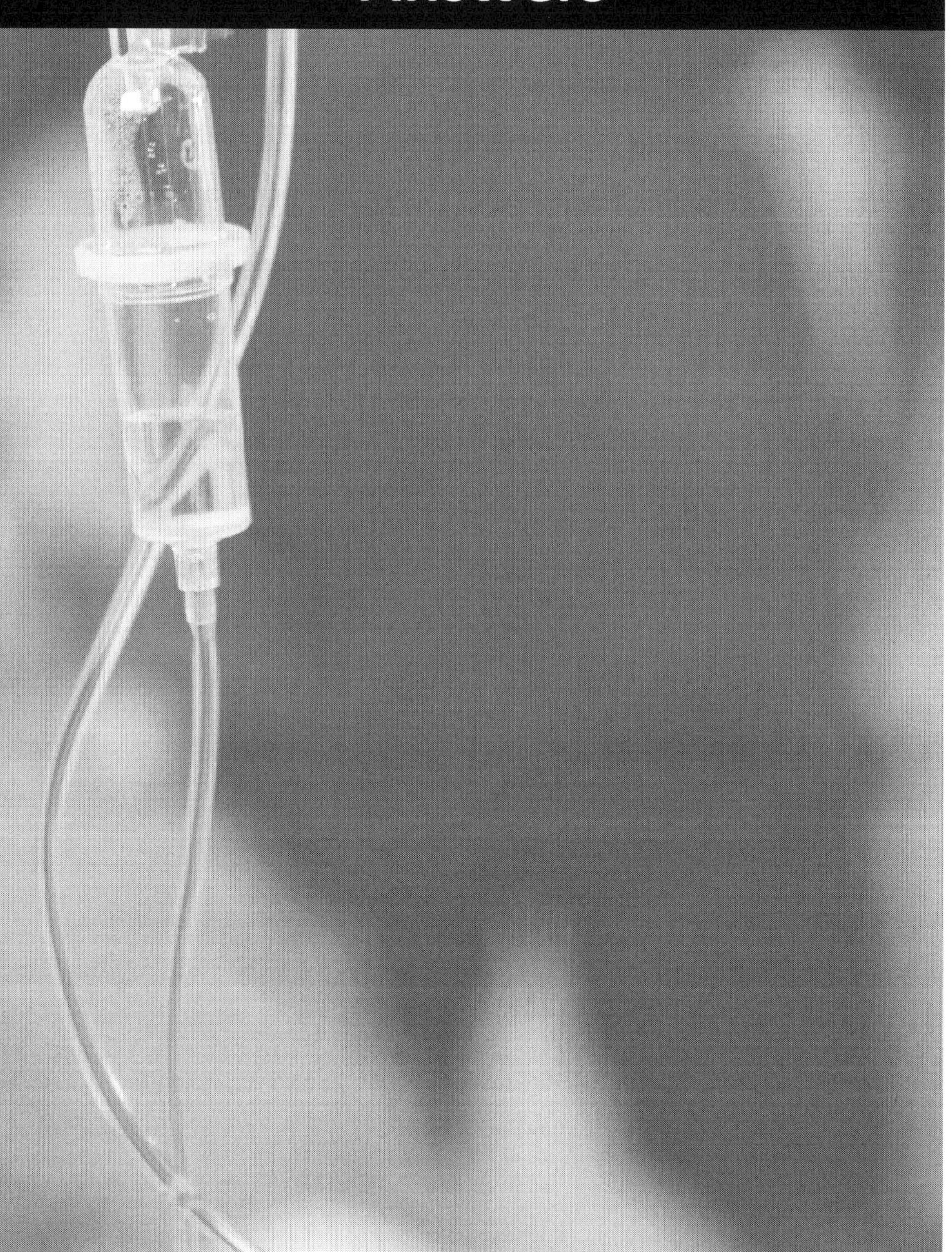

1. Which stage of anesthesia causes loss of consciousness and eyelid reflex?
B. Stage II - Stage II (excitement stage) begins at unconsciousness through loss of eyelid reflex and return of regular breathing

2. Which of the following is referred to as the overdose stage of anesthesia?
D. Sage IV - Stage IV (overdose stage) is marked by nonreactive dilated pupils, hypotension, and cessation of breathing.

3. Which stage is referred to as the excitement stage of anesthesia?
B. Stage II - Stage II (excitement stage) begins at unconsciousness through loss of eyelid reflex and return of regular breathing.

4. Stage I of anesthesia is considered the ____ stage.
A. Amnesia - Stage I (amnesia stage) starts at the administration of the anesthetic to unconsciousness.

5. In which stage of anesthesia does surgery take place?
C. Stage III (surgical anesthesia stage) - Stage III (surgical anesthesia stage) begins with regular breathing through cessation of breathing. This is the stage where surgery takes place.

6. Which of the following is the correct order for general anesthesia phases?
B. Induction, maintenance, emergence, and recovery - The order of the phases of general anesthesia is as follows: Induction is the phase where the patient moves from alert to asleep. Maintenance is the phase where the surgical procedure takes place. Emergence is where the patient is brought back to consciousness and the procedure is ending. Recovery begins in the OR and continues in PACU.

7. What is the purpose of the Sellick's maneuver?
D. Reduce the chance of aspiration - The Sellick's maneuver is used during anesthesia induction to occlude the esophagus preventing aspiration.

8. Which of the following is **NOT** a regional anesthesia?
D. MAC block - Regional anesthesia includes nerve plexus block, Bier block, and spinal block. A MAC block is monitored anesthesia care and is a nerve block that is given topically or locally in combination with sedatives.

9. To administer a Bier block what supply would be needed?
A. Tourniquet - The supplies needed to administer a Bier block include: tourniquet, Esmarch bandage, IV catheter.

10. Where is a spinal block administered?
C. Subarachnoid space - The spinal block is administered into the cerebrospinal fluid in the subarachnoid space within the lumbar region (L2-3 or L3-4 disk spaces) of the vertebrae.

11. Where is the epidural anesthesia administered?
D. Epidural space of the vertebrae - The epidural anesthesia is administered above the dura matter into the epidural space of the vertebrae.

12. Which of the following is **NOT** an anesthetic agent?
B. Oxygen - Nitrous oxide, sevoflurane, desflurane, and isoflurane are anesthetic agents. Oxygen is not classified as an anesthetic agent.

13. Which of the following is **NOT** an induction agent?
A. Ketamine hydrochloride - Induction agents allow the transition from stage 1 to stage 3 of consciousness more pleasant. These agents include: Propofol (Diprivan), Etomidate (Amidate), Thiopental sodium (Pentothal sodium), and Methohexital sodium (Brevital).

14. Which of the following is the most commonly used dissociative agent for surgery?
D. Ketamine hydrochloride (Ketalar) - Ketamine hydrochloride is the dissociative agent most commonly used in surgery.

15. Which of the following anesthesia medications produce hypnosis and depress the CNS?
B. Pentothal and Sodium - Pentothal and Sodium are in the category of induction agents. Induction agents produce hypnosis and anesthesia, depress the CNS, and are not analgesics.

16. Which of the following are nerve conduction blockers?
C. Xylocaine and Marcaine - Xylocaine, Marcaine, Carbocaine, Cocaine, Duranest, and Naropin block nerve conduction. Succinylcholine prevents muscle contraction and Ethrane maintains unconsciousness.

17. Which of the following cause pupil dilation?
D. Both B and D - Pupil dilation is caused by mydriatic and cycloplegic drugs. Viscoelastic agents are used to replace the vitreous humor.

18. Which of the following solutions is similar to plasma?
B. Ringer's solution - Ringer's solution has serum electrolytes and is similar to plasma.

19. Which of the following are used to correct acidosis, electrolyte, and fluid imbalance?
B. Ringer's solution and lactated ringer's solution - Ringer's and lactated ringer's solutions are used to correct acidosis, electrolyte and fluid imbalance in the patient.

20. When a patient has metabolic alkalosis what solution should be administered?
A. 0.9% saline solution - When a patient has metabolic alkalosis the patient 0.9% saline solution should be administered.

21. Which of the following can be used when a patient has large blood loss?
D. Whole blood and packed red blood cells - When a patient has blood loss, whole blood and packed red blood cells (PRBC) can be administered to the patient.

22. What condition would the blood expander, Hespan, be used to correct?
B. Hypovolemia - Hespan, a plasma expander, would be administered to a patient that is hypovolemic or in hypovolemic shock.

23. During surgery the patient begins having the following signs and symptoms: tachycardia, increased levels of carbon dioxide, and unstable blood pressure, and muscular contracture. What condition is the patient more than likely presenting?
A. Malignant hyperthermia - Malignant hyperthermia signs and symptoms include: muscle contraction, increased levels of carbon dioxide, unstable blood pressure, perspiration, cyanosis, mottled skin, and rise in body temperature.

24. Which of the following is a medication for Malignant Hyperthermia?
D. Dantrolene - Dantrolene is the only medication to reverse malignant hyperthermia at this time.

25. What treatment should be followed during surgery when a patient goes into malignant hyperthermia?
B. Stop anesthesia, administer 100% oxygen, Dantrolene, chilled IV fluids, and use chilled saline lavage - When a surgical patient goes into malignant hyperthermia anesthesia needs to stop, 100% oxygen and Dantrolene needs to be administered as well as chilled IV fluids and chilled lavage of the body cavities.

26. What fluid needs to be mixed with Dantrolene prior to administering the Dantrolene?
C. Sterile injectable water - Sterile injectable water is mixed with Dantrolene for administration to a patient with malignant hyperthermia.

27. What is the loading dose of Dantrolene?
C. 2.5 mg/kg - 2.5 mg/kg of Dantrolene is administered as a loading dose. This is followed by 1mg/kg every 5 minutes until 10mg/kg is administered.

28. What class of drug are opiates?
B. Class II - Opiates/opiods are in the class II controlled substances category. Some of these drugs include: Demerol, Sublimaze, and Sufenta.

29. Which of the following is used in the OR setting for pain management?
C. Codeine - Medications used in the OR setting for pain management vary: Codeine, Sublimaze, Demerol, Morphine, Tylenol, Advil, Naprosyn, and Toradol are a few.

30. Heparin and Coumadin are found in which of the following category?
D. Anticoagulants - Heparin and Coumadin are classified as anticoagulants. They assist in preventing blood from clotting and are used in some vascular surgeries.

31. What do Gelfoam, Avitene, and Surgicel do?
D. Stimulate clot formation - Hemostatic agents assist in reducing/stopping bleeding. They block on open vessel and attract platelets to aid the clotting process. Gelfoam, Gel film, Avitene, Oxycel, Surgicel, Collastat, Hemopad, and Thrombinar are all Hemostatic agents.

32. What solution is used to stain the cervical mucosa during a conization?
B. Lugol's solution - Schiller's and Lugol's solutions are topical solutions used to stain the cervical mucosa during a conization procedure.

33. Schiller's solution is used in which of the following procedures?
A. Conization - Schiller's solution is used to stain the cervical mucosa during a conization procedure.

34. Which of the following anesthetic agents is called 'milk of amnesia'?
C. Propofol - Propofol (Diprivan) is called 'Milk of Amnesia' because of its milky appearance.

35. Which of the following is **NOT** a parenteral application of medication?
C. Buccal - Buccal, sublingual, instillation and inhalation are all topical drug administration routes. Intradermal, subcutaneous, intramuscular, intravenous, intra-articular, intrathecal, and intracardiac are all parenteral routes of administration of drugs. Oral and rectal administration of drugs is enteral administration.

36. What is a solution prepared with water called?
B. Aqueous solution - Aqueous solutions are made with water.

37. Which drug causes pupil dilation?
C. Both A and B - Mydriatic and cycloplegic drugs cause the iris to dilate by paralyzing it.

38. When the pupil needs to be constricted what drug would be used?
B. Miotic drugs - Miotic drugs help the pupil constrict by causing the sphincter of the iris to become smaller.

39. When sensations of sensory and motor eye function need to be blocked, what would the surgeon use?
A. Retrobulbar anesthesia - Retrobulbar anesthesia is used to block the eye sensations (sensory and motor function).

40. Which of the following is **NOT** an eye lubricant?
C. Carbachol - Carbachol (Carbacel) is used to constrict the sphincter of the iris. The solutions used to lubricate the eye during surgery include BSS, Lacri-lube, and Dura tears.

41. What can be used to facilitate hemostasis at the surgical site?
C. Lidocaine with epinephrine - Lidocaine with epinephrine is usually used to help with pain and hemostasis.

42. This is when a substance is enhanced by a chemical/drug.
B. Agonist - When a substance is enhanced by a drug is an agonistic interaction.

43. This is used to prevent the agonist from working.
B. Antagonist - The antagonist is used to bind to the receptor site of the agonist to prevent the agonist from attaching to the receptor.

44. This is the time it takes a medication to take effect.
A. On set - On set is the time it takes a medication to take effect.

45. This is the term used for the duration a medication is effective within the patient.
D. Duration - The duration a medication is effective within the patient is referred to as duration.

46. This is an effect that is expected as a result of a drug.
B. Side effect - The side effect is an expected result of a drug. Examples: dry mouth, diarrhea, drowsiness

47. This is the amount of a drug needed to produce the desired effect.
D. Therapeutic effect - The therapeutic effect is the amount of drug needed to produce the desired effect without producing harmful effects to the patient.

48. This is when a medication produces a harmful effect to the patient.
A. Adverse effect - When a medication produces a harmful effect in the patient this is an adverse effect of the medication.

49. This is a term used when a patient needs a higher dose of medication to produce the desired effect.
C. Tolerance - Tolerance is when a patient needs a higher dose of medication to produce the desired effect.

50. This is when a patient has a physiological or psychological dependency for a medication.
B. Addiction - An addiction is when a patient has a physiological or psychological dependency for a medication.

51. What is the meaning of NPO?
C. Nothing by mouth - NPO (Non per os or nil per os) is nothing by mouth.

52. This is when a substance is enhanced by a chemical/drug.
A. Agonist - When a substance is enhanced by a drug is an agonistic interaction.

53. This is when a medication produces a harmful effect to the patient.
A. Adverse effect - When a medication produces a harmful effect in the patient this is an adverse effect of the medication.

54. This is when a patient has a physiological or psychological dependency for a medication.
B. Addiction - An addiction is when a patient has a physiological or psychological dependency for a medication.

55. Which of the following word suffixes is synonymous with the word pain?
D.-algia - The suffix -algia is synonymous with the word pain.

56. Which of the following is an air tight glass vessel commonly used to hold medications for hypodermic injection?
A. Ampule - An ampule is the air tight glass vessel commonly used to hold medications for hypodermic injection.

57. Which of the following refers to a medication that reduces or eliminates pain?
C. Analgesic - The term analgesic refers to a medication that reduces or eliminates pain.

58. Which of the following refers to a drug that neutralizes the effects of another drug?
B. Antagonist - The term antagonist refers to a drug that neutralizes the effects of another drug.

59. Which of the following refers to a medication used to kill microorganisms?
A. Antibiotic - Antibiotic is medication to treat infections by killing the microorganism that is causing the infection.

60. Which of the following refers to an agent used to prevent the formation of blood clots?
D. Anticoagulant - The term anticoagulant refers to an agent used to prevent the formation of blood clots.

61. When two liquids are put together but will not mix it is called:
C. Emulsion - An emulsion is a solution made of two liquids that will not mix.

62. What term is defined as an accumulation of fluid in the intercellular space.
B. Edema - Edema is the abundance of fluid in the intercellular space.

63. When the doctor hands off a tissue to be sent to pathology and it needs to be preserved, it is placed:
A. In formalin - The specimen that needs to be preserved will be put in formalin, a preservative liquid.

64. A mydriatic is a drug that:
D. Causes the pupil to dilate - Mydriatic drugs cause the pupil to dilate.

65. Miotic drugs make
D. The pupil constrict - Miotic drugs make the pupils constrict.

66. The study of how drugs move, how they are absorbed, and excreted from the body.
A. Pharmacokinetics - Pharmacokinetics is the study of how drugs move through the body, how they are absorbed and excreted.

67. Which of the following is **NOT** a parenteral route of drug administration?
C. Buccal - Topical administration includes buccal, sublingual, instillation, and inhalation. Parenteral routes of drug administration include intradermal, subcutaneous, intramuscular, intravenous, intra-articular, intrathecal, and intracardiac. Enteral routes include oral and rectal.

68. What term is defined as a sweetened aqueous solution?
A. Syrup - Syrup is a sweetened aqueous solution.

69. Which is prepared with alcohol?
B. Tincture - A tincture solution is one made with alcohol.

70. What term is used for anesthesia vapors escaping the tubing and anesthesia machine?
C. Waste anesthetic gases - The gases that escape the anesthesia machine and tubing are called waste anesthesia gases.

71. Which medication is used to prevent vasospasms?
A. Papaverine - Papaverine is used to prevent vasospasms.

72. What does tumescent liposuction involve?
D. A mixture of local anesthetic, epinephrine, saline, and Wydase - The Tumescent liposuction uses a mixture of Wydase, saline, epinephrine and a local anesthetic. This mixture 'liquefies' the fat to make removal easier.

73. How should Gelfoam be prepared for a craniotomy?
D. Placed in thrombin - Gelfoam is usually cut into small squares or strips and placed in thrombin to aid in hemostasis.

Pathophysiology

Questions

1. What is the condition when the eyes are not aligned properly?
A. Pterygium
B. Strabismus
C. Chalazion
D. Dacryocystitis

2. What term is defined as the chest being depressed because the sternum is displaced posteriorly?
A. Pectus excavatum
B. Sternal fissure
C. Pectus carinatum
D. Sternal cleft

3. When there is an accumulation of air in the pleural cavity causing the lung to collapse it is called:
A. Cardiac tamponade
B. Bronchitis
C. Penetrating wound
D. Pneumothorax

4. What is it called when the foreskin will not retract over the glans penis?
A. Hypospadias
B. Torsion
C. Phimosis
D. Hypertrophy

5. Which of the following is when the testes fail to descend into the scrotum?
A. Cryptorchism
B. Testicular torsion
C. Hypospadias
D. Epispadias

6. What term is used when bleeding occurs in the brain between the cranium and dural mater?
A. Aneurysm
B. Subdural hematoma
C. Neuroma
D. Epidural hematoma

7. What condition is caused when the cerebral spinal fluid cannot move through the ventricular system?
A. Dysraphism
B. Hydrocephalus
C. Hemorrhage
D. Aneurysm

8. Where would an intramedullary spinal tumor be found?
A. Inside the dural matter but not inside the spinal cord
B. Outside the spinal cord
C. Inside the spinal cord
D. Through all layers of the spinal cord

9. Which nerve is affected in carpal tunnel syndrome?
A. The caudal plexus
B. The brachial plexus
C. The ulnar nerve
D. The median nerve

10. Which of the following pathological conditions would a gastrostomy be performed?
A. Esophageal stricture
B. Cholesteatoma
C. Hernia
D. Strangulated bowel

11. Which of the following repairs the protrusion of abdominal contents through a weakening of the abdominal lining?
A. Gastrostomy
B. Billroth I
C. Herniorrhaphy
D. Stoma

12. What part of the body does pilonidal disease affect?
A. Sacrococcygeal area
B. Axilla area
C. Inguinal area
D. Thoracic area

13. Which of the following procedures will be performed for cancer in the head of the pancreas?
A. Cholecystectomy
B. Mastectomy
C. Whipple
D. Tracheotomy

14. When a female patient presents with a prolapsed bladder which of the following would the surgeon perform?
A. Hysterectomy
B. Colporrhaphy
C. Vulvectomy
D. Cholecystectomy

15. What organ does pterygium affect?
A. Eye
B. Ovary
C. Colon
D. Lung

16. Which of the following is a condition of the upper eyelid?
A. Entropion
B. Ptosis
C. Sclera buckle
D. Cataract

17. Tinnitus is a condition of which organ?
A. Eye
B. Ear
C. Ovary
D. Duodenum

18. Which of the following is pathology of the middle ear?
A. Otitis media
B. Otitis externa
C. Meniere's syndrome
D. Vitrectomy

19. What is epistaxis?
A. Inflamed turbinates
B. Broken nose
C. Polyps in the sinus
D. Nosebleed

20. What is a viral infection of the throat?
A. Tonsillitis
B. Epistaxis
C. Pharyngitis
D. Tinnitus

21. What structure is associated with micrognathia?
A. Maxilla and/or mandible
B. Orbit and nasal bones
C. Mandible and orbit
D. Hyoid and odontoid

22. Which of the following is a deformity of the palate?
A. Cheiloschisis
B. Palatoschisis
C. Neoplasm
D. Syndactyly

23. Which of following is an autoimmune disease?
A. De Quervain's disease
B. Rheumatoid arthritis
C. Gynecomastia
D. Carpal tunnel syndrome

24. What is the condition where the foreskin will not retract over the glans penis?
A. Hypospadias
B. Cryptorchism
C. Torsion
D. Phimosis

25. What is it called when the bone becomes inflamed?
A. Osteomyelitis
B. Osteoporosis
C. Hallux valgus
D. Bunion

26. Torn meniscus is located in which joint?
A. Knee
B. Shoulder
C. Elbow
D. Hip

27. Which of the following is a congenital deformity where the sternum becomes pronounced anteriorly?
A. Pectus excavatum
B. Thoracic outlet syndrome
C. Aneurysm
D. Pectus carinatum

28. Cardiac tamponade is defined as
A. Dilation of the arterial wall due to weakening
B. When the pericardium becomes filled with blood or fluid which compresses the heart
C. When the mitral valve is weak and blood flows backward in the heart
D. When the atria beats faster than 350 beats per minute

29. What condition is present when there is no opening between the right ventricle and the right atrium?
A. Tetralogy of Fallot
B. Patent ductus arteriosus
C. Coarctation of the aorta
D. Tricuspid atresia

30. A patient with peripheral vascular disease presents with cramping in the lower leg, the pain subsides when the patient rests. What do these symptoms suggest the patient is experiencing?
A. Claudication
B. Thrombus
C. Occlusion
D. Embolus

31. This is a pathology that can occur when the abdominal aorta wall becomes thin.
A. Arteriosclerosis obliterans
B. Claudication
C. Aneurysm
D. Occlusion

32. Seizures, coma, headache, nausea, and aphasia are symptoms of which of the following?
A. Cardiac pathologies
B. Vascular pathologies
C. Neural pathologies
D. Skeletal pathologies

33. Lumbar spondylosis:
A. Spinal canal constriction
B. Lumbar disc disease
C. Bone spurs
D. Vessel occlusion

34. What is it called when the cranial sutures close prematurely?
A. Hydrocephalus
B. Spina bifida
C. Craniosynostosis
D. None of the above

35. This is when the ligament of Osborne entraps the ulnar nerve.
A. Ulnar nerve compression
B. Carpal tunnel syndrome
C. Hydrocephalus
D. Hematoma

36. What is ischemic disease?
A. Fast heart rate
B. Stroke
C. Fast respiration
D. Brittle bone

37. Which of the following terms means cancerous growth?
A. Benign
B. Node
C. Malignant
D. Nodular

38. Which of the following refers to a congenital heart condition where the blue skin color associated with cyanosis is not produced?
A. Acyanotic defect
B. Cardiomyopathy
C. Pulmonary stenosis
D. None of the above

39. Which of the following is a condition that causes changes in blood pressure or heart rate, chronic diarrhea, and darkening of the skin and occurs when the adrenal glands do not produce enough of their hormones?
A. Cushing's syndrome
B. Addison's disease
C. Crohn's disease
D. All of the above

40. Which of the following is another name for renal cell carcinoma?
A. Nephroblastoma
B. Adenocarcinoma
C. Nephropathy
D. None of the above

41. Which of the following terms refers to the temporary cessation of breathing?
A. Apnea
B. Anaerobic
C. Aqueous
D. Asystole

42. Which of the following refers to an irregular or abnormal heart rhythm?
A. Tachycardia
B. Bradycardia
C. Cardiomyopathy
D. Arrhythmia

43. Which of the following refers to a lab test used to evaluate the lungs by measuring the levels of oxygen and CO2 in arterial blood?
A. Computed axial tomography
B. Aspiration biopsy
C. Capnography
D. Arterial blood gases (ABGs)

44. Which of the following refers to the failure of the ventricles of the heart to contract?
A. Diastole
B. Asystole
C. Systole
D. None of the above

45. Which of the following terms is used to describe the fatty plaque that accumulates against the wall of an artery?
A. Atheroma
B. Atherosclerosis
C. Cholesteatoma
D. None of the above

46. Which of the following refers to an irregular heart beat characterized by uneven electrical activity in the atria?
A. Ventricular fibrillation
B. Atriomegaly
C. Atrial fibrillation
D. None of the above

47. When the intrauterine fetus presents feet or buttocks first at delivery this is called?
A. Breech
B. Lightening
C. Parity
D. Descent

48. Which of the following heart rates will be labeled bradycardia?
A. Heart rate below 60 beats per minute or slower
B. Heart rate below 70 beats per minute or slower
C. Heart rate below 80 beats per minute or slower
D. None of the above

49. Define compound fracture.
A. A fracture where the bone breaks into many pieces but the skin stays intact.
B. A fracture where the bone only breaks on one side and remains in the skin.
C. A fracture where the bone is not broken through and through.
D. A fracture where the bone is broken and part of the bone pushes through the skin.

50. When a bone is broken in more than three pieces it is:
A. Compound fracture
B. Comminuted fracture
C. Green stick fracture
D. Simple fracture

51. Which of the following is a clouded/opaque crystalline lens?
A. Ptosis
B. Cataract
C. Entropion
D. None of the above

52. This is a person that has an infectious pathogen in their system but does not get sick from it.
A. Vector
B. Carrier
C. Hybrid
D. None of the above

53. What is gas, air, or tissue that floats through the circulatory system called?
A. Embolus
B. Emboli
C. Thrombus
D. Plaque

54. What term is used when an opening forms between two structures that should not be there?
A. Lumen
B. Fistula
C. Fossa
D. Fomite

55. Which of the following affects only the epidermis?
A. First-degree burn
B. Second degree burn
C. Third degree burn
D. Fourth degree burn

56. When a patient's tissue oxygen levels are below normal range:
A. Hyperoxia
B. Hypovolemia
C. Hypervolemia
D. Hypoxia

57. Which of the following is the definition for hypotension:
A. High blood pressure
B. Low blood pressure
C. Low blood volume
D. High blood volume

58. Which of the following is the definition for hypothermia:
A. Core body temperature below 65 degrees Celsius
B. Core body temperature below 70 degrees Celsius
C. Core body temperature below 75 degrees Celsius
D. Core body temperature below 80 degrees Celsius

59. When a disease moves from its original position to other positions it is called:
A. Mitigate
B. Transient
C. Metastasis
D. Stationary

60. Which of the following is a medical emergency caused by high end-tidal carbon dioxide, tachycardia, muscle rigidity, and high body temperature?
A. Hyperthermia
B. Fever
C. Malignant hypothermia
D. Malignant hyperthermia

61. Which of the following conditions is characterized by a drooping of the eyelids?
A. Glaucoma
B. Cataract
C. Pterygium
D. Ptosis

62. What is the term used to represent more digits than 5 on hands or feet?
A. Polydactyly
B. Syndactyly
C. Multiple digits
D. Pentadigit

63. When there is an accumulation of air in the pleural cavity it is referred to as:
A. Pneumonectomy
B. Pneumatic
C. Pneumothorax
D. Pleura

66. What is the term used for when the foreskin cannot be retracted over the glans penis?
A. Phimosis
B. Philtrum
C. Hypospadias
D. Cryptorchism

67. When the sternum is posteriorly displaced making the chest look concave.
A. Pectus carinatum
B. Pectus excavatum
C. Mediastinum
D. None of the above

68. Which of the following is a congenital chest deformity where the sternum is protruding?
A. Pectus carinatum
B. Pectus excavatum
C. Mediastinum
D. None of the above

69. Which of the following are used to assess the surface area burned on a patient?
A. Abbreviated Burn Severity Index
B. Rule of nines
C. Lund-Browder
D. Both B and C

70. When the digits of the feet and/or hands fail to separate it is called:
A. Webbing
B. Syndactyly
C. Deformity
D. All of the above

71. This is something a patient feels, a perception about a condition, disease, or illness.
A. Sign
B. Symptom
C. Emotion
D. None of the above

72. Which of the following is an infection acquired during a surgical procedure?
A. Surgical site infection
B. Nosocomial infection
C. Both A and B
D. None of the above

73. When a disease affects the entire system.
A. Local
B. Metastasis
C. Systemic
D. None of the above

74. What is the condition where the tissue between the fingers and toes fail to separate during fetal development?
A. Dactyly
B. Duck digits
C. Syndactyly
D. None of the above

75. What term means constriction?
A. -stasis
B. Stenosis
C. Stent
D. None of the above

76. When the bone is twisted and fractures it is referred to as which of the following?
A. Greenstick fracture
B. Comminuted fracture
C. Spiral fracture
D. Transverse fracture

77. Define septicemia.
A. When the blood stream has infective agents in it
B. Surgical reconstruction of the nasal septum
C. Failure of the circulatory system to bring blood to the organs
D. None of the above

78. A patient presents with his right arm injured by heat exposure. The epidermis and part of the dermis have been affected. There is redness, blisters, and it is very painful. The patient has:
A. First degree burn
B. Second degree burn
C. Third degree burn
D. Fourth degree burn

79. Which defines tricuspid atresia?
A. The absence of the tricuspid valve between the left ventricle and the left atrium
B. The absence of the tricuspid valve between the right ventricle and right atrium
C. The absence of the bicuspid valve between the right ventricle and right atrium
D. The absence of the bicuspid valve between the left ventricle and the left atrium

80. When neck muscles are in a state of abnormal contraction it is called:
A. Contracture
B. Sprain
C. Torticollis
D. Strain

81. A client presents with upper limb pain, weakness in the hand, paresthesia of fingers and drooping shoulder girdle. The patient is having symptoms of:
A. Carpal tunnel syndrome
B. Thoracic outlet syndrome
C. Sciatica
D. Thoracalgia

82. Which of the following affect all layers of the skin and appears white in color?
A. First-degree burn
B. Second-degree burn
C. Third-degree burn
D. All of the above

83. Tendonitis is defined:
A. Inflammation of a muscle
B. Inflammation of a structure
C. Inflammation of a vessel
D. Inflammation of a tendon

84. Damage to tissue of the body:
A. Wound
B. Trauma
C. Injury
D. All of the above

85. When the ventricle contracts abnormally fast, it is called:
A. Atrial tachycardia
B. Ventricular tachycardia
C. Ventricular bradycardia
D. Atrial bradycardia

86. When the ventricles of the heart have abnormal opening between them.
A. Ventricular septal defect
B. Atrial septal defect
C. Cardiac defect
D. Septal defect

87. Which of the following is not an aneurysm form?
A. Saccular
B. Fusiform
C. Internal
D. Dissecting

88. Which of the following is a condition where an opening occurs between the left and right ventricle of the heart:
A. Patent ductus arteriosus
B. Pulmonary stenosis
C. Coarctation of the aorta
D. Ventricular septal defect

89. What is pediatric aortic coarctation?
A. Expansion of the aorta
B. Narrowing of the aorta
C. Stenosis of the subclavian artery
D. Blockage of the jugular vein

90. What syndrome presents with the signs and symptoms of fullness in the ear, tinnitus, vertigo, and intermittent hearing loss?
A. Meniere's syndrome
B. Cushing syndrome
C. Compartmental syndrome
D. None of the above

91. What procedure is done to remove part of the bony portion of the mastoid air cells?
A. Myringotomy
B. Stapedotomy
C. Mastoidectomy
D. Otosclerosis

92. Which of the following is the condition where the nasal mucosa is inflamed and over produces mucous?
A. Sinusitis
B. Rhinitis
C. Polyps
D. Epistaxis

93. What is the condition that causes the mucosal lining in the paranasal sinuses to become inflamed?
A. Sinusitis
B. Rhinitis
C. Polyps
D. Epistaxis

94. Which of the following is not in a basic nasal set?
A. Cottle speculum
B. Halsey needle holder
C. Graefe forceps
D. Pottsmith scissors

95. What term is used when the pharyngeal tonsils are inflamed?
A. Adenoiditis
B. Laryngitis
C. Epiglottitis
D. Pharyngitis

96. What is an embolus?
A. Piece(s) of thrombus that is floating throughout the vascular system
B. A stationary clot
C. Cholesterol build up
D. None of the above

97. What degree burn is it when the epidermis is affected but not blistered?
A. First degree burn
B. Second degree burn
C. Third degree burn
D. Fourth degree burn

98. Which of the following is the medical term for cleft palate?
A. Cheiloschisis
B. Blepharochalasis
C. Palatoschisis
D. Dermatochalasis

99. What is used to determine the total body surface area burned?
A. Lund-Browder
B. Rule of Nines
C. Abbreviated Burn Severity Index
D. A and B

100. What term is used when the digits fail to separate during development?
A. Syndactyly
B. Hypoplasia
C. Neoplasm
D. Palatoschisis

101. Which of the following anatomical structures are affected in radial dysplasia?
A. Digits three and four, ulna, and soft tissue
B. Hallux, ulna, and soft tissue
C. Digits and ulna
D. Hallux, radius, and soft tissue

102. Which of the following is the medical term for hair lip?
A. Palatoschisis
B. Cheiloschisis
C. Dermatochalasis
D. Palatoschisis

103. What is caused by the palmar fascia contracting and nodules forming on the fourth or fifth digit?
A. Dupuytren's Disease
B. De Quervain's Disease
C. Trigger Finger
D. Polydactyly

104. What is the definition of gynecomastia?
A. Over development of the female breast
B. Over development of the male breast
C. Tumor is the uterus
D. Cyst in the breast

105. Which of the following conditions causes snapping and locking the fingers and thumb?
A. Polydactyly
B. Dupuytren's Disease
C. Trigger finger
D. DeQuervain's Disease

106. Which of the following is an autoimmune disease where the synovial tissue is attacked causing damage to the cartilage and bone?
A. Human Immunodeficiency Virus
B. Rheumatoid arthritis
C. Ganglion cyst
D. Multiple sclerosis

107. Which of the following conditions is a stenosing tenosynovitis?
A. Dupuytren's disease
B. Pheochromocytoma
C. Cushing syndrome
D. De Quervain's disease

108. What term is used for the condition where the rectum prolapses into the vaginal vault?
A. Rectocele
B. Cystocele
C. Colposcopy
D. Colporrhaphy

109. Which stage of labor is defined as the span between complete dilation of the cervix and birth of the infant?
A. Stage one
B. Stage two
C. Stage three
D. Stage four

110. What term is used when a structure becomes stiff and hard?
A. Stenotic
B. Sclerotic
C. Stent
D. Septic

111. Tendonitis is defined:
A. Inflammation of a tendon
B. Inflammation of a muscle
C. Inflammation of a structure
D. Inflammation of a vessel

Pathophysiology

Answers

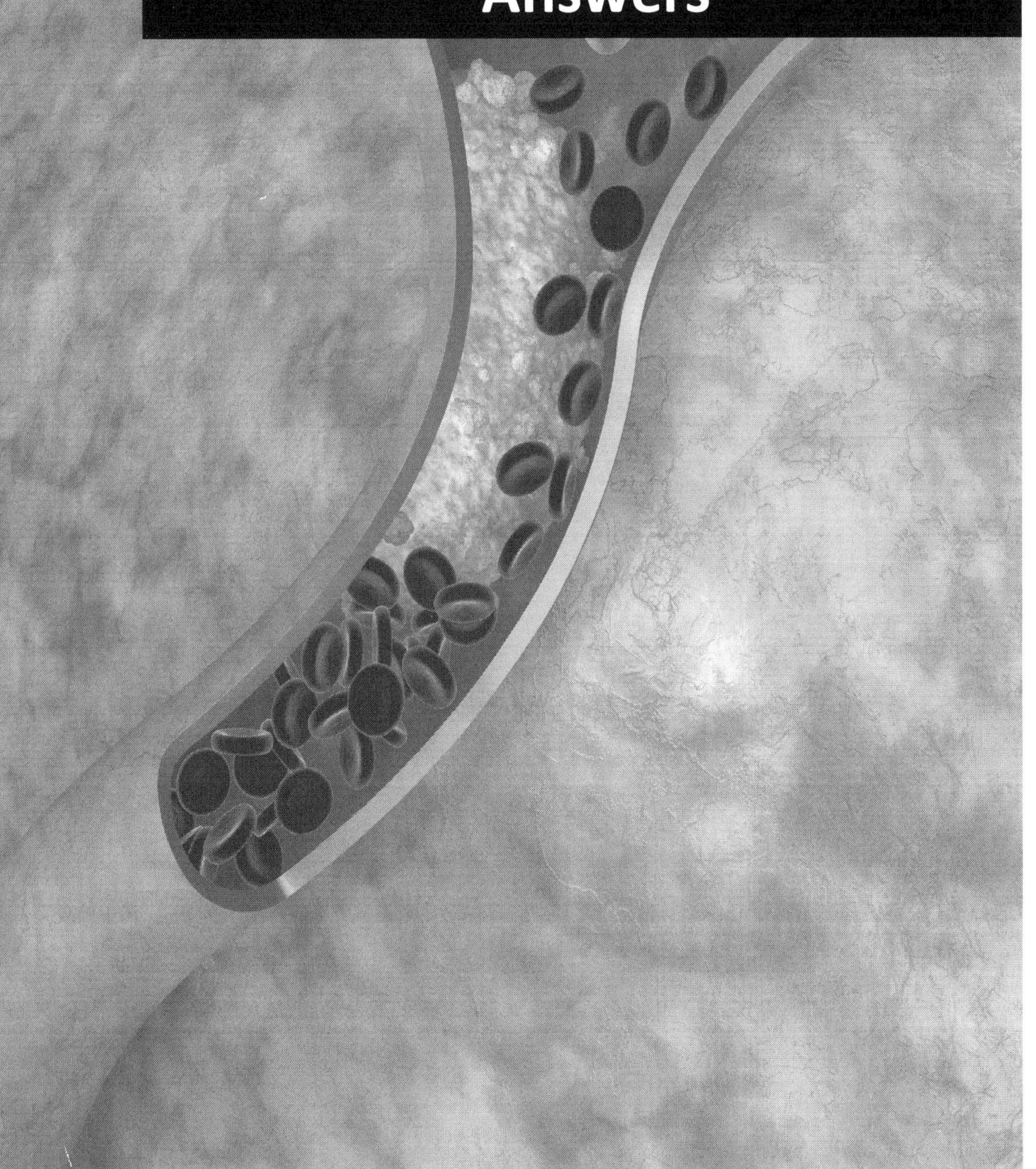

1. What is the condition when the eyes are not aligned properly?
B. Strabismus - Strabismus is when the eyes are misaligned or one is deviated.

2. What term is defined as the chest being depressed because the sternum is displaced posteriorly?
A. Pectus excavatum - Pectus excavatum is when the sternum is displaced posteriorly making the chest look as though it is a funnel shape.

3. When there is an accumulation of air in the pleural cavity causing the lung to collapse it is called:
D. Pneumothorax - Pneumothorax occurs when the lung cannot expand and collapses because there is air or alveolar gas in the pleural cavity.

4. What is it called when the foreskin will not retract over the glans penis?
C. Phimosis - Phimosis is the condition where the prepuce will not retract over the glands penis.

5. Which of the following is when the testes fail to descend into the scrotum?
A. Cryptorchism - Cryptorchism is when the testes fail to drop into the scrotum.

6. What term is used when bleeding occurs in the brain between the cranium and dural mater?
D. Epidural hematoma - Epidural hematoma is when the vessels in the brain bleed between the skull and dura matter.

7. What condition is caused when the cerebral spinal fluid cannot move through the ventricular system?
B. Hydrocephalus - Hydrocephalus can be caused by cerebral spinal fluid not being moved through the ventricular system.

8. Where would an intramedullary spinal tumor be found?
C. Inside the spinal cord - The intramedullary spinal tumor is found inside the spinal cord. The intradural spinal tumor is located inside the dural matter and outside the spinal cord. The extradural spinal tumor is located on the outside of the spinal cord.

9. Which nerve is affected in carpal tunnel syndrome?
D. The median nerve - The median nerve becomes entrapped within the transverse carpal ligament causing carpal tunnel syndrome.

10. Which of the following pathological conditions would a gastrostomy be performed?
A. Esophageal stricture - A gastrostomy may be performed for esophageal strictures, tumors of the larynx, pharynx, esophagus, and the proximal stomach.

11. Which of the following repairs the protrusion of abdominal contents through a weakening of the abdominal lining?
C. Herniorrhaphy - Herniorrhaphy is performed to correct a protrusion of internal organs through a weak abdominal lining.

12. What part of the body does pilonidal disease affect?
A. Sacrococcygeal area - Pilonidal disease is an abscess in the sacrococcygeal area that will not heal.

13. Which of the following procedures will be performed for cancer in the head of the pancreas?
C. Whipple - The Whipple procedure is used to remove the head of the pancreas due to cancer.

14. When a female patient presents with a prolapsed bladder which of the following would the surgeon perform?
B. Colporrhaphy - The colporrhaphy would be performed to repair the bladder or rectum that has 'fallen' into the vaginal vault.

15. What organ does pterygium affect?
A. Eye - Pterygium affects the cornea of the eye. It is a condition where the conjunctiva grows onto the cornea.

16. Which of the following is a condition of the upper eyelid?
B. Ptosis - Ptosis is when the upper eyelid begins to droop because the levator aponeurosis becomes weak.

17. Tinnitus is a condition of which organ?
B. Ear - The ear is the organ tinnitus affects. It is a ringing in the ear.

18. Which of the following is pathology of the middle ear?
A. Otitis media - Otitis media is inflammation of the inner ear.

19. What is epistaxis?
D. Nosebleed - Epistaxis is nose bleeds caused by the nasal mucosa drying, nose picking, chronic inflammation, and/or hypertension.

20. What is a viral infection of the throat?
C. Pharyngitis - Pharyngitis is a viral or bacterial infection of the throat.

21. What structure is associated with micrognathia?
A. Maxilla and/or Mandible - Micrognathia is a deformity of the jaw in which the jaw does not develop to full size. It can affect the mandible, maxilla, or both.

22. Which of the following is a deformity of the palate?
B. Palatoschisis - Palatoschisis is a deformity of the palate.

23. Which of following is an autoimmune disease?
B. Rheumatoid arthritis - Rheumatoid arthritis is an autoimmune disease of the synovial tissues.

24. What is the condition where the foreskin will not retract over the glans penis?
D. Phimosis - Phimosis is a condition where the foreskin will not retract over the glans penis.

25. What is it called when the bone becomes inflamed?
A. Osteomyelitis - Osteomyelitis is an inflammation of the bone.

26. Torn meniscus is located in which joint?
A. Knee - The meniscus is located in the knee joint.

27. Which of the following is a congenital deformity where the sternum becomes pronounced anteriorly?
D. Pectus carinatum - When the sternum protrudes anteriorly it is called pectus carinatum.

28. Cardiac tamponade is defined as
B. When the pericardium becomes filled with blood or fluid which compresses the heart - Cardiac tamponade is when the pericardium becomes filled with blood or fluid compressing the heart.

29. What condition is present when there is no opening between the right ventricle and the right atrium?
D. Tricuspid atresia - Tricuspid atresia is the absence of the opening and the tricuspid valve resulting in no opening between the right ventricle and the right atrium.

30. A patient with peripheral vascular disease presents with cramping in the lower leg, the pain subsides when the patient rests. What do these symptoms suggest the patient is experiencing?
A. Claudication - Claudication is when there is exercise onset cramping that dissipates with rest in a patient with peripheral vascular disease.

31. This is a pathology that can occur when the abdominal aorta wall becomes thin.
C. Aneurysm - Aneurysm is a pathology where the wall of the aorta becomes thin and bulges.

32. Seizures, coma, headache, nausea, and aphasia are symptoms of which of the following?
C. Neural pathologies - Neural pathologies can have the following symptoms: seizure, coma, headache, nausea, aphasia, intracranial pressure.

33. Lumbar spondylosis:
B. Lumbar disc disease - Lumbar spondylosis is a disease of the lumbar discs and bone caused by osteoarthritis.

34. What is it called when the cranial sutures close prematurely?
C. Craniosynostosis - Craniosynostosis is when the cranial suture closes prematurely, before age 2.

35. This is when the ligament of Osborne entraps the ulnar nerve.
A. Ulnar nerve compression - The ligament of Osborne can entrap the ulnar nerve causing a pathology called ulnar nerve Compression.

36. What is ischemic disease?
B. Stroke - Stroke is ischemic disease.

37. Which of the following terms means cancerous growth?
C. Malignant - Malignant means cancerous growth.

38. Which of the following refers to a congenital heart condition where the blue skin color associated with cyanosis is not produced?
A. Acyanotic defect - The term acyanotic defect is the congenital heart condition that does not produce the blue skin color associated with cyanosis.

39. Which of the following is a condition that causes changes in blood pressure or heart rate, chronic diarrhea, and darkening of the skin and occurs when the adrenal glands do not produce enough of their hormones?
B. Addison's disease - Addison's disease is a condition brought on when the adrenal glands do not produce enough of their hormones causing changes in blood pressure or heart rate, chronic diarrhea, and darkening of the skin.

40. Which of the following is another name for renal cell carcinoma?
B. Adenocarcinoma - Another name for renal cell carcinoma is adenocarcinoma. Adenocarcinoma is the most common type of kidney cancer.

41. Which of the following terms refers to the temporary cessation of breathing?
A. Apnea - The term apnea is used to describe the temporary cessation of breathing.

42. Which of the following refers to an irregular or abnormal heart rhythm?
D. Arrhythmia - The term arrhythmia refers to an irregular or abnormal heart rhythm.

43. Which of the following refers to a lab test used to evaluate the lungs by measuring the levels of oxygen and CO2 in arterial blood?
D. Arterial blood gases (ABGs) - Arterial blood gasses is a lab test used to evaluate the lungs by measuring the levels of oxygen and CO2 in arterial blood.

44. Which of the following refers to the failure of the ventricles of the heart to contract?
B. Asystole - Failure of the ventricles of the heart to contract is known as asystole.

45. Which of the following terms is used to describe the fatty plaque that accumulates against the wall of an artery?
A. Atheroma - Atheroma is a fatty plaque that accumulates against the wall of an artery. Atheromas cause atherosclerosis.

46. Which of the following refers to an irregular heart beat characterized by uneven electrical activity in the atria?
C. Atrial fibrillation - Atrial fibrillation is irregular heart beat characterized by uneven electrical activity in the atria.

47. When the intrauterine fetus presents feet or buttocks first at delivery this is called?
A. Breech - Breech is when the intrauterine fetus presents feet or buttock first at delivery.

48. Which of the following heart rates will be labeled bradycardia?
A. Heart rate below 60 beats per minute or slower - Heart rate 60 beats per minute or slower is labeled as bradycardia.

49. Define compound fracture.
D. A fracture where the bone is broken and part of the bone pushes through the skin. - A compound fracture is a fracture where the bone is broken and part of the bone pushes through the skin.

50. When a bone is broken in more than three pieces it is:
B. Comminuted fracture - A comminuted fracture is when the bone fragments into many pieces.

51. Which of the following is a clouded/opaque crystalline lens?
B. Cataract - A cataract is the clouding of the crystalline lens in the eye. It is caused by trauma or age.

52. This is a person that has an infectious pathogen in their system but does not get sick from it.
B. Carrier - A carrier is a person the has an infectious pathogen in their system but does not get sick from it.

53. What is gas, air, or tissue that floats through the circulatory system called?
A. Embolus - Embolus is something that is floating through the circulatory system that can get lodged in a vessel. It can be a piece of tissue, air or gas.

54. What term is used when an opening forms between two structures that should not be there?
B. Fistula - A fistula is an opening that forms between two structures that should be separate.

55. Which of the following affects only the epidermis?
A. First-degree burn - First-degree burn: epidermis, no blisters, red, no scar tissue. Second-degree burn: dermis and epidermis, blisters, red, painful, and scar Third-degree burn: all skin affected (epidermis and dermis), blisters, charring, permanent damage of tissue. Fourth-degree burn: tissue damaged to bone including nerve, vessels, and muscle can affect bone density, reconstruction will take place

56. When a patients tissue oxygen levels are below normal range:
D. Hypoxia - Hypoxia is a condition where the oxygen level in the tissue is below normal range.

57. Which of the following is the definition for hypotension:
B. Low blood pressure - Hypotension is low blood pressure.

58. Which of the following is the definition for hypothermia:
A. Core body temperature below 65 degrees Celsius - Hypothermia is a core body temperature that falls below 65 degrees Celsius.

59. When a disease moves from its original position to other positions it is called:
C. Metastasis - Metastasis is the movement of a disease from its original position to another location within the body.

60. Which of the following is a medical emergency caused by high end-tidal carbon dioxide, tachycardia, muscle rigidity, and high body temperature?
D. Malignant hyperthermia - Malignant hyperthermia is a medical emergency caused by high end-tidal carbon dioxide, tachycardia, muscle rigidity, and high body temperature.

61. Which of the following conditions is characterized by a drooping of the eyelids?
D. Ptosis - Ptosis is the condition of the eye where the lid is drooping. It is caused by a weak levator muscle.

62. What is the term used to represent more digits than 5 on hands or feet?
A. Polydactyly - Polydactyly is when the hands or the feet have more than five digits.

63. When there is an accumulation of air in the pleural cavity it is referred to as:
C. Pneumothorax - Pneumothorax is a condition where there is an accumulation of air in the pleural cavity. Pneumonectomy is a procedure where the lung is excised.

66. What is the term used for when the foreskin cannot be retracted over the glans penis?
A. Phimosis - Phimosis is a condition where the foreskin of the glans penis cannot retract.

67. When the sternum is posteriorly displaced making the chest look concave.
B. Pectus excavatum - Pectus excavatum is a congenital chest deformity where the sternum is posteriorly positioned and the chest looks concave.

68. Which of the following is a congenital chest deformity where the sternum is protruding?
A. Pectus carinatum - Pectus carinatum is a congenital chest deformity where the sternum is protruding.

69. Which of the following are used to assess the surface area burned on a patient?
D. Both B and C - The Lund-Browder and Rule of nines are the methods used to estimate the body surface affected by burns. The Abbreviated Burn Severity Index uses five criteria to determine the severity of the patient's condition.

70. When the digits of the feet and/or hands fail to separate it is called:
B. Syndactyly - Syndactyly is an abnormality that occurs when the digits of the hands and feet do not separate.

71. This is something a patient feels, a perception about a condition, disease, or illness.
B. Symptom - Signs and symptoms are associated with conditions, illness, and disease.

72. Which of the following is an infection acquired during a surgical procedure?
A. Surgical site infection - A surgical site infection is an infection acquired during a surgical procedure.

73. When a disease affects the entire system.
C. Systemic - Systemic means it affects the entire system not just a part.

74. What is the condition where the tissue between the fingers and toes fail to separate during fetal development?
C. Syndactyly - Syndactyly is the genetic condition where the tissue between the fingers and toes do not seperate.

75. What term means constriction?
B. Stenosis - Stenosis means constriction or narrowing.

76. When the bone is twisted and fractures it is referred to as which of the following?
C. Spiral fracture - Spiral fractures occur when the bone has been twisted and the fracture curves around the bone.

77. Define septicemia.
A. When the blood stream has infective agents in it - Septicemia is when a pathogen or its toxins are within the blood stream.

78. A patient presents with his right arm injured by heat exposure. The epidermis and part of the dermis have been affected. There is redness, blisters, and it is very painful. The patient has:
B. Second degree burn - First degree burns affect the epidermis without blistering. The skin is red, hot and painful to touch.

79. Which defines tricuspid atresia?
B. The absence of the tricuspid valve between the right ventricle and right atrium - Tricuspid atresia is the absence of the tricuspid valve between the right ventricle and the right atrium.

80. When neck muscles are in a state of abnormal contraction it is called:
C. Torticollis - Torticollis is a condition where the cervical muscles are in an abnormal state of contraction. It is also called wryneck.

81. A client presents with upper limb pain, weakness in the hand, paresthesia of fingers and drooping shoulder girdle. The patient is having symptoms of:
B. Thoracic outlet syndrome - Thoracic outlet syndrome's signs and symptoms include but not limited to paresthesia of fingers, pain in the upper arm, hand muscle wasting, and shoulder girdle drooping. It is caused by compression of the brachial plexus nerve trunk and subclavian vessels.

82. Which of the following affect all layers of the skin and appears white in color?
C. Third-degree burn - Third-degree burn affects the epidermis, dermis, and subcutaneous tissue.
First-degree burn affects the only the epidermis. It appears as a pink/red color with no blisters.
Second-degree burn affects the epidermis and the dermis. It appears as pink, red, or mottled white with blisters.

83. Tendonitis is defined:
D. Inflammation of a tendon - Inflammation of a tendon is tendonitis.

84. Damage to tissue of the body:
D. All of the above - Wound, trauma, and injury are all terms used when referring to damage to the body, whether intentional, traumatic, or chronic.

85. When the ventricle contracts abnormally fast, it is called:
B. Ventricular tachycardia - When the ventricle contracts quickly three or more times in succession, 140-250/minute, it is called ventricular tachycardia.

86. When the ventricles of the heart have abnormal opening between them.
A. Ventricular septal defect - Ventricular septal defect is when there is an opening between the left and right ventricle of the heart that does not allow proper blood flow through the heart.

87. Which of the following is not an aneurysm form?
C. Internal - The forms of aneurysms: saccular, fusiform and dissecting.

88. Which of the following is a condition where an opening occurs between the left and right ventricle of the heart:
D. Ventricular septal defect - Ventricular septal defect is a condition where the right and left ventricle have an opening between them that should not be there.

89. What is pediatric aortic coarctation?
B. Narrowing of the aorta - Pediatric aortic coarctation is a narrowing of the aorta. It is surgically repaired by excising the stricture and anastomosing the free edges.

90. What syndrome presents with the signs and symptoms of fullness in the ear, tinnitus, vertigo, and intermittent hearing loss?
A. Meniere's syndrome - Meniere's syndrome affects the cochlea and/or the vestibule. It presents with ringing in the ears (tinnitus), vertigo, and intermittent hearing loss

91. What procedure is done to remove part of the bony portion of the mastoid air cells?
C. Mastoidectomy - When a patient has mastoiditis, a mastoidectomy may be performed. This procedure removes part of the bony sections of the mastoid air cells.

92. Which of the following is the condition where the nasal mucosa is inflamed and over produces mucous?
B. Rhinitis - Rhinitis is when the nasal mucosa over produces mucous and becomes inflamed.

93. What is the condition that causes the mucosal lining in the paranasal sinuses to become inflamed?
A. Sinusitis - Sinusitis is inflammation of the lining of the mucosa located in the paranasal sinuses.

94. Which of the following is not in a basic nasal set?
D. Pottsmith scissors - Pottsmith scissors are found in a vascular set.

95. What term is used when the pharyngeal tonsils are inflamed?
A. Adenoiditis - Adenoiditis is when the pharyngeal tonsils are inflamed.

96. What is an embolus?
A. Piece(s) of thrombus that is floating throughout the vascular system - When a thrombus (buildup of plaque/ cholesterol) breaks free or pieces break free and travel throughout the vascular system it is called an embolus.

97. What degree burn is it when the epidermis is affected but not blistered?
A. First degree burn - A first degree burn only affects the epidermis without blistering. A second degree burn will blister and goes to the dermis at varying degrees. Third degree burns affect all layers of the skin and if the nerves are damaged can be painless. A fourth degree burn covers the epidermis, dermis, muscles, and even bone.

98. Which of the following is the medical term for cleft palate?
C. Palatoschisis - Palatoschisis is the medical term for cleft palate. Cheiloschisis is the medical term for cleft or hair lip. Blepharochalasis is the medical term used when the eyelid loses its tone and looks wrinkled. Dermatochalasis is the medical term for the skin on the eyelid when it hypertrophies.

99. What is used to determine the total body surface area burned?
D. A and B - Lund-Browder charts and the Rule of Nines are used to determine the total body surface area burned.

100. What term is used when the digits fail to separate during development?
A. Syndactyly - Syndactyly is the term used when the digits fail to separate during development. This condition can involve the soft tissue only or the bone and fingernails.

101. Which of the following anatomical structures are affected in radial dysplasia?
D. Hallux, radius, and soft tissue - Club hand (radial dysplasia), is a deformity of the thumb, radius, and soft tissues.

102. Which of the following is the medical term for hair lip?
B. Cheiloschisis - Cheiloschisis is the medical term for cleft or hair lip. Palatoschisis is the medical term for cleft palate. Blepharochalasis is the medical term used when the eyelid loses its tone and looks wrinkled. Dermatochalasis is the medical term for the skin on the eyelid when it hypertrophies.

103. What is caused by the palmar fascia contracting and nodules forming on the fourth or fifth digit?
A. Dupuytren's Disease - Dupuytren's disease is a condition where the palmar fascia becomes contracted and nodules form on the fourth and fifth digits.

104. What is the definition of gynecomastia?
B. Over development of the male breast - Gynecomastia is the over development of the male breast. It usually is seen at the onset of puberty.

105. Which of the following conditions causes snapping and locking the fingers and thumb?
C. Trigger finger - When the finger or thumb becomes inflamed and the tendons enlarge the condition is referred to as trigger finger. It is painful and the digit will lock and make a painful snapping noise.

106. Which of the following is an autoimmune disease where the synovial tissue is attacked causing damage to the cartilage and bone?
B. Rheumatoid arthritis - Rheumatoid arthritis attacks the connective tissues, synovial tissues, and can cause damage to the articular cartilage.

107. Which of the following conditions is a stenosing tenosynovitis?
D. De Quervain's disease - De Quevrain's disease is a stenosing tenosynovitis syndrome of the hand. It is known as the "washerwoman's sprain".

108. What term is used for the condition where the rectum prolapses into the vaginal vault?
A. Rectocele - Rectocele is when the rectum prolapses into the vaginal vault usually caused by pelvic muscles that have been torn or stretched from pregnancy.

109. Which stage of labor is defined as the span between complete dilation of the cervix and birth of the infant?
B. Stage two - Stage one: onset of labor until the cervix is dilated completely.

110. What term is used when a structure becomes stiff and hard?
B. Sclerotic - Sclerosis (sclerotic) is the hardening or stiffening of a structure.

111. Tendonitis is defined:
A. Inflammation of a tendon - Inflammation of a tendon is tendonitis.

SECTION 2

PERIOPERATIVE CARE

Preoperative Preparation & Management

Aseptic Technique / Preference card / Time Out
Instruments and supplies
Operating room set up
Surgical scrub / Gown / Glove
Patient transportation / Positioning / Preparation
Draping

Intraoperative Procedures & Management

Supplies
Instruments
Procedures

Postoperative Procedures & Management

Patient care
Operating Room Breakdown and Cleaning

Preoperative Preparation & Management

Questions

Aseptic Technique - Preference Card - Time out

1. Where should the ST open the gown and gloves prior to setting up the back table?
A. Operating table
B. Basin stand
C. Mayo stand
D. Back table

2. What is the correct procedure to follow when the ST's glove needs replacing during an operation?
A. ST removes the glove and regloves using closed technique
B. Another sterile team member removes the glove by grasping the glove and gown cuff and pulling off the glove; ST regloves
C. Anesthesiologist removes the glove; ST regloves using closed glove technique
D. Circulator removes the glove by grasping the glove and gown cuff and pulling off the contaminated glove; ST uses closed technique to reglove

3. What should be worn in the semi-restricted and restricted areas of the operating room?
A. Gown and gloves
B. OR attire
C. Street clothes
D. None of the above
E. All of the above

4. When dressing to enter the OR suite what should be put on first?
A. Scrubs
B. Shoe covers
C. Hair cover
D. Order of dress does not matter

5. What part of the sterile gown is considered not sterile?
A. The cuff
B. The chest area
C. The forearm area
D. None of the above

6. What is the technique for opening a small wrapped package to the sterile back table?
A. Check package integrity, hold package in one hand and break the seal, grasp the tab and lift the flap away from the body grasping this flap with the hand that is holding the package, the next flap is grasped and wrapped around the holding hand without reaching over the item and secured in the holding hand, the third flap is grasped at the edge and wrapped around the holding hand so that the holding hand is now completely covered by the wrapper. Gently toss the item onto the back table.
B. Grasp the tab and lift the flap away from the body grasping this flap with the hand that is holding the package, the next flap is grasped and wrapped around the holding hand without reaching over the item and secured in the holding hand, the third flap is grasped at the edge and wrapped around the holding hand so that the holding hand is now completely covered by the wrapper. Gently toss the item onto the back table.
C. Check package integrity, hold package in one hand and break the seal, grasp the tab and lift the flap away from the body grasping this flap with the hand that is holding the package, the third flap is grasped at the edge and wrapped around the holding hand so that the holding hand is now completely covered by the wrapper. Gently toss the item onto the back table.
D. Break the seal, grasp the tab and lift the flap away from the body grasping this flap with the hand that is holding the package, the next flap is grasped and wrapped around the holding hand without reaching over the item and secured in the holding hand, the third flap is grasped at the edge and wrapped around the holding hand so that the holding hand is now completely covered by the wrapper. Gently toss the item onto the back table.

7. How should the STSR grasp the second, third, and forth flap of the back table pack when opening it?
A. Grasp the flap on the edge of the cuff
B. Grasp the corners of the cover
C. Grasp the flap under the cuff
D. None of the above

8. Which of the following refers to the absence of bacteria, viruses, and microorganisms?
A. Sterile
B. Asepsis
C. Decontamination
D. None of the above

9. Which of the following is **NOT** found on the surgeon's preference card?
A. Patient position for surgery
B. Skin prep
C. Suture
D. Patient's allergies

10. Where would the surgeon's preference for dressings, skin prep, and medications be found?
A. Supply room
B. Supply cart
C. Nurse's station
D. Surgeons preference card

11. When does the time out occur?
A. Immediately prior to incision
B. When patient enters the operating room
C. When the surgeon calls for it
D. When the patient is positioned for surgery

12. Which of the following is not included in the time out?
A. Patient name
B. Operative procedure
C. Operative side and site
D. Operating room number

Instruments and Supplies

13. What should be checked before opening peel packed supplies for surgery?
A. Tears and punctures
B. Chemical indicators have changed
C. Integrity of the package and dates are current
D. All of the above

14. Prior to placing instruments onto the back table, what should be checked in a container system instrument set once the cover is removed?
A. Chemical indicator and filter
B. Integrity of the instruments
C. Count is correct
D. Scissors are sharp

15. Which of the following is not checked prior to opening the instrument set?
A. External chemical indicators
B. Filters on the inside of the case container
C. Seals are intact
D. Both B and C

16. When opening a basin set what order should it be opened to maintain aseptic technique?
A. Unfold the first flap toward the body, unfold the side flaps, finally unfold the fourth flap away from the body
B. Unfold the sides first, unfold the next flap away from the body, finally, unfold the fourth flap toward the body
C. Unfold the first flap away from the body, unfold the side flaps, finally unfold the fourth flap toward the body
D. Unfold the first flap away from the body, unfold the second flap toward the body, finally, unfold the sides

17. What is the Julian date?
A. The date of manufacture
B. The date of sterilization
C. The date the instrument is used for surgery
D. None of the above

18. Which of the following are used to test the steam sterilizer to guarantee the sterilization process has taken place?
A. Haemophilus influenzae
B. Microsporum sp
C. Treponema pallidum
D. Bacillus stearothermophilus

19. What is the surgical technologist looking for once the lid of the instrument set is removed?
A. The surgical technologist is looking to see if the filter is dry.
B. The surgical technologist is looking to see if the filter is intact and if the inside of the lid is dry.
C. The surgical technologist is looking to see if the inside of the lid is dry.
D. The surgical technologist is looking to see if the filter is dry and intact and if the inside of the lid is dry.

Operating Room Set Up

20. When preparing the operating room for a procedure where should the back table be situated?
A. Against the wall
B. 3 feet from the wall
C. 6-12 inches from the wall
D. 12-18 inches away from the wall

21. What should be added to the operating table for a ganglionic cyst removal?
A. Foot board
B. Allen stirrups
C. Tourniquet
D. Hand table attachment

22. Where should the sterile field be established for the surgical procedure in the operating room?
A. The wall closest to the door
B. The wall farthest away from the door
C. Close to the anesthesia provider
D. Next to the OR bed

23. What method is used to maintain the pediatric patient's body temperature?
A. Overhead radiant heater
B. Forced-air warmers
C. Water circulating blankets
D. All of the above

24. Which of the following supplies will be needed in a carpal tunnel release procedure?
A. K-wires
B. Rongeur
C. Esmarch bandage
D. Weck sponges

25. Which of the following will be needed for augmentation or reduction mammoplasty?
A. Cooley clamp
B. Hohmann retractor
A. Footboard for operating table
D. Arm table for the operating table

26. When setting the OR up for a procedure, what is the minimum number of operational suction units needed in the operating room?
A. 1
B. 2
C. 3
D. 4

27. Which of the following equipment is necessary for digit re-plantation surgery?
A. Loupes
B. C-arm
C. K-wires
D. All of the above

28. When gathering instruments and supplies for a parotidectomy which of the following should be included?
A. Thyroid set
B. Fiber-optic headlight and light source
C. Nerve hooks
D. All of the above

29. Which of the following are the components of the pneumatic tourniquet?
A. Cuff, pressure device, ace wrap
B. Cuff, tubing, pressure device, power source
C. Tubing, pressure device, power source
D. Tubing, power source, wrap

30. Which of the following is the correct order when opening the back table pack?
A. Check package integrity, orient pack on back table, break seal, unfold first flap away from you, unfold second flap towards you, insert hand under the cuff and grasp and unfold third flap, finally insert your hand under the cuff grasped and extend the last flap to cover the table
B. Check package integrity, orient pack on back table, break seal, unfold first flap toward you, unfold second flap away from you, insert hand under the cuff and grasp and unfold third flap, finally insert your hand under the cuff grasped and extend the last flap to cover the table
C. Check package integrity, break seal, unfold first flap away from you, unfold second flap towards you, insert hand under the cuff grasp and unfold third flap, insert your hand under the cuff grasp and extend the last flap to cover the table, adjust table cover so that it is straight
D. All of the above

31. When organizing the back table how many times should the surgical technician handle each item?
A. Once
B. Twice
C. Three times
D. Four times

32. Where should small basins and medicine cups be placed on the back table?
A. Near the middle of the back table
B. Near the left side of the back table
C. Near the edge of the back table
D. Anywhere that is convenient

33. When a procedure requires a medial sternotomy which of the following should the surgical technologist be sure is in the operating room prior to surgery?
A. Camera
B. Allen Stirrups
C. Sternal saw
D. Kidney lift

34. When using nitrogen as the energy source for power tools in surgery, what should the operating pressure be set on?
A. 50-70 psi
B. 40-60 psi
C. 80-100 psi
D. 90-110 psi
E. None of the above

35. What should the insufflator pressure be set on for a laparoscopic procedure?
A. 12-15 mm Hg
B. 15-17 mm Hg
C. 10-12 mm Hg
D. 18-20 mm Hg
E. None of the above

36. Which of the following is a piece of equipment used to support the administration of anesthesia and monitor the patient during surgical procedures?
A. Anesthesia cart
B. Back table
C. Anesthesia machine
D. All of the above

37. When preparing the OR for an ear procedure how should the operating table be situated?
A. The table should remain as it is: head at the head of the table
B. The table is reversed: head at the foot of the bed
C. The table should remain as it is and lowered to accommodate stools
D. The table is reversed: head at the foot of the bed and put into Trendelenburg

38. Which of the following instruments are used to excise the tonsil?
A. White tonsil forceps
B. Sage tonsil snare
C. Allis
D. Tonsil sponge

39. When preparing the instruments, supplies, and back table for a tracheotomy what should the STSR check?
A. The camera has been white balanced
B. Jorgensen scissors are sharp
C. Ligating clip appliers are working
D. Patency of the tracheotomy tube balloon

40. How many Raney clip appliers should be opened for a craniotomy?
A. 4
B. 3
C. 2
D. 1

41. What equipment will need to be added to the set up in a carpal tunnel release procedure?
A. Stools and arm table
B. Stools
C. Arm table
D. Pin fixation device
E. Arm table and pin fixation device

42. Which of the following items are needed when performing a laparoscopic procedure?
A. Camera
B. Insufflator
C. Video monitor
D. All of the above

43. Which of the following does cryotherapy use?
A. Nitrous oxide
B. CO2
C. O2
D. Nitrous oxide and CO2

Surgical Scrub - Gown - Glove

44. What PPE should be worn when performing hand surgery that includes bone repair?
A. Lead gloves
B. Lead aprons
C. Extra latex gloves
D. None of the above

45. When should the surgical attire be put on?
A. Before the sterile field has been established
B. Once the patient enters the OR
C. After the sterile field has been established
D. After the patient has been draped

46. Which gloving technique is used after the surgical scrub and sterile gown have been donned?
A. Closed glove technique
B. Open glove technique
C. Any technique
D. The circulator should assist the surgical technologist

47. Who fastens the back of the gown?
A. Surgeon
B. Surgical technologist
C. Nurse
D. Circulator

48. When donning the surgical gown what actions/motion should be used?
A. One arm at a time
B. 'Swimming' motion
C. Push into the sleeves by raising arms
D. None of the above

49. Which of the following is **NOT** operating room attire (PPE)?
A. Scrubs
B. Hair and shoe covers
C. Mask
D. Sterile gown

50. Which of the following is the sterile area for the surgical gown?
A. Front of the entire gown and the sleeves (circumferentially) to 2 inches above the elbow
B. Front of the gown-waist to mid-chest and the sleeves (circumferentially) to 2 inches above the elbow
C. Front of the gown-waist to mid-chest and the entire sleeve (circumferentially)
D. The entire gown is sterile

51. What should be added to the surgical attire when a C-arm is being used during surgical procedures?
A. Glasses
B. Extra gloves
C. Lead aprons
D. Shoe covers

52. How should the surgical mask be worn?
A. Snugly with gaps at the sides for ventilation
B. Snugly without gaps at the sides
C. Straps crossed at the back of the head
D. Straps crossed at the back of the head and loose at the sides for ventilation

53. What is the most comfortable order for gloves to be worn when double gloving?
A. Outer glove normal size, inner glove 1/2 to 1 size larger
B. Outer glove 1/2 to 1 size larger, inner glove normal size
C. Both gloves normal size
D. Both gloves 1/2 to 1 size larger

54. When is the surgical scrub performed?
A. Prior to establishing the sterile field
B. When the surgeon performs the surgical scrub
C. After establishing the sterile field
D. Once the patient has been transferred to the OR table

55. What is the surgical scrub intended to do?
A. Remove all microbes from the skin
B. Remove as many microbes as possible from the hands
C. Remove as many microbes as possible from the skin from the hands to 2" above the elbow
D. All of the above
E. None of the above

56. What/who dictates the method of surgical scrub to be performed by the surgical team?
A. Healthcare facility policy
B. Surgeons policy
C. American Medical Association
D. Surgical team policy

57. Which of the following describes the timed method for the surgical scrub?
A. The hands and arms are scrubbed for a specific number of strokes
B. The hands and arms are scrubbed for prescribed length of time
C. Waterless scrub solution is rubbed on hands and arms for 5 minutes
D. None of the above

58. What is it called when the surgical technologist performs a surgical scrub that uses counted brush strokes?
A. Timed method
B. Waterless scrub method
C. Surgical scrub
D. Counted brush stroke method

59. What is the first step in the surgical scrub?
A. Wet hands and arms
B. Clean subungual space
C. Inspect hands and arms
D. Scrub finger tips

60. How many planes should the fingers and arms be divided into when performing the surgical scrub?
A. Two
B. Three
C. Four
D. No divisions

61. Where does the surgical scrub start and finish?
A. Finger tips to the elbow
B. Finger tips to 2 inches below the elbow
C. Finger tips to 2 inches above the elbow
D. Hands and arms

62. When performing the surgical scrub how should the hands and arms be positioned?
A. Hands should remain above the elbows and the elbows should remain bent
B. Hands should remain below the elbows and the elbows should remain straight
C. Hands should be toward the bottom of the basin and elbows slightly bent
D. Hands should be level with the hip and elbows even with sink lip

63. How should the hands and arms be dried after the surgical scrub?
A. A circular scrubbing motion should be used while bending slightly at the waist
B. A rubbing motion should be used while bending slightly at the knees
C. A patting motion should be used while bending slightly at the waist
D. A patting motion should be used while standing erect

64. When gloving how should the glove be positioned on the hand prior to putting it on?
A. The glove should be positioned palm to palm, thumb to thumb, fingertips of glove pointed toward elbow
B. The glove should be positioned palm to palm, fingertips to fingertips and the fingertips of glove pointed away from elbow
C. The glove should be positioned palm to palm, thumb to thumb, fingertips pointed away from the elbow
D. The glove should be positioned back of the glove to palm, thumb to thumb, fingertips of glove pointed toward elbow

65. When assisting other sterile team members with their gown, how should the surgical technologist protect her hands from possible contamination?
A. Hold the gown at the neck area allowing the gown to fall back over the hands
B. Hold the gown at the shoulder area allowing the gown to fall back over the hands
C. Hold the gown at the arms allowing the other team member to slide their arms in
D. Hold the gown wherever it is comfortable allowing the other team member to slide their arms in

Patient Transportation - Positioning - Preparation

66. Which of the following is **NOT** a method used in the operating room to warm the patient?
A. Warmed gastric lavage
B. Warming lamps
C. Thermal caps
D. Manually rubbing the patient's arms and legs

67. Which of the following is **NOT** a risk factor for hypothermia?
A. Patient age
B. Bear huggers
C. Surgical procedure length
D. Cold lavage fluid

68. What is the goal of positioning?
A. Patient comfort
B. Surgeon comfort
C. Best visualization of surgical site
D. Best access and visualization of surgical site, and least amount of stress to patient body and joints

69. When performing a meniscal tear procedure what are the prep parameters?
A. The leg circumferentially mid-thigh to mid-calf
B. The leg circumferentially mid-calf to hip
C. The entire leg circumferentially hip to foot
D. The leg circumferentially ankle to mid-thigh

70. What angle should the arm board not extend past?
A. 45° angle
B. 60° angle
C. 50° angle
D. 90° angle

71. Which team member directs the movement of the anesthetized patient?
A. Surgeon
B. Anesthesia provider
C. Circulator
D. Surgical technologist

72. What are the three basic surgical positions?
A. Supine, medial, and prone
B. Prone, lateral, and medial
C. Supine, prone, and lateral
D. Supine, prone, medial, and lateral

73. When the patient is in the supine position during an operation, which of the following areas are at risk for tissue injury?
A. Occiput, scapula, olecranon, sacrum, ilium, and calcaneus
B. Occiput, scapula, olecranon, sternum, ischial tuberosity, and calcaneus
C. Occiput, scapula, olecranon, sacrum, ischial tuberosity, and calcaneus
D. Occiput, sternum, olecranon, sacrum, talus

74. Where should the safety straps be placed when the patient is in the supine position?
A. At the waist
B. On the knee
C. 2" below the knee
D. 2" above the knee

75. What position will the patient be placed in a total hip arthroplasty?
A. Lateral
B. Prone
C. Supine
D. Trendelenburg

76. Which surgical position should use shoulder braces?
A. Supine position
B. Lithotomy position
C. Trendelenburg position
D. Fowler's position

77. Which of the following describes the Trendelenburg position?
A. Supine, head and torso lowered, feet elevated and knees slightly bent
B. Supine, feet and legs lowered, head and torso elevated
C. Prone, feet and legs lowered, head and torso elevated
D. Prone, head and torso lowered, feet elevated and knees slightly bent

78. What attachments should be used when preparing the table for a patient who will be put into the lithotomy position?
A. Cranial head rest
B. Stirrups
C. Kidney lift
D. Shoulder supports

79. Which of the following is not an area accessed with the prone position?
A. Abdominal cavity
B. Posterior cranium
C. Posterior lower extremity
D. Spine

80. Which of the following is not a modification of the supine position?
A. Fowler's position
B. Kraske position
C. Reverse Trendelenburg position
D. Lithotomy position

81. When preparing the operating room for a vaginal hysterectomy what positioning equipment should be in the room?
A. Cranial head rest
B. Footboard
C. Arm table
D. Stirrups

82. What should be done to the stretcher once it is placed next to the operating room bed before transferring the patient to the OR bed?
A. Stretcher wheels should be locked
B. Sheets on stretchers should be straightened
C. Bed rails raised
D. Nothing should take place

83. What can be used to move the patient from a supine to prone position for a surgical procedure?
A. Allen stirrups
B. Bed rails
C. Wilson frame
D. Mayfield head rest

84. What should be added to the operating table when the reverse Trendelenburg position is going to be used?
A. Arm board
B. Foot board
C. Stirrups
D. Nothing needs to be added to the table

85. Which term is used when the patient is on the operating room table in a supine position and the head of the table is angled toward the floor?
A. Trendelenburg position
B. Lithotomy position
C. Reverse Trendelenburg position
D. Reverse lithotomy position

86. What positioning equipment would be used for surgery on a hip fracture ?
A. Pin fixation device
B. Gigli saw
C. Fracture table
D. Gardner-Wells fixation device

87. Which of the following would not be found in an orthopedic instrument set?
A. Hohmann retractor
B. Love-Kerrison rongeur
C. Chandler elevator
D. Lambotte osteotome

88. When a meniscal tear is being arthroscopically repaired which of the following will be needed?
A. Allen stirrups
B. Minnesota retractor
C. Doppler
D. Shaver

89. When prepping the patient for a craniotomy:
A. Only enough hair should be shaved to allow incision
B. Entire head should be shaved
C. Head is never shaved for craniotomies
D. A four inch by four inch area is shaved

90. What are the parameters for prepping a shoulder for an arthroscopic procedure?
A. Shoulder, neck, scapula, arm to wrist
B. Shoulder, neck, arm circumferentially to elbow, chest to navel
C. Shoulder, neck, scapula, and chest
D. Shoulder, neck, scapula, chest, and arm circumferentially to elbow

91. What is used to make the stab incision for an arthroscopy surgery?
A. #15 blade
B. #12 blade
C. # 11 blade
D. #10 blade

92. What position is used to perform rotator cuff repair?
A. Prone
B. Lateral
C. Supine
D. Semi-Fowler's

93. Which of the following is the prep parameters for a nasal procedure?
A. Eyebrows to chin
B. Nose to hair line
C. Chin to nose
D. Hairline and beyond the chin

94. What are the prep parameters for mentoplasty?
A. From nose down the neck bilaterally to shoulders
B. From hairline down the neck to the shoulders bilaterally covering entire face
C. From the bottom lip down the neck
D. From the jugular notch to the lower eyelid

95. When performing a vaginal hysterectomy what position will the patient be placed?
A. Trendelenburg
B. Lithotomy with reverse Trendelenburg
C. Lithotomy with slight Trendelenburg
D. Lithotomy

96. What position would a patient be placed for a colonoscopy?
A. Prone
B. Kraske
C. Trendelenburg
D. Supine

97. When placing the patient in the lateral position, the patient will be:
A. On his side
B. On his back
C. On his stomach
D. None of the above

98. What is another term used for Supine Position?
A. Dorsal reclined position
B. Supine recumbent position
C. Prone recumbent position
D. Dorsal recumbent position

Draping

99. What is used to extend the sterile field, create a sterile barrier, and expose the operative site?
A. Gowns
B. Drapes
C. Sheets
D. All of the above

100. Which of the following is not a characteristic of a surgical drape?
A. Absorbent
B. Fluid-resistant
C. Lint free
D. Static free

101. What type of drape is used for ear surgery?
A. Thoracotomy drape
B. Laparotomy drape
C. Turban style head drape
D. None of the above

102. When preparing the towels for draping what order should they be placed in?
A. First towel cuff is toward the ST and the remaining three face away from the ST
B. First towel cuff is away from the ST and the next three cuffs face the ST
C. All towel cuffs face the ST
D. All towel cuffs face away from the ST

103. Which of the following is the correct order for placing surgical towels on the operative site prior to the drape?
A. 1st towel is placed on the side of the patient the person applying the towel is on, 2nd towel is placed superiorly, 3rd towel is placed inferiorly, 4th towel is placed opposite the 1st
B. 1st towel is placed on the opposite side of the patient the person applying the towel is on, 2nd towel is placed superiorly, 3rd towel is placed inferiorly, 4th towel is placed on the same side the person applying the towels is on
C. 1st towel is placed on the side of the patient the person applying the towel is on, 2nd towel is placed inferiorly, 3rd towel is placed superiorly, 4th towel is placed opposite the 1st
D.1st towel is placed on the opposite side of the patient the person applying the towel is on, 2nd towel is placed opposite the first, 3rd towel is placed superiorly, 4th towel is placed inferiorly

104. When placing drapes:
A. Drapes cannot be relocated without permission of the surgeon
B. Drapes can be pulled into position
C. Drapes cannot be relocated
D. Drapes can be taken off an reapplied

105. How does a sterile team member protect gloved hands when applying drapes to the patient?
A. The gloved hand is covered with a sterile towel and the towel is discarded
B. The drape is handed to the circulator
C. The gloved hand does not need protection
D. The drape is cuffed over the gloved hand

106. What instrument is used to secure cords to the drape?
A. Alice clamps
B. Crile clamps
C. STATS
D. Non-perforating towel clamps

107. When draping the perineum which drape is applied first?
A. Legging
B. Under-the-buttock drape
C. Fenestrated sheet
D. Laparotomy sheet

108. Which part of the drape is extended first when draping for an abdomen procedure?
A. The head end of the sheet
B. The arms of the sheet
C. The foot end of the sheet
D. It does not matter

109. When a surgical procedure involves an extremity, what order should the drapes be applied?
A. U-drape, extremity drape, stockinette
B. Sheet, stockinette, extremity drape
C. Stockinette, U-drape, extremity drape
D. Sheet, U-drape, stockinet, extremity drape

110. A stockinette would be used in which of the following surgeries?
A. Craniotomy
B. Appendectomy
C. Carpal tunnel release
D. Abdominal hysterectomy

111. In which of the following procedures would a split sheet drape be used?
A. Thyroidectomy
B. Herniorrhaphy
C. Tuboplasty
D. Total knee arthroplasty

112. What type of drape is used for a cranial procedure?
A. 4 towels
B. Craniotomy drape
C. Laparotomy drape
D. Fenestrated sheet

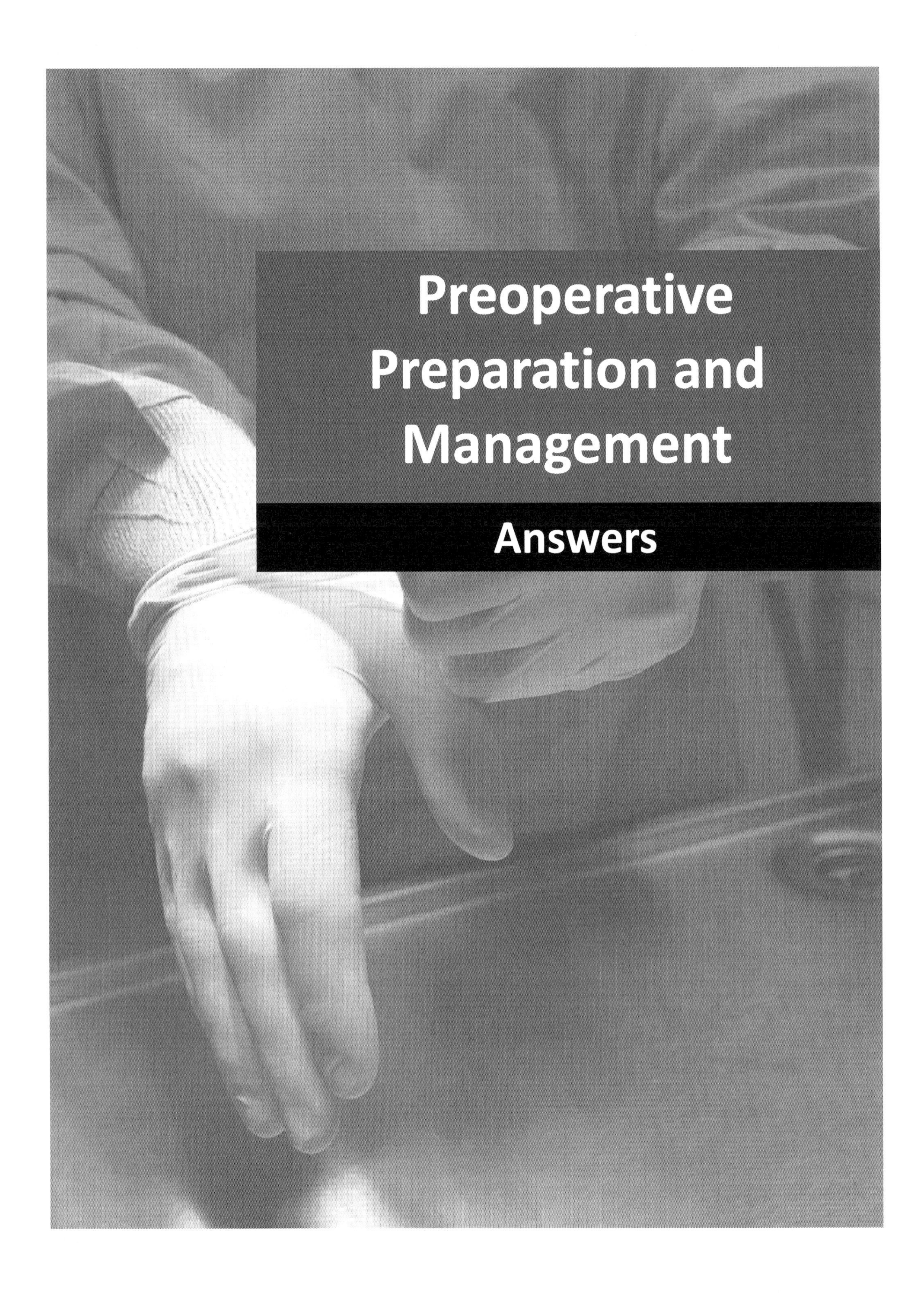
Preoperative
Preparation and
Management
Answers

Aseptic Technique - Preference Card - Time out

1. Where should the ST open the gown and gloves prior to setting up the back table?
C. Mayo stand - To prevent contaminating the back table, the ST should open gown and gloves on the mayo stand.

2. What is the correct procedure to follow when the ST's glove needs replacing during an operation?
D. Circulator removes the glove by grasping the glove and gown cuff and pulling off the contaminated glove; ST uses closed technique to reglove - The circulator should grasp the glove at the cuff and pull both the glove and cuff. The ST should then use closed glove technique to reglove.

3. What should be worn in the semi-restricted and restricted areas of the operating room?
B. OR attire - Operating room attire should be worn in restricted and semi-restricted areas of the operating room to prevent microbial spread between patients and employees.

4. When dressing to enter the OR suite what should be put on first?
C. Hair cover - The hair cover should be put on first prevent hair or dandruff from being shed onto the scrubs. Hair is a major contamination source therefore, care should be taken to cover your hair prior to dressing into scrubs.

5. What part of the sterile gown is considered not sterile?
A. The cuff - The cuff and the back of the sterile gown are considered not sterile and should be covered with the sterile gloves.

6. What is the technique for opening a small wrapped package to the sterile back table?
A. Check package integrity, hold package in one hand and break the seal, grasp the tab and lift the flap away from the body grasping this flap with the hand that is holding the package, the next flap is grasped and wrapped around the holding hand without reaching over the item and secured in the holding hand, the third flap is grasped at the edge and wrapped around the holding hand so that the holding hand is now completely covered by the wrapper. Gently toss the item onto the back table. - Check package integrity, hold package in one hand and break the seal, grasp the tab and lift the flap away from the body grasping this flap with the hand that is holding the package, the next flap is grasped and wrapped around the holding hand without reaching over the item and secured in the holding hand, the third flap is grasped at the edge and wrapped around the holding hand so that the holding hand is now completely covered by the wrapper. Gently toss the item onto the back table.

7. How should the STSR grasp the second, third, and forth flap of the back table pack when opening it?
C. Grasp the flap under the cuff - When opening the back table pack the STSR needs to cover the hands with the edge of the drape to prevent contaminating the table. To do this slide hands under the cuff, grasp, and gently pull the drape in the correct direction extending the drape over the edge of the table.

8. Which of the following refers to the absence of bacteria, viruses, and microorganisms?
B. Asepsis - The term asepsis refers to the absence of bacteria, viruses, and microorganisms. Sterile is the term used when all microorganisms have been killed.
Decontamination is when gross debris is removed from surgical instruments.

9. Which of the following is **NOT** found on the surgeon's preference card?
D. Patient's allergies - Surgeon's name, position, glove size, equipment, supplies, instrumentation, suture, dressings, skin prep, and medications are items listed on the surgeon's preference card.

10. Where would the surgeon's preference for dressings, skin prep, and medications be found?
D. Surgeons preference card - The surgeon's preference card has information that is particular to the surgeons likes for particular surgeries.

11. When does the time out occur?
A. Immediately prior to incision - The time out takes place immediately prior to incision.

12. Which of the following is not included in the time out?
D. Operating room number - The time out includes the patient's name, correct site, correct side, and the procedure. All members of the surgical team have to agree prior to incision.

Instruments and Supplies

13. What should be checked before opening peel packed supplies for surgery?
D. All of the above - The integrity of the package should be checked this includes date, tears, punctures and indicators have changed.

14. Prior to placing instruments onto the back table, what should be checked in a container system instrument set once the cover is removed?
A. Chemical indicator and filter - Once the set has been opened the loose chemical indicator should be seen and if it has changed indicating the set has been exposed to sterilization the surgical technologist removes the set being careful to keep the instruments away from the body while the circulator checks the filters that are in the bottom of the case. These indicators should be intact without tears or holes. At this point the surgical technologist may put the instruments onto the back table.

15. Which of the following is not checked prior to opening the instrument set?
B. Filters on the inside of the case container - Prior to opening an instrument case the seals should be checked, external chemical indicators have changed, and if chemical tape has been used on the wrapper it should be intact and has changed.

16. When opening a basin set what order should it be opened to maintain aseptic technique?
C. Unfold the first flap away from the body, unfold the side flaps, finally unfold the fourth flap toward the body - When opening a basin set check the integrity of the package, set the basin on the ring stand, open the first flap away from the body, the side flaps are unfolded next, and finally the fourth flap is opened toward the body.

17. What is the Julian date?
B. The date of sterilization - The Julian date is the date of sterilization of the instrument or supply. It is a single number that represents the month, date and year. For example March 1, 2013 would be 60.

18. Which of the following are used to test the steam sterilizer to guarantee the sterilization process has taken place?
D. Bacillus stearothermophilus - Bacillus stearothermophilus is the biological indicator used to guarantee the sterilization process has been met.

19. What is the surgical technologist looking for once the lid of the instrument set is removed?
D. The surgical technologist is looking to see if the filter is dry and intact and if the inside of the lid is dry. - The surgical technologist is looking to see if the inside of the lid is dry and the filter is intact and dry.

Operating Room Set Up

20. When preparing the operating room for a procedure where should the back table be situated?
D. 12-18 inches away from the wall - The sterile field should be situated on the farthest wall from the door of the OR and the table should be placed 12-18 inches away from the wall.

21. What should be added to the operating table for a ganglionic cyst removal?
D. Hand table attachment - When performing hand surgery a hand table needs to be added to the operating table. A footboard is attached when using reverse Trendelenburg position. Allen stirrups are used in gynecology procedures. And a tourniquet is not attached to the table it is placed on the extremity.

22. Where should the sterile field be established for the surgical procedure in the operating room?
B. The wall farthest away from the door - The sterile field should be situated on the farthest wall from the door of the OR.

23. What method is used to maintain the pediatric patient's body temperature?
D. All of the above - Because pediatric patients are at a higher risk of hypothermia it is important to have warming devices in the OR. Overhead radiant heaters, forced-air warmers, water circulating blankets, thermal caps, blankets, fluid warmers, and warmed gastric lavage are all sources used to thermo regulate patients.

24. Which of the following supplies will be needed in a carpal tunnel release procedure?
C. Esmarch bandage - The Esmarch bandage is needed to exsanguinate the arm prior to tourniquet placement in the carpal tunnel procedure. Rongeurs are instruments used to remove bone. Weck sponges are used in ophthalmic procedures. K-wires are used in repairing broken bone.

25. Which of the following will be needed for augmentation or reduction mammoplasty?
A. Footboard for operating table - The patient will need to be moved into the Fowler's position via footboard to check the breasts for symmetry and size then returned to the supine position.

26. When setting the OR up for a procedure, what is the minimum number of operational suction units needed in the operating room?
B. 2 - Two operational suction units need to be in the operating room. One is used for airway maintenance and the other is used for the procedure.

27. Which of the following equipment is necessary for digit re-plantation surgery?
D. All of the above - Loupes are necessary to anastomose vessels. C-arm is needed to properly align bone structures. K-wires are used on the small bones to stabilize them.

28. When gathering instruments and supplies for a parotidectomy which of the following should be included?
D. All of the above - The following supplies are suggested for a parotidectomy: fiber-optic headlight and light source, basic neck set, thyroid set, nerve hooks, extra skin hooks, and extra right-angle clamps.

29. Which of the following are the components of the pneumatic tourniquet?
B. Cuff, tubing, pressure device, power source - The components of a pneumatic tourniquet include; cuff, tubing, pressure device, and power source.

30. Which of the following is the correct order when opening the back table pack?
A. Check package integrity, orient pack on back table, break seal, unfold first flap away from you, unfold second flap towards you, insert hand under the cuff and grasp and unfold third flap, finally insert your hand under the cuff grasped and extend the last flap to cover the table - When opening the back table pack check package integrity, orient pack on the table, break the seal, unfold the first flap away from you, unfold the second flap toward you, reposition self, insert hand under the cuff grasped and extend the third flap to cover the table move to the other side

31. When organizing the back table how many times should the surgical technician handle each item?
A. Once - When organizing the back table the surgical technician should handle the item only once, placing it in the final location onto the back table.

32. Where should small basins and medicine cups be placed on the back table?
C. Near the edge of the back table - Medicine cups and small basins need to be placed near the edge of the table so the circulator has access to place solutions or medicines in them.

33. When a procedure requires a medial sternotomy which of the following should the surgical technologist be sure is in the operating room prior to surgery?
C. Sternal saw - A sternal saw and sternal retractor are needed to perform a medial sternotomy.

34. When using nitrogen as the energy source for power tools in surgery, what should the operating pressure be set on?
C. 80-100 psi - The operating pressure for nitrogen should be between 80 and 100 psi.

35. What should the insufflator pressure be set on for a laparoscopic procedure?
A. 12-15 mm Hg - The insufflator should be set on 12-15 mm Hg for a laparoscopic procedure.

36. Which of the following is a piece of equipment used to support the administration of anesthesia and monitor the patient during surgical procedures?
C. Anesthesia machine - Anesthesia machine - The anesthesia machine is a piece of equipment used to support the administration of anesthesia and monitor the patient during surgical procedures.
An anesthesia cart is a portable cart used to hold the supplies needed to administer anesthetics.
The back table is where the sterile instruments and supplies are placed for the surgical procedure.

37. When preparing the OR for an ear procedure how should the operating table be situated?
B. The table is reversed: head at the foot of the bed - The operating table should be reversed; head at the foot of the bed for leg room of the surgical team when they sit to perform the surgery

38. Which of the following instruments are used to excise the tonsil?
B. Sage tonsil snare - The Sage tonsil snare, as well as the Bovie can excise the tonsil.

39. When preparing the instruments, supplies, and back table for a tracheotomy what should the STSR check?
D. Patency of the tracheotomy tube balloon - The balloon on the tracheotomy tube should be checked for patency prior to the procedure. A tracheotomy procedure is not done laparoscopically so cameras are not necessary. Jorgensen scissors are used in hysterectomy procedures and ligating clip appliers are used in thyroidectomy and vascular procedures.

40. How many Raney clip appliers should be opened for a craniotomy?
C. 2 - Two Raney clip appliers are adequate for a craniotomy. After passing one clip applier to the surgeon the surgical technologist should have the second loaded and prepared to pass to keep the procedure moving smoothly.

41. What equipment will need to be added to the set up in a carpal tunnel release procedure?
A. Stools and arm table - The carpal tunnel release procedure will need to have an arm table and stools added to the set up because the procedure is usually done in a sitting position.

42. Which of the following items are needed when performing a laparoscopic procedure?
D. All of the above - Laparoscopic procedures utilize trocars, Veress needle, camera, video monitor, insufflators, light source, light cords, and a laparoscopic tower.

43. Which of the following does cryotherapy use?
D. Nitrous oxide and CO_2 - CO_2 and nitrous oxide are the gases used to freeze tissue in cryotherapy.

Surgical Scrub - Gown - Glove

44. What PPE should be worn when performing hand surgery that includes bone repair?
B. Lead aprons - When hand surgery includes bone repair the surgical team needs to be sure to wear lead aprons because x-ray will be needed to check proper bone alignment.

45. When should the surgical attire be put on?
C. After the sterile field has been established - The sterile field is established, the surgical scrub takes place then the surgical attire is put on.

46. Which gloving technique is used after the surgical scrub and sterile gown have been donned?
A. Closed glove technique - The closed glove technique should be used after the surgical scrub has taken place and the sterile gown has been donned.

47. Who fastens the back of the gown?
D. Circulator - The circulator ties the gown once the sterile team members has donned it.

48. When donning the surgical gown what actions/motion should be used?
B. 'Swimming' motion - When putting the surgical gown on great care must be taken to prevent contamination. The STSR should use a swimming motion to get the gown onto the arms.

49. Which of the following is **NOT** operating room attire (PPE)?
D. Sterile gown - Operating room attire consists of hair and shoe covers, mask, and scrubs. Sterile attire includes the PPE and sterile gown, gloves, and eye protection.

50. Which of the following is the sterile area for the surgical gown?
B. Front of the gown-waist to mid-chest and the sleeves (circumferentially) to 2 inches above the elbow - The gown is considered sterile from the mid-chest to waist of the front of the gown and the sleeves, circumferentially, to 2 inches above the elbow.

51. What should be added to the surgical attire when a C-arm is being used during surgical procedures?
C. Lead aprons - A C-arm uses x-ray, therefore the surgical team should add lead aprons to their surgical attire to protect themselves from radiation exposure.

52. How should the surgical mask be worn?
B. Snugly without gaps at the sides - Masks are worn snugly across the nose and mouth without gaps at the sides and straps do not cross at the back of the head.

53. What is the most comfortable order for gloves to be worn when double gloving?
A. Outer glove normal size, inner glove 1/2 to 1 size larger - When double gloving it is suggested that the inner glove be 1/2 to 1 size larger than normal size and the outer glove be normal size.

54. When is the surgical scrub performed?
C. After establishing the sterile field - The surgical scrub takes place once the sterile field has been established.

55. What is the surgical scrub intended to do?
C. Remove as many microbes as possible from the skin from the hands to 2" above the elbow - The surgical scrub is intended to render the hands and arms to 2" above the elbow surgically clean by removing as many microbes as possible from the skin.

56. What/who dictates the method of surgical scrub to be performed by the surgical team?
A. Healthcare facility policy - The healthcare facility policy dictates the surgical scrub method.

57. Which of the following describes the timed method for the surgical scrub?
B. The hands and arms are scrubbed for prescribed length of time - The time to method for surgical scrub is when the hands and arms are scrubbed for prescribed length of time.

58. What is it called when the surgical technologist performs a surgical scrub that uses counted brush strokes?
D. Counted brush stroke method - When the surgical technologist uses a scrub that uses counted brush strokes it is called counted brush stroke method.

59. What is the first step in the surgical scrub?
C. Inspect hands and arms - Surgical scrub: inspect hands, arms, cuticles and nails, open brush packet, turn on water, wet hands and arms, clean subungual spaces, wet brush and begin scrubbing fingertips and nails, scrub each of the four finger planes, scrub each web, divide and scrub hand in four planes, divide arm into four planes and scrub each, scrub continues to 2 inches above the elbow. Use circular motions. Rinse from finger tips to elbow.

60. How many planes should the fingers and arms be divided into when performing the surgical scrub?
C. Four - The fingers and arms should be divided into four planes when performing the surgical scrub.

61. Where does the surgical scrub start and finish?
C. Finger tips to 2 inches above the elbow - The surgical scrub starts at the fingertips and goes to 2 inches above the elbow.

62. When performing the surgical scrub how should the hands and arms be positioned?
A. Hands should remain above the elbows and the elbows should remain bent - The hands should remain above the elbows with the elbows bent during the surgical scrub.

63. How should the hands and arms be dried after the surgical scrub?
C. A patting motion should be used while bending slightly at the waist - When drying hands and arms after the surgical scrub you should bend slightly at the waist so the towel does not come in contact with the scrubs and use a patting motion to dry the arms and hands.

64. When gloving how should the glove be positioned on the hand prior to putting it on?
A. The glove should be positioned palm to palm, thumb to thumb, fingertips of glove pointed toward elbow - When closed gloving the hands should remain inside the cuffs, position the glove palm to palm, thumb to thumb, and fingertips of glove pointed towards the elbow.

65. When assisting other sterile team members with their gown, how should the surgical technologist protect her hands from possible contamination?
B. Hold the gown at the shoulder area allowing the gown to fall back over the hands - When assisting a team member with gowning the surgical technologist should grasp the gown at the shoulders allowing the gown to fold over the hands protecting them.

Patient Transportation - Positioning - Preparation

66. Which of the following is **NOT** a method used in the operating room to warm the patient?
D. Manually rubbing the patient's arms and legs - Maintaining the patient's core temperature reduces cardiac events, wound infections, and may reduce the loss of blood and the patient's hospital stay. Blankets and thermal caps, bear huggers, warming lamps, warmed blood and IV fluid, as well as warmed gastric lavage and peritoneal irrigation are methods to keep the patient's body temperature in the normal range.

67. Which of the following is **NOT** a risk factor for hypothermia?
B. Bear huggers - The risk factors for hypothermia in a surgical patient include: anesthesia agents, cold fluids (irrigating, IV, blood), age extremes, length of procedure, muscle relaxants, and vasodilatation agents.

68. What is the goal of positioning?
D. Best access and visualization of surgical site, and least amount of stress to patient body and joints - When positioning a patient the goal is to have the best visualization and access with the least amount of stress applied to the patient's skin, joints and body.

69. When performing a meniscal tear procedure what are the prep parameters?
C. The entire leg circumferentially hip to foot - The prep for a knee procedure would be circumferentially from hip to foot.

70. What angle should the arm board not extend past?
D. 90° angle - The arm boards should not extend beyond a 90° angle to prevent hyperextension of the shoulder as well as compression of the brachial plexus.

71. Which team member directs the movement of the anesthetized patient?
B. Anesthesia provider - The anesthetized patient is moved on the direction of the anesthesia provider.

72. What are the three basic surgical positions?
C. Supine, prone, and lateral - The three basic positions for surgery are supine, lateral, and prone.

73. When the patient is in the supine position during an operation, which of the following areas are at risk for tissue injury?
C. Occiput, scapula, olecranon, sacrum, ischial tuberosity, and calcaneus - The areas that are at risk for tissue damage when the patient is in the supine position include the occiput, sacrum, olecranon, scapula, ischial tuberosity, and calcaneus.

74. Where should the safety straps be placed when the patient is in the supine position?
D. 2" above the knee - The safety straps should be place 2" proximal to the knee on a supine patient.

75. What position will the patient be placed in a total hip arthroplasty?
A. Lateral - The patient will be placed in a lateral position. The affected hip will be exposed and prepped.

76. Which surgical position should use shoulder braces?
C. Trendelenburg position - Trendelenburg position uses shoulder braces to support the patient and prevent patient from sliding toward the head of the bed.

77. Which of the following describes the Trendelenburg position?
A. Supine, head and torso lowered, feet elevated and knees slightly bent - The Trendelenburg position places the patient supine, head and torso lowered, feet elevated and knees slightly bent.

78. What attachments should be used when preparing the table for a patient who will be put into the lithotomy position?
B. Stirrups - Stirrups will be used when placing a patient into the lithotomy position.

79. Which of the following is not an area accessed with the prone position?
A. Abdominal cavity - The spine, posterior lower extremity, posterior cranium, and dorsal surface are accessed in the prone position.

80. Which of the following is not a modification of the supine position?
B. Kraske position - Fowler's position, sitting position, Trendelenburg position, and reverse Trendelenburg position are the modifications of supine position.

81. When preparing the operating room for a vaginal hysterectomy what positioning equipment should be in the room?
D. Stirrups - Stirrups are used to position the patient's legs for a vaginal hysterectomy.

82. What should be done to the stretcher once it is placed next to the operating room bed before transferring the patient to the OR bed?
A. Stretcher wheels should be locked - Once the stretcher is in place next to the bed the wheels need to be locked to prevent the stretcher from rolling away while transferring patient to the stretcher.

83. What can be used to move the patient from a supine to prone position for a surgical procedure?
C. Wilson frame - The Wilson frame is an operating table that is used when a procedure requires the patient to be moved from a supine position to a prone position. Allen stirrups are used to support the lower leg in gynecologic procedures. The Mayfield head rest is used in craniotomy procedures.

84. What should be added to the operating table when the reverse Trendelenburg position is going to be used?
B. Foot board - The reverse Trendelenburg is used to displace the abdominal organs toward the feet and a footboard will be added to the table to prevent the patient from sliding off the table .

85. Which term is used when the patient is on the operating room table in a supine position and the head of the table is angled toward the floor?
A. Trendelenburg position - The Trendelenburg position puts the patient in a supine, head angled down incline position. Reverse Trendelenburg position puts the patient in a supine, feet angled down position. Lithotomy position is when the patient is supine with legs in the Allen stirrups. Reverse lithotomy is not a position used.

86. What positioning equipment would be used for surgery on a hip fracture ?
C. Fracture table - The fracture table is used to position the patient for hip fracture surgery.
The Gigli saw is used to cut bone for craniotomies. The Gardner-Wells and the Mayfield fixation devices are used to help position the patient for neurosurgeries.

87. Which of the following would not be found in an orthopedic instrument set?
B. Love-Kerrison rongeur - The Love-Kerrison rongeur is found in the neurosurgery set.

88. When a meniscal tear is being arthroscopically repaired which of the following will be needed?
D. Shaver - A shaver is used to arthroscopically repair a meniscal tear. The Doppler is used in vascular surgery to determine blood flow through the vessels. Allen stirrups are used to place patients in the lithotomy position. The Minnesota retractor is used in oral and maxillofacial surgeries.

89. When prepping the patient for a craniotomy:
A. Only enough hair should be shaved to allow incision - An area large enough for the incision should be shaved.

90. What are the parameters for prepping a shoulder for an arthroscopic procedure?
D. Shoulder, neck, scapula, chest, and arm circumferentially to elbow - The prep parameters include shoulder, neck, scapula, chest, and arm circumferentially to elbow

91. What is used to make the stab incision for an arthroscopy surgery?
C. # 11 blade - The #11 blade is used to put a stab incision in skin for trocar insertion.

92. What position is used to perform rotator cuff repair?
D. Semi-Fowler's - The Semi-Fowler position is used to repair the rotator cuff.

93. Which of the following is the prep parameters for a nasal procedure?
D. Hairline and beyond the chin - The prep should begin at the upper lip moving to the hairline and then down past the chin.

94. What are the prep parameters for mentoplasty?
B. From hairline down the neck to the shoulders bilaterally covering entire face - The correct prep for a mentoplasty would cover the entire face from the hairline down the face and neck to the shoulders bilaterally.

95. When performing a vaginal hysterectomy what position will the patient be placed?
C. Lithotomy with slight Trendelenburg - The position the patient needs to be in for a vaginal hysterectomy is Lithotomy with slight Trendelenburg.

96. What position would a patient be placed for a colonoscopy?
B. Kraske - A colonoscopy would be performed with the patient in the Kraske or lateral position. Prone position is when the patient is lying face down. Trendelenburg is when the patient is supine and the operating table is angled slightly head down. Supine is when the patient is lying on her back with arms at the sides.

97. When placing the patient in the lateral position, the patient will be:
A. On his side - Lateral position is when the patient is on his side. Supine is when the patient is on his back. Prone is when the patient is on his stomach.

98. What is another term used for Supine Position?
D. Dorsal recumbent position - Dorsal recumbent position is another term used for supine position.

Draping

99. What is used to extend the sterile field, create a sterile barrier, and expose the operative site?
B. Drapes - Drapes are used to create a sterile barrier, expose the surgical site and to extend the sterile field.

100. Which of the following is not a characteristic of a surgical drape?
A. Absorbent - A drape needs to be lint and static free, fluid-resistant, strong, and flexible.

101. What type of drape is used for ear surgery?
C. Turban style head drape - The turban head drape is used in ear surgeries to hold back the patients hair.

102. When preparing the towels for draping what order should they be placed in?
B. First towel cuff is away from the ST and the next three cuffs face the ST - The four towels are prepared with a 2" cuff. The first towel faces away from the ST and the remaining three face the ST.

103. Which of the following is the correct order for placing surgical towels on the operative site prior to the drape?
A. 1st towel is placed on the side of the patient the person applying the towel is on, 2nd towel is placed superiorly, 3rd towel is placed inferiorly, 4th towel is placed opposite the 1st - When placing towels to square off the operative site the 1st towel is placed on the side of the patient the person applying the towel is on, 2nd towel is placed superiorly, 3rd towel is placed inferiorly, 4th towel is placed opposite the 1st.

104. When placing drapes:
C. Drapes cannot be relocated - Once drapes are placed they cannot be relocated, pulled, or removed and reapplied.

105. How does a sterile team member protect gloved hands when applying drapes to the patient?
D. The drape is cuffed over the gloved hand - When draping, the gloved hand is cuffed in the drape to protect it from contamination.

106. What instrument is used to secure cords to the drape?
D. Non-perforating towel clamps - Non-perforating towel clamps are used to secure cords to the drapes.

107. When draping the perineum which drape is applied first?
B. Under-the-buttock drape - The order for draping the perineum is as follows: under-the-buttock drape, leggings, and fenestrated sheet.

108. Which part of the drape is extended first when draping for an abdomen procedure?
C. The foot end of the sheet - When draping for an abdominal procedure the foot end of the drape is unfolded first, the head end is next, and finally the arms are covered.

109. When a surgical procedure involves an extremity, what order should the drapes be applied?
D. Sheet, U-drape, stockinet, extremity drape - When draping for an extremity the sheet is laid under the extremity, the U-drape(s) is applied, the stockinette is rolled on, then the extremity drape is applied.

110. A stockinette would be used in which of the following surgeries?
C. Carpal tunnel release - Carpal tunnel release uses a stockinette. Craniotomy uses a craniotomy drape. Appendectomies and abdominal hysterectomies use laparotomy drapes.

111. In which of the following procedures would a split sheet drape be used?
D. Total knee arthroplasty - A split sheet drape would be used in a total knee arthroplasty. Herniorrhaphy and tuboplasty use a laparotomy drape. Thyroidectomy uses a thyroid sheet. A total knee uses a split sheet.

112. What type of drape is used for a cranial procedure?
B. Craniotomy drape - The craniotomy drape is the drape that will be used. It has a plastic adhesive to keep it in place and a pouch that hangs from the cranium toward the surgeon's feet to catch blood or irrigation that flows down from the surgical site. Towels are not drapes. Towels are used to square off the surgical site.

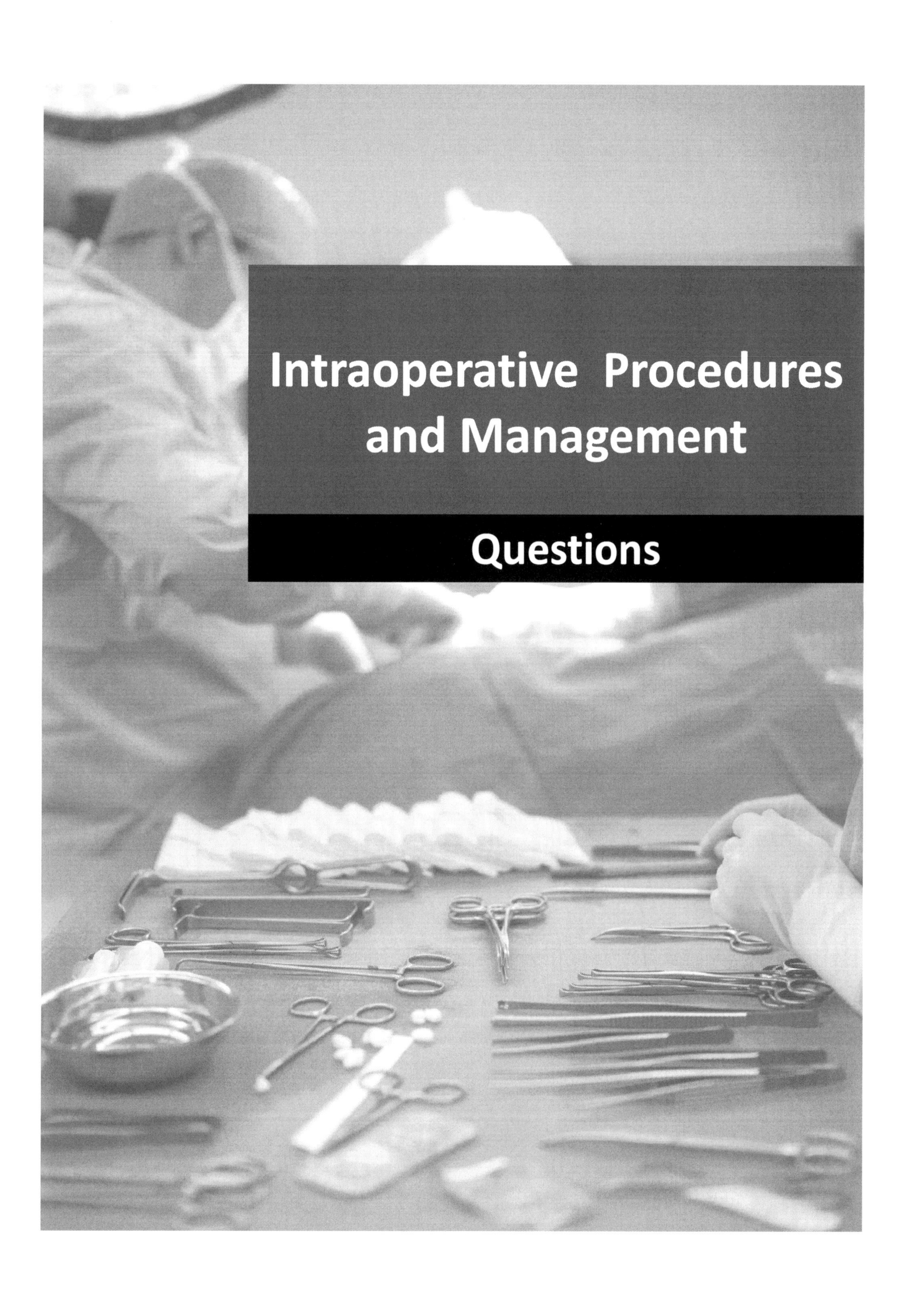
Intraoperative Procedures and Management
Questions

Supplies

1. Which of the following are used to immobilize, absorb drainage, reduce edema, and eliminate dead space?
A. Rigid dressing
B. Pressure dressing
C. Wet-to-dry dressing
D. Queen Ann's dressing

2. What is used to inflate a Foley catheter?
A. Water
B. Air
C. Sterile water
D. None of the above

3. Which surgery would polymethyl methacrylate be used?
A. Neurologic
B. Orthopedic
C. Cardiovascular
D. Ophthalmic

4. How much Sterile water is used to fill a 5 cc catheter balloon?
A. 2-6cc
B. 5-8cc
C. 5-10cc
D. 8-10 cc

5. What are cervical cone biopsy samples placed on?
A. Telfa
B. Raytec
C. Laps
D. None of the above

6. Which of the following catheters are referred to as a "red rubber"?
A. Coudé
B. Foley
C. Robinson
D. Tenckhoff

7. How many cc's does an asepto syringe hold?
A. 100 cc
B. 110 cc
C. 120 cc
D. 125 cc

8. Which of the following would be needed for a thoracoscopy procedure?
A. Trocars, water-seal drainage system, stents, catheter
B. Trocars, lens defogger, chest tube drain, stents
C. Trocars, chest tube drain, lens defogger, stents, catheter
D. Trocars, water-seal drainage system, lens defogger, chest tube drain

9. What supplies will the surgical technologist need to gather and place in the operating room when a cast will be applied during a surgical procedure?
A. Webril, stockinette, water, plaster casting, and scissors
B. Lukewarm water, plaster casting, and stockinette
C. Heavy scissors, Webril, stockinette, and water
D. Lukewarm water, Webril, stockinette, plaster casting, and heavy scissors

10. When performing a carpal tunnel release procedure, what equipment may be used to provide a blood free surgical site?
A. Tourniquet
B. Esmarch bandage
C. Traction
D. Positioning

11. What is needed when repairing a Colles fracture?
A. Satterlee bone saw
B. Foot board
C. Penrose drain
D. Lead aprons

12. Which suture would be used to repair an Achille's tendon tear?
A. Monocryl
B. Tycron
C. Ethilon
D. Plain Gut

13. What kind of dressing could be used with nasal procedures?
A. Queen Ann's collar
B. Band-aid
C. Mustache dressing
D. None of the above

14. When using a laryngoscope what should be available?
A. Defogger
B. Esmarch
C. Casting material
D. Tourniquet

15. Identify the materials from which vascular stents are made.
A. Stainless steel mesh
B. Titanium
C. Polypropylene
D. All of the above

16. Which graft does not need to be pre-clotted?
A. Woven polyester
B. Knitted velour polyester
C. All grafts need pre-clotting
D. Pre-clotting is not necessary for grafts

17. What is used to reinforce the anastomosis in vascular surgery?
A. Methyl methacrylate
B. Synthetic graft
C. Stent
D. Pledgets

18. Which of the following drain might be used in a rhytidectomy?
A. Hemovac
B. Jackson-Pratt
C. Cystostomy tube
D. Fogarty

19. Which of the following supplies should be available but not opened until needed in a groin hernia repair?
A. Penrose drain
B. Mesh
C. Blades
D. None of the above

20. What is meant by the term *monofilament* when speaking of suture?
A. Single thread
B. Double thread
C. Animal fiber thread
D. Manmade fiber thread

21. What is the diameter of a suture called?
A. Thickness
B. Gauge
C. Strength
D. Multifilament

22. When discussing suture, what is capillarity?
A. The ability of multifilament to prevent fluid movement down the suture
B. The ability of monofilament to move fluid down the suture
C. The ability of multifilament to move fluid down the suture
D. The ability of monofilament to prevent fluid movement down the suture

23. What material is used for natural suture?
A. Cellulose
B. Silk
C. Gut
D. All of the above

24. Which of the following is the largest gauge suture?
A. #1
B. #2
C. 2-0
D. 6-0

25. Which suture gauge is the most commonly used to close subcuticular skin layer?
A. 0
B. #3
C. 3-0
D. 6-0

26. Which of the following is used on peritoneum, fascia, or contaminated areas?
A. Maxon
B. Chromic gut
C. Stainless steel
D. Ethicon

27. Which is a non-absorbable suture?
A. Maxon
B. Vicryl
C. Dexon
D. Prolene

28. What are strands called that are precut, not attached to a needle, and are placed into the opened hand of the surgeon.
A. Free-tie
B. Stick tie
C. Ligature reel
D. Tie on a pass

29. How many cutting needles are there?
A. 2
B. 3
C. 4
D. 5

30. Which of the following would be used in a thoracoscopy procedure?
A. Osteotome
B. Septum speculum
C. Penfield dissectors
D. Water-seal drainage system
E. All of the above

31. What is used to filter blood, deoxygenate blood, oxygenate blood and return it to the circulatory system during a CABG?
A. Pulse oximeter
B. Pump oxygenator
C. Pulse generator
D. Ventilator

32. Which of the following refers to suture type that can be broken down by the tissues and fluids of the body?
A. Absorbable suture
B. Non-absorbable suture
D. Monofilament
C. Answer A and B

33. Which of the following is a suture that is braided or twisted together?
A. Suture
B. Absorbable suture
C. Multifilament suture
D. Monofilament suture

34. What supply is the term 'swaged' associated with?
A. Catheters
B. Sponges
C. Suture
D. Syringes

35. What term is defined as: the amount of pull a suture strand can take before it breaks?
A. Tensile strength
B. Tendon strength
C. Tension strength
D. Torsion

36. Which type of surgery would a pledget most likely be used?
A. Orthopedic surgery
B. Peripheral vascular surgery
C. Maxillofacial surgery
D. Otorhinolaryngologic surgery

37. Venous compression device:
A. A device used in surgery to assist arterial blood return to assist in preventing thrombophlebitis.
B. A device used in surgery to assist arterial blood pooling in the extremities.
C. A device used in surgery to assist lymphatic drainage.
D. A device used in surgery to assist venous blood return to assist in the prevention of thrombophlebitis.

Diagnostics

38. Which of the following diagnostic tool is used to check for calculi within the common bile duct?
A. Cholangiogram
B. Fluoroscopy
C. Cholangiography
D. None of the above

39. What is used to keep the skin graft flat so it will pass through the mesh device evenly?
A. Telfa
B. Derma-carrier
C. Raytec
D. The graft can be placed in the mesh device by itself.

40. Which of the following records the electric activity of the brain?
A. ECG
B. EKG
C. EEG
D. ESU

41. What does the term LASER stand for?
A. Light amplification by stimulated emission of radiation
B. Long amplitude simulated emission of radiation
C. Low altitude simulated emission of radiation
D. Light attenuated simulated emission of radiation

42. Which of the following is used to measure the oxygen levels in blood?
A. Pump oxygenator
B. Pulse oximeter
C. Pulse
D. Pulse generator

43. Which device is used to measure left atrial and left ventricular pressures?
A. Tenckhoff catheter
B. Swan-Ganz catheter
C. Foley catheter
D. Robinson

44. Which of the following uses electrons colliding with a metal target in an x-ray tube to produce an image for the radiologist to use to diagnose a condition?
A. CAT Scan
B. X-rays
C. MRI Scan
D. Both A and B

45. What device will the operating staff use to view x-rays?
A. Viewing box
B. Light box
C. CT box
D. None of the above

46. NPO means:
A. Nothing by mouth
B. Nil per os
C. Both A and B
D. None of the above

Procedures

47. What is a lumpectomy?
A. It is a breast procedure removing a tumor and a margin of tissue around the tumor.
B. It is a breast procedure that removes a mass and not the entire breast.
C. It is a breast procedure that removes the entire mammary gland.
D. It is the removal of one breast.

48. Which of the following incisions would be used for a cesarean section?
A. Thoracolumbar
B. Pfannenstiel
C. Paramidline
D. McBurney

49. Where is the reservoir for ventriculoperitoneal shunt placed?
A. Peritoneal cavity
B. Taped against the abdomen
C. Behind and above the ear
D. There is no reservoir

50. What has to be repaired for a digit re-plantation to be viable?
A. One artery, one vein, one nerve
B. Two arteries, one vein
C. One artery and two veins
D. Two arteries, two veins, and one nerve

51. Which of the following terms are defined as a joint that is surgically fused?
A. Laminectomy
B. Arthrocentesis
C. Arthrodesis
D. Osteomyelitis

52. The procedure is a Cesarean section. What suture is used to close the uterine incision?
A. 2-0 absorbable suture
B. 4-0 nonabsorbable suture
C. 3-0 absorbable suture
D. 7-0 suture

53. What condition is corrected with a Nissen fundoplication?
A. Esophageal stricture
B. Hiatal hernia
C. Cancer of the stomach
D. None of the above

54. What is the skin graft called when it is harvested from a cadaver and used on a person?
A. Xenograft
B. Autologous graft
C. Heterograft
D. Homograft

55. When can traction be used to align fractures?
A. Preoperatively
B. Intraoperatively
C. Postoperatively
D. All of the above

56. Which of the following is not a gynecologic incision?
A. Gibson
B. Pfannestiel
C. Maylard
D. Cherney

57. When the retina is detached which of the following could be used?
A. Bowman probe
B. Cryotherapy unit
C. Bulldogs
D. Potts scissors

58. Which of the following are options for genitourinary incisions?
A. Gibson
B. Scrotal
C. Inguinal
D. All of the above

59. Which of the following are used for ACL grafts?
A. Patellar tendon
B. Hamstring
C. Quadriceps tendon
D. All of the above

60. What is connected when a femorofemoral bypass is performed?
A. Iliac arteries
B. Popliteal arteries
C. Common femoral arteries
D. Femoral artery to saphenous vein

61. Which of the following techniques are used in scar revision?
A. Z-plasty and M-plasty
B. M-plasty, Y-V plasty
C. W-plasty and Z-plasty
D. A, B, and C

62. Which of the following procedures would use a needle to evaluate the fluid in the intrapleural space of the lungs?
A. Thoracentesis
B. Thoracoscopy
C. Bronchoscopy
D. Mediastinoscopy

63. Which of the following category of instruments will be used to excise an appendix?
A. Grasping
B. Cutting
C. Suturing
D. Holding

64. Which of the following breaks up the lens while it irrigates and aspirates simultaneously?
A. Vitrectomy
B. Keratoplasty
C. Phacoemulsification
D. Dacryocystitis

65. What does the graft connect in an axillofemoral bypass?
A. Brachiocephalic vein to the femoral artery
B. Abdominal aorta to the iliac artery
C. Axillary artery to the femoral artery
D. Thoracic aorta to the saphenous vein

66. Which approach should be used when accessing the lower ureter?
A. Lumbar incision
B. Scrotal incision
C. Inguinal incision
D. Gibson incision

67. When the STSR sets up for a trabeculectomy and iridectomy she should be sure to have which of the following instruments, equipment, and supplies?
A. BSS
B. Weck sponges
C. Loupe
D. All of the above

68. Which of the following is not used to occlude a vessel?
A. Stapler
B. Hemoclip applier
C. Ligatures
D. Rochester-Pean forceps

69. What position is the patient placed for a transurethral resection of the prostate?
A. Lithotomy
B. Supine
C. Lateral
D. Reverse Trendelenburg

70. When reducing a fracture in the operating room which piece of equipment would be used to check alignment?
A. Lasers
B. Fluoroscopy
C. Hohmann retractor
D. Bone holding clamp

71. What is it called when the nose is operated on for aesthetic purposes?
A. Rhinoplasty
B. Cheiloplasty
C. Palatoplasty
D. Abdominoplasty

72. Which of the following are the factors that affect digit replantation?
A. Type and location of amputation, extent of damage, how well the severed digit is preserved
B. Type and location of amputation, extent of damage, elapsed time between injury and surgery, and how well the severed digit is preserved
C. Type and location of amputation, elapsed time between injury and surgery, how well the severed digit is preserved
D. Type and location of amputation and how well the severed digit is preserved

73. Which of the following will be needed when the surgical procedure calls for arch bar application?
A. Army Navy retractor
B. Wire cutters
C. Iris scissors
D. Midas drill

74. Which of the following is used for blunt dissection during laparoscopic procedures?
A. Endo harmonic scalpel
B. Blunt grasper
C. Cone tip dissector
D. None of the above

75. What procedure is a uterine sound used in?
A. Hysterectomy
B. Rectocele
C. Dilation and curettage
D. Cesarean section

76. What condition is being repaired when the eyelid is elevated and the surgeon creates an upper fold in the eyelid?
A. Entropion
B. Ptosis
C. Glaucoma
D. Cataract

77. What information needs to be documented when implants are used?
A. Type of implant, size of implant, serial number, implant site
B. Number of implants used, type of implant, size of implant, serial number
C. Number of implants used, size of implant, serial number, implant site
D. Number of implants used, type of implant, size of implant, serial number, implant site

78. Which of the following can be used in ophthalmic and vascular procedures?
A. Tonometer
B. Strabismus scissors
C. Yasargil scissors
D. Serrefine clamps

79. Which of the following is used to dilate the urethra in a TURP?
A. Van Buren sound
B. Hegar dilator
C. Penfield
D. None of the above

80. Which of the following are ophthalmic surgical forceps?
A. Colibri forceps and Bishop-Harmon forceps
B. Pott-Smith and Cushing bayonet forceps
C. Pott-Smith and Colibri forceps
D. Cushing bayonet and Bishop-Harmon forceps

81. Which of the following would be used for a nephrectomy?
A. Flank incision
B. Pfannesteil incision
C. Upper paramedian
D. Midline

82. When a bone graft is performed, which of the following is the best donor sit for cancellous bone?
A. Femur
B. Scapula
C. humerus
D. Iliac crest

83. Which of the following instruments would be used in a thyroidectomy?
A. Dennis clamp
B. Bakes dilator
C. Doyen forceps
D. Bipolar forceps

84. Which of the following procedures would be done for a lung biopsy?
A. Electrocardiography
B. Mediastinoscopy
C. Chamberlin procedure
D. Thoracoscopy

85. Which of the following would be used to immobilize the lumbar vertebrae and lower thoracic vertebrae?
A. Spica cast
B. Minerva jacket
C. Body jacket
D. None of the above

86. What are Hegar uterine dilators use for?
A. Dilation of the uterus
B. Dilation of vessels
C. Dilation of the cervix
D. Dilation of the aorta

87. Which of the following is **NOT** used as a blunt dissector during surgery?
A. Lap sponge
B. Kitner
C. Peanut
D. Cherries

88. Which of the following is used with a pneumothorax?
A. Endotracheal tube
B. Penrose drain
C. Fogarty catheter
D. Chest tube

89. A splenectomy is being performed on the patient. What incision will most likely be used?
A. Pfannenstiel
B. Subcostal
C. Thoracolumbar
D. Transverse

90. Which of the following would be needed for neurosurgery?
A. Microscope
B. Headlight
C. Burr
D. All of the above

91. Which of the following is **NOT** a treatment for Atheroma?
A. Stent
B. Pacemaker
C. Percutaneous transluminal coronary angioplasty
D. Intracoronary thrombolysis

92. What is the surgical approach for a pediatric atrial septal defect?
A. Median sternotomy
B. Thoracotomy
C. Subcostal
D. Pfannensteil

93. Which of the following is **NOT** an approach for a prostatectomy procedure?
A. Perineal
B. Retropubic
C. Scrotal
D. Suprapubic

94. Which of the following is defined as a joint that is reconstructed or completely replaced to allow for normal function?
A. Arthrodesis
B. Arthroplasty
C. Arthroscopy
D. Osteogenesis

95. Which of the following is a treatment for hydrocephalus?
A. Ventriculoperitoneal shunt
B. Ventriculoscopy
C. Ventriculoatrial shunt
D. All of the above
E. None of the above

96. What does a commissurotomy separate?
A. Ligaments
B. Mitral valve commissura
C. Tendons
D. Chordae tendineae

97. Which of the following is not a sterile procedure?
A. Bronchoscopy
B. Thoracoscopy
C. Cardiac catheterization
D. Mediastinoscopy

98. What structure is cut to relieve carpal tunnel symptoms?
A. Median nerve
B. Extensor retinaculum
C. Retinaculum
D. Transverse carpal ligament

99. Which of the following is **NOT** a surgical patient position for an intrathoracic procedure?
A. Posterolateral
B. Anterolateral
C. Supine
D. Prone with Trendelenburg

100. Which of the following are adult cardiac surgical procedures?
A. Pericardectomy, aortocoronary bypass, valve replacements, heart transplants, coronary angioplasty, and pacemaker implants
B. Pericardectomy, aortocoronary bypass, valve replacements, heart transplants, peripheral vessel angioplasty, and pacemaker implants
C. .Pericardectomy, aortocoronary bypass, valve replacements, endarterectomy, coronary angioplasty, and pacemaker implants
D. Pericardectomy, aortocoronary bypass, valve replacements, heart transplants, coronary angioplasty, and aortofemoral bypass

101. Which of the following is used to oxygenate and filter blood during a cardiopulmonary bypass?
A. Closed-seal drainage unit
B. Defibrillator unit
C. Pump oxygenator
D. None of the above

102. During cardiopulmonary bypass how is the myocardium protected?
A. Hyperthermia
B. Hypothermia
C. Stenting
D. Both A and B

103. Which procedure would use a figure-eight suture technique?
A. Simple nephrectomy
B. Vaginal hysterectomy
C. Appendectomy
D. CABG

104. Which of the following is the position used for a Marshall-Marchetti-Krantz procedure ?
A. Supine
B. Supine with Trendelenburg
C. Lithotomy
D. Supine with reverse Trendelenburg

105. What is the name of the procedure where the prepuce is removed?
A. Circumcision
B. Orchiectomy
C. TURP
D. Urethroplasty

106. What is the maximum time the tourniquet should be used on an upper extremity before deflating the tourniquet?
A. One hour
B. One and half hours
C. Two hours
D. Thirty minutes

107. In which procedure would Hesselbach's triangle be encountered?
A. Diaphragmatic hernia surgery
B. Ventral hernia surgery
C. Groin hernia surgery
D. Midline incisional hernia surgery

108. Tetany and death can be caused by the removal of what structure(s)?
A. Pancreas
B. Parathyroid glands
C. Spleen
D. Thyroid gland

109. Which of the following are options for a coronary bypass graft?
A. Femoral artery
B. Saphenous vein
C. Internal mammary artery
D. B and C

110. Which of the following is used in aortic valve replacement?
A. Human cadaver valves
B. Pig valve
C. Cow pericardium
D. All of the above

111. What structure will the pacemaker electrode pass through to get placed into the heart?
A. Subclavian vein
B. Carotid artery
C. Jugular vein
D. Brachial artery

112. When performing a pediatric cardiac procedure, what will be used to cut the sternum?
A. Mayo scissors
B. Sternal saw
C. Scalpel
D. Potts-Smith scissors

113. Which of the following is a concern for the surgical team with a pediatric patient?
A. Hyperthermia so the OR temperature should be lowered prior to patient arrival
B. Parent anxiety so the STSR should be sure to call the waiting room during the procedure
C. Hypothermia so the OR temperature should be raised prior to patient arrival
D. None of the above

114. What makes up a full thickness skin graft?
A. The epidermis and half the dermis
B. The dermis, the epidermis and sometimes the subcutaneous tissue
C. The dermis and subcutaneous tissue
D. The epidermis

115. What dressing would be used for a thyroidectomy?
A. Bolster dressing
B. Wet to dry dressing
C. Rigid dressing
D. Queen Ann's collar

116. When doing a simple nephrectomy what can be used for the blunt dissection of the renal pedicle?
A. Peanut sponge
B. Sponge stick
C. A and B
D. None of the above

117. Kidneys are harvested from which of the following?
A. Living relatives
B. Cadavers
C. Unrelated living donors
D. None of the above
E. All of the above

118. When performing a GU endoscopy what position is used?
A. Lithotomy
B. Supine
C. Reverse Trendelenburg
D. Fowlers

119. What is a skin graft called when it is harvested from a pig or a calf and used on a person?
A. Homograft
B. Xenograft
C. Autologous graft
D. None of the above

120. What incision is used in an Abdominoplasty?
A. Low longitudinal incision
B. Right inguinal incision
C. Low oblique incision
D. Low transverse incision

121. What structures are removed in a male radical cystectomy?
A. Bladder, prostate, seminal vesicles
B. Bladder, urethra, prostate
C. Kidney, bladder, urethra
D. Kidney, bladder, prostate

122. What is transplanted in a keratoplasty surgery?
A. Cataract
B. Cornea
C. Iris
D. Vitreous humor

123. What PPE should be worn during a total knee arthroplasty to assist in preventing infection?
A. Double glove
B. Laser goggles
C. Body exhaust system
D. Respirator

124. Which of the following is the correct order of a TKA?
A. Femoral resection, preparation, alignment; tibial preparation, resection, sizing; patellar preparation; trial reduction; implant placement
B. Femoral preparation, alignment, resection sizing; patellar preparation; tibial resection, preparation; trial reduction; implant placement
C. Femoral preparation, alignment, resection, sizing; tibial preparation, resection, sizing; patellar preparation; trial reduction; implant placement
D. Femoral preparation, alignment, resection, sizing; tibial preparation, resection, sizing; trial reduction; patellar preparation; implant placement

125. Which of the following is the closing order for a laparotomy procedure?
A. Peritoneum, Scarpa's fascia, subcuticular layer, skin
B. Fascia, peritoneum, subcuticular layer, skin
C. Peritoneum, subcuticular layer, fascia, skin
D. Subcuticular layer, fascia, peritoneum, skin

126. What is the name of the procedure that incises the tympanic membrane?
A. Mastoiditis
B. Stapedotomy
C. Myringotomy
D. Stapectomy

127. Which of the following can repair female incontinence?
A. TURP procedure
B. Marsupialization procedure
C. Cystectomy
D. Marshall-Marchetti-Krantz procedure

128. What eye structure is adjusted to correct strabismus?
A. Cornea
B. Eye muscles
C. Retina
D. Sclera

129. What are the prep parameters for a rotator cuff procedure?
A. Shoulder to elbow
B. Elbow to shoulder and chest on affected side
C. Wrist to shoulder and chest on affected side
D. Shoulder and chest on affected side

130. What is considered the safest method to remove foreign bodies from the throat?
B. Flexible bronchoscopy
C. Tracheotomy
D. Endoscope
A. Rigid bronchoscopy

131. Once the skin has been harvested where should it go while waiting to be meshed prior to being transplanted?
A. Body temperature sterile saline
B. Body temperature water
C. Cold saline
D. Room temperature water

132. What equipment is used to help position the patient in a knee to chest position for surgery?
A. Wilson frame
B. Fracture table
C. Andrew's frame
D. Halo frame

133. When performing an above the knee amputation, where will the femur be resected?
A. 2-4" proximal to the knee joint
B. 4-6" proximal to the knee joint
C. 4-6" distal to the knee joint
D. 6-8" proximal to the knee joint

134. What is used to prevent the drill from overheating and causing thermal necrosis of the bone?
A. Water poured into surgical site
B. Exchange drills periodically
C. Irrigation fluid dripped onto the drill bit
D. Use a slow drill speed

135. When using the reamers in a total hip arthroplasty what order should they be passed to the surgeon?
A. Largest to smallest
B. Smallest to largest
C. The circulator will tell the STSR the order
D. Order is not important

136. What does ORIF stand for?
A. Closed reduction internal fixation
B. Open reduction intermittent fixation
C. Open reduction internal fixation
D. Open reference internal fixation

137. When performing a rotator cuff repair what position will the patient be placed?
A. Lateral position
B. Semi-Fowler's position
C. Prone position
D. Trendelenburg position

138. What instrument will be used when removing the femoral head in a total hip arthroplasty procedure?
A. Reciprocating saw
B. Oscillating saw
C. Gigli saw
D. Bovi

139. Which procedure is done for cosmetic purposes?
A. Turbinectomy
B. Polypectomy
C. Caldwell-Luc
D. Rhinoplasty

140. What instrument will be used to begin the opening in the femur for the femoral component of the hip prosthesis?
A. Power reamer
B. Rasp
C. T-handle reamer
D. None of the above

141. What are the procedural steps for peripheral artery angioplasty?
A. Arterial needle/cannula punctures artery, guide wire placed, balloon catheter placed, balloon inflated, optional stent placed.
B. Arterial needle/cannula punctures artery, balloon catheter placed, balloon inflated, guide wire placed, optional stent placed.
C. Arterial needle/cannula punctures artery, guide wire placed, balloon inflated, balloon catheter placed, optional stent placed.
D. Arterial needle/cannula punctures artery, guide wire placed, balloon catheter placed, balloon inflated, optional stent placed a punctures artery, guide wire placed, optional stent placed, balloon catheter placed, balloon inflated.

142. What areas are used for skin graft donor sites?
A. Back
B. Abdomen and chest
C. Thigh
D. All of the above

143. What procedure is done to remove part of the bony portion of the mastoid air cells?
A. Myringotomy
B. Mastoidectomy
C. Stapedotomy
D. Otosclerosis

144. What is removed during a T & A procedure?
A. Palatine and pharyngeal tonsils
B. Palatine and adenoid tonsils
C. Lingual and adenoid tonsils
D. Pharyngeal and lingual tonsils

145. Which laser is commonly used for larynx and oropharynx surgeries?
A. Argon laser
B. YAG laser
C. Krypton laser
D. Carbon dioxide laser

146. Which of the following is **NOT** a common peripheral vascular surgery?
A. Bypass
B. Endarterectomy
C. Aneurysmectomy
D. Coronary angioplasty

147. What is used to maintain the lumen of a vessel after an angioplasty procedure?
A. Endarterectomy
B. Stent
C. Balloon angioplasty
D. None of the above

148. When using an autogenous vein for a bypass procedure, what needs to happen to the vein?
A. It needs to be flushed with water
B. It needs to be stretched
C. The valves need to be stripped from the vein
D. All of the above

149. Which of the following defines rhytidectomy?
A. Face lift
B. Eyelid repair
C. Underdeveloped jaw
D. Mole removal

150. What is the procedure that removes excess fat and skin from the upper or lower eyelid?
A. Rhytidectomy
B. Mentoplasty
C. Liposuction
D. Blepharoplasty

151. Which of the following procedures would an umbilical template be used?
A. Mentoplasty
B. Blepharoplasty
C. Abdominoplasty
D. Rhytidectomy

152. What is it called when a patient donates their own skin for their skin graft?
A. Autologous
B. Homograft
C. Heterograft
D. Xenograft

153. What procedure is done to prevent spontaneous abortion?
A. Shirodkar's procedure
B. CPD
C. Cervical cerclage
D. A and C

154. What order will the digit re-plantation be performed?
A. Tendons, bones, blood vessels, then nerves
B. Bones, tendons, blood vessels, then nerves
C. Blood vessels, bones, nerves, then tendons
D. Bones, nerves, vessels, then the tendons

155. Which of the following is used to irrigate the vessels to prepare them for anastomosis?
A. Heparin
B. Papaverine
C. Water
D. Sterile saline

156. Which of the following is a surgical procedure that would use a periareolar line incision or an inframammary fold incision?
A. Reduction mammoplasty
B. Augmentation mammoplasty
C. Abdominoplasty
D. TRAM

157. Which of the following is used in a TRAM?
A. Longissimus muscle
B. Pectoralis minor
C. Serratus posterior inferior
D. Rectus abdominis muscle

158. What incision would be used for an appendectomy?
A. Thoracolumbar
B. Pfannestiel
C. McBurney's
D. Inguinal

159. Which hernia is more likely seen in a female?
A. Direct inguinal hernias
B. Indirect inguinal hernias
C. Femoral hernias
D. All types of hernia's are seen equally in both men and women

160. When performing a gastrectomy, which incision would **NOT** be used?
A. Pfannenstiel
B. Upper midline incision
C. Bilateral subcostal incision
D. Thoracoabdominal incision

161. The Whipple procedure is done for which organ?
A. Spleen
B. Colon
C. Liver
D. Pancreas

162. What is the name of the procedure that removes the entire mammary gland?
A. Mastectomy
B. Dissection
C. Lumpectomy
D. Mammoplasty

163. During cranial procedures saline irrigation should be:
A. Below body temperature
B. Body temperature
C. Above body temperature
D. It does not matter what temperature the irrigation fluid is in a cranial procedure.

164. When a bone flap is removed where will it be placed?
A. It is placed in the kick bucket
B. It is placed on the mayo stand
C. It is placed on the back table soaking in normal saline and antibiotic
D. It is wrapped in a moist laparotomy sponge and placed on the back table

165. Where is the distal drain tube placed in hydrocephalus treatment?
A. Peritoneal cavity
B. Right atrium of the heart, peritoneal cavity
C. Right ventricle of the heart, peritoneal cavity
D. Left atrium of the heart

166. When a patient has a pituitary gland tumor which procedure is used to remove it?
A. Craniotomy
B. Ventriculoscopy
C. Laminectomy
D. Transphenoidal hypophysectomy

167. What is the most common cause for a Cesarean section to be performed?
A. Cephalopelvic disproportion
B. Herpes
C. Labor failing to progress
D. None of the above

168. Which of the following correctly describes an episiotomy?
A. An episiotomy in an incision made in the perineum to ease the process of delivering babies and to prevent tearing of the perineum during delivery.
B. An episiotomy in an incision made in the clitoris to ease the process of delivering babies and to prevent tearing of the vulva during delivery.
C. An episiotomy is the process of suturing the vulva after delivery of a baby.
D. An episiotomy is an incision used to perform a cesarean section.

169. Which of the following procedures would use Mersilene tape?
A. Cervical cerclage
B. Shirodkar's procedure
C. Answer A and B
D. None of the above

170. What is called when the uterus, both fallopian tubes and ovaries are removed through the abdomen?
A. Total hysterectomy
B. LAVH
C. Salpingectomy
D. Total abdominal hysterectomy with bilateral salpingo-oophorectomy

171. What organs are excised in a total pelvic exenteration?
A. Vagina, uterus, cervix, fallopian tubes, and ovaries
B. Uterus, fallopian tubes, ovaries, and bladder
C. Uterus, fallopian tubes, cervix, bladder and rectum
D. Vagina, uterus, cervix, fallopian tubes, ovaries, bladder, and rectum

172. Which of the following needles would be used on thick tough tissue?
A. Tapered
B. Blunt
C. Cutting
D. Any needle tip will do

173. What suture is used for an appendectomy?
A. Purse string suture
B. Traction suture
C. Primary suture
D. Doctor's choice

174. What is used to prevent the suture from cutting into tissue?
A. Vessel loops
B. Bolsters
C. Adhesive
D. None of the above

175. Which gauge suture would be used to close the fascia in an abdominal procedure?
A. 0
B. #2
C. 2-0
D. 5-0

176. Which of the following is used for blunt dissection during laparoscopic procedures?
A. Cone tip dissector
B. Endo harmonic scalpel
C. Blunt grasper
D. All of the above

177. Which of the following surgical techniques utilizes heat to remove, erode or vaporize tissues?
A. Cryotherapy
B. Ablation
C. Fluoroscopy
D. None of the above

178. Which of the following procedures refers to the surgical removal of the adrenal gland?
A. Stapedectomy
B. Odontectomy
C. Splenectomy
D. Adrenalectomy

179. Which of the following refers to a surgically made connection between adjacent blood vessels or parts of the intestine?
A. Fistula
B. Anastomosis
C. Fenestration
D. None of the above

180. Which of the following is a surgical procedure utilized to reconstruct damaged blood vessels?
A. Arthroscopy
B. Bronchoscopy
C. Angioplasty
D. Mentoplasty

181. Which of the following refers to the surgical fixation of a patient's joint in order to provide support and relieve pain?
A. Arthroscopy
B. Arthrodesis
C. Arthroplasty
D. Arthrotomy

182. Which of the following refers to the surgical reconstruction or replacement of a patient's joint?
A. Arthroscopy
B. Arthrotomy
C. Arthroplasty
D. None of the above

183. Which of the following refers to a surgical procedure that utilizes an endoscope to visualize a patient's joint space?
A. Arthroscopy
B. Arthroplasty
C. Arthrotomy
D. Arthrodesis

184. Which of the following refers to the surgical opening of a joint?
A. Arthroplasty
B. Arthroscopy
C. Arthrotomy
D. None of the above

185. Which of the following refers to a plastic reconstructive surgical procedure that is used to increase the size of the breasts?
A. Augmentation
B. Mammoplasty
C. Mentoplasty
D. Augmentation mammoplasty

186. What procedure is used to remove foreign objects that are lodged in the airway?
A. Endoscopy
B. Tracheostomy
C. Bronchoscopy
D. None of the above

187. Define *cystoscopy*.
A. This is a procedure for bladder diagnostics.
B. This is a scope procedure to treat bladder cancer.
C. This is a procedure where a scope is passed through the urethra into the bladder to perform diagnostic tests and or to treat the bladder.
D. This is a procedure where the scope passes through the vagina to check the bladder.

188. What is the definition of *cystectomy*?
A. Surgical removal of the uterus
B. Surgical removal of the kidney
C. Surgical removal of the stomach
D. Surgical removal of the bladder

189. What is the name of the procedure that will repair a cleft lip?
A. Cheiloschisis
B. Chelation
C. Cheilectomy
D. Cheiloplasty

190. In which of the following procedures would cannulation need to be used?
A. Roux-N-Y
B. Cholecystectomy
C. Coronary artery bypass graft
D. None of the above

191. When a surgeon separates tissue with a sponge stick what is it called?
A. Sharp dissection
B. Blunt dissection
C. Dissection
D. None of the above

192. When a surgical wound opens partially or totally:
A. Rupture
B. Incision
C. Avulsion
D. Dehiscence

193. What term is used when an injury needs to have necrotic tissue and or debris removed from it?
A. Debridement
B. Decontaminate
C. Antisepsis
D. Dehiscence

194. When something is exsanguinated it:
A. Has all the water removed
B. Has all the blood replaced
C. Has all the blood removed
D. Both A and B

195. When a total pelvic exenteration procedure is done on a female patient which of the following is not removed?
A. Vagina
B. Ovaries
C. Rectum
D. Cecum

196. What supply would be used to exsanguinate an extremity prior to tourniquet application?
A. Ace wrap
B. Gauze wrap
C. Esmarch bandage
D. None of the above

197. During labor and delivery what will the doctor do to prevent tearing of the perineum?
A. Episiotomy
B. Perineotomy
C. Pfannenstiel incision
D. Nothing

198. When a tissue is completely removed to be transplanted (usually on the chest):
A. Pedicle flap
B. Free flap reconstruction
C. In situ
D. Both A and C

199. When performing a laparoscopic procedure, what term is used to place air/gas into the abdominal cavity for visualization purposes?
A. Inflation
B. Ensufflation
C. Insufflation
D. None of the above

200. What structure can be ligated?
A. Blood vessels
B. Muscles
C. Nerves
D. None of the above

201. What term means: to wash out?
A. Levege
B. Lysis
C. Lavage
D. Suction

202. What dressing would be used on the top lip?
A. Cigar dressing
B. Mustache dressing
C. Queen Ann's collar
D. None of the above

203. What is the safest method for passing scalpels?
A. Neutral zone
B. Laying it on the Mayo stand
C. Hand to hand
D. Placing the scalpel on the drape to be picked up by the STSR

204. In which of the following procedures is the lung surgically removed?
A. Pneumothorax
B. Pneumonia
C. Pleurectomy
D. Pneumonectomy

205. The definition of phacoemulsification:
A. The process of irrigating the lens of the eye using ultrasonic energy
B. The process of fragmenting the lens using ultrasonic energy
C. The process of removing aqueous humor from the eyeball
D. The process of breaking up and aspirating the lens from the eye that uses ultrasonic energy

206. Which of the following is a procedure where tissue remains attached to its blood supply and is relocated through a tunneling procedure under the skin?
A. Free flap reconstruction
B. Reconstruction
C. Pedicle flap reconstruction
D. All of the above

207. Which of the following is a treatment of a condition or disease that is not a cure but allows the patient to be more comfortable by reducing the symptoms?
A. Palliative
B. Enteral
C. Parenteral
D. Buccal

208. What procedure 'lifts' the face and removes wrinkles?
A. Mentoplasty
B. Rhytidectomy
C. Rhinoplasty
D. Acromioplasty

209. The patient is being treated for malignant neoplasms. What treatment would be used?
A. Antibiotic therapy
B. Radiculopathy
C. Radiation therapy
D. All of the above

210. Which procedure removes the prostate gland?
A. Suprapubic prostatectomy
B. Suprapubic vesicourethral suspension
C. Suprapubic cystostomy
D. None of the above

211. Which procedure is used to drain the bladder when the urethra is blocked or cannot be penetrated?
A. Suprapubic prostatectomy
B. Suprapubic vesicourethral suspension
C. Suprapubic cystostomy
D. None of the above

212. The patient's comes in to repair esotropia. What procedure will he have done?
A. Scleral buckle
B. Keratoplasty
C. Strabismus correction
D. Cataract extraction

213. What term refers to the spleen being removed?
A. Splenectomy
B. Splenomegaly
C. Splenotomy
D. All of the above

214. The procedure is a mastectomy with a breast reconstruction because of cancer. The mastectomy is complete and the reconstruction is underway. The surgical technologist passes a Crile to the surgeon to use in the reconstruction procedure that was used during the mastectomy. What possible problem did the surgical technologist do?
A. The surgical technologist did nothing incorrect.
B. The surgical technologist possibly allowed seeding to take place.
C. The surgical technologist should have used a clean Crile.
D. None of the above

215. What is it called when the rectus abdominis muscle is used in breast reconstruction surgery?
A. TURP
B. TIA
C. TRAM
D. None of the above

216. Which of the following is an examination of the thoracic cavity with a scope?
A. Thoracoscopy
B. Thoracocentesis
C. Thorascope
D. None of the above

217. Which of the following is the definition of Thoracocentesis?
A. An instrument used to examine the thoracic cavity
B. The process of examining the thoracic cavity through a rigid scope
C. Pain within the chest cavity
D. The process of inserting a needle into the pleural space to analyze pleural effusion

218. When two granulated surfaces are approximated it is called:
A. First intention
B. Second intention
C. Third intention
D. None of the above

219. Which of the following is a suture technique?
A. Pursestring suture
B. Blanket suture
C. Sutura
D. None of the above

220. When an abdominal hysterectomy is being performed, what instrument would be used to assist in manipulating the uterus?
A. Babcock
B. Tenaculum
C. Pennington retractor
D. Kocher clamp

221. Which instrument is used to cut the cornea during a Keratoplasty procedure?
A. Trephine
B. Cookie Cutter template
C. Beaver blade with handle
D. None of the above

222. What will the doctor use to redirect body fluid to another part of the body?
A. Stent
B. Shunt
C. Catheter
D. Syringe

223. What is retracted with a vessel loop?
A. Vessels
B. Nerves
C. Ducts
D. All of the above

224. Which type of surgery would a pledget most likely be used?
A. Orthopedic surgery
B. Maxillofacial surgery
C. Peripheral vascular surgery
D. Otorhinolaryngologic surgery

Instruments

225. What instrument would be used to harvest a skin graft?
A. Ferris-Smith
B. Padgett and Reese
C. Mesh graft
D. A and B

226. Which of the following are urethral instruments?
A. Hegar dilator
B. Vanburen sound
C. Heaney-Ballantine clamp
D. Raney clip

227. Which instrument finish is used in laser procedures?
A. Ebony
B. Mirror
C. Matte
D. Gold plating

228. Which of the following category of instruments will be used to stop the flow of fluid/blood?
A. Cutting
B. Holding
C. Clamping
D. Suctioning

229. Which of the following would be found in a gynecology instrument set?
A. Hulka tenaculum
B. Hegar dilators
C. Auvard speculum
D. All of the above

230. Which part of the instrument is designed to lock it?
A. Ratchet
B. Jaws
C. Finger rings
D. Box lock

231. What is used to expand the harvested skin for grafting purposes?
A. Ferris-Smith
B. Weck
C. Dermatome
D. Mesh graft device

232. Which of the following is a grasping/holding instrument?
A. Crile forceps
B. Skin hook
C. Ferris-Smith tissue forceps
D. Gelpi retractor

233. Which of the following would be found in a general instrument set?
A. Intraluminal stapler
B. Harrington retractor
C. Endo Kittner
D. Schroeder tenaculum

234. Which of the following will be used in obstetrics and gynecology?
A. Hank dilators
B. Lacrimal probe
C. Ball tip probe
D. Vascular dilators

235. Which of the following is a hand held retractor?
A. Weitlaner retractor
B. Gelpi retractor
C. Volkman retractor
D. Barraquer eye speculum

236. Where would the shank of the instrument be located?
A. Between the tip and the jaws
B. Between the finger rings and the ratchet
C. Between the ratchet and the box lock
D. None of the above

237. What type of instrument can be used to retract the tongue during an adenoidectomy?
A. McIvor mouth gag
B. Wieder tongue depressor
C. Army Navy retractor
D. None of the above

238. Which of the following would be found in a plastic surgery instrument set?
A. Skin hooks
B. Beaver blade and handle
C. Littler scissors
D. All of the above

239. Which of the following would not be found in a typical dental set?
A. Iris scissors
B. McGill
C. Minnesota retractor
D. Gingival probe

240. Which of the following is not a gynecologic instrument?
A. Auvard weighted speculum
B. Minnesota retractor
C. Luikart forceps
D. Sims curettes

241. Which of the following is used to make a sponge stick?
A. Tonsil sponge
B. Raytec sponge
C. Laparotomy sponge
D. Kitner

242. Which instrument would be used to pull the ribs back together after a rib retraction?
A. Rib contractor
B. Scapula retractor
C. Forceps
D. Rib shears

243. Which of the following would **NOT** be used in ophthalmic surgery?
A. Scleral hooks
B. Graefe knife
C. Raney clip
D. Westcott scissors

244. What instrument is used to cut the cornea in a keratoplasty surgery?
A. McPherson-Vanna scissors
B. Beaver Blade
C. Trephine
D. Mayo scissors

245. What suture would be used to close the cornea incision in a cataract extraction procedure?
A. 4-0
B. 5-0
C. 7-0
D. 10-0

246. What instruments need to be added to the set up when an internal fixation of the femoral shaft is performed?
A. Power reamer
B. Hohmann retractor
C. Lowman bone holding clamp
D. Bone rongeur

247. What is used to prepare the acetabulum for the prosthesis?
A. Bone rasp
B. Oscillating saw
C. Acetabular reamer
D. Acetabulum does not need prepping

248. Which of the following knife blades are popular in oropharyngeal surgery?
A. #10
B. #11
C. #12
D. # 15

249. Which of the following instruments are used to excise the tonsil?
A. White tonsil forceps
B. Sage tonsil snare
C. Allis
D. Tonsil sponge

250. Which of the following is not a peripheral vascular instrument?
A. Beaver knife
B. Castroviejo needle holders
C. Hemoclips
D. Raney clip appliers

251. What instrument would be used to make the tunnel for a bypass surgery?
A. Tunneler
B. Mayo scissors
C. Curette
D. Probe

252. What instrument could be used to remove the plaque from the carotid artery during an endarterectomy?
A. Diethrich scissors
B. Key elevator
C. Freer elevator
D. None of the above

253. Which is used to anastomose the femoral artery in an artery bypass procedure?
A. 5-0, 6-0 Prolene, double armed
B. 8-0, 9-0 Prolene, single armed
C. 5-0, 6-0 Monocryl, double armed
D. 2-0, 3-0 Vicryl, single armed

254. Which of the following is not needed for an aneurysmectomy procedure?
A. Cell saver
B. Raney clips
C. Heparin
D. Grafts

255. Which of the following would be added to the set up for a rhytidectomy procedure?
A. Caliper
B. Castroviejo needle holder
C. Jeweler's forceps
D. All of the above

256. Which of the following are used for a skin graft harvest procedure?
A. Dermatome, tongue blades, derma-carrier, mineral oil
B. Mineral oil, mesh graft device, derma-carrier
C. Dermatome, derma-carrier, mesh graft device, mineral oil
D. Dermatome, mineral oil, sterile tongue blades, derma-carrier, mesh graft device

257. Which of the following would **NOT** be found in a laparotomy set?
A. Army Navy retractor and O'Sullivan- O'Conner retractor
B. Yankauer and Poole suction
C. Mosquito's and criles
D. Babcock and Tonsil Schnidt

258. What is used to retract the spermatic cord during a herniorrhaphy?
A. Ribbon retractor
B. Army Navy retractor
C. Penrose drain
D. Goelet retractor

259. When performing a gastrectomy, which of the following instruments might be used?
A. Heaney forceps
B. Bookwalter
C. Bowman probe
D. Minnesota retractor

260. When a laparoscopic cholecystectomy is being done, which of the following will be needed?
A. Veress needle
B. Trocars
C. Light cord
D. All of the above

261. Which of the following is a cranial immobilizer?
A. A fracture table
B. A beanbag
C. A three pin fixation system
D. All of the above

262. What instrument is used to clip a cranial aneurysm?
A. Aneurysm clips
B. Hemoclips
C. Raney clips
D. Silk ties

263. Which of the following can be used to cut the cranium between the bur holes during a craniotomy?
A. Gigli saw
B. Air powered craniotome saw
C. Electric craniotome saw
D. All of the above

264. When performing a tuboplasty what instruments should be added to the set up?
A. Minnesota retractor
B. Toomey syringe
C. Microsurgical instruments
D. Lambotte osteotome

265. What instrument is used to grasp the cervix during a vaginal hysterectomy?
A. Babcock
B. Tenaculum
C. Heaney forceps
D. Kelly

266. How is the needle placed into the needle holder?
A. One third the distance between the swage and the needle tip
B. Half way from the swage and the needle tip
C. A quarter of the distance between the swage and the needle tip
D. Anywhere on the needle will work

267. What direction should the needle point be directed when passing the needle to the surgeon?
A. Toward the ceiling
B. Toward the surgeon
C. Toward the patient
D. Away from the surgeon

268. Which of the following staples and cuts?
A. Linear stapler
B. Ligating clip
C. Intraluminal staplers
D. Linear cutter

269. Which of the following category of instruments will be used to stop the flow of fluid/blood?
A. Clamping
B. Cutting
C. Holding
D. Suctioning

270. Which of the following category of instruments will be used to excise an appendix?
A. Grasping
B. Cutting
C. Suturing
D. Holding

271. Which of the following is a grasping/holding instrument?
A. Crile forceps
B. Skin hook
C. Gelpi retractor
D. Ferris-Smith tissue forceps

272. Which of the following is not used to occlude a vessel.
A. Stapler
B. Hemoclip applier
C. Ligatures
D. Rochester-Pean forceps

273. Which of the following would be found in a general instrument set?
A. Intraluminal stapler
B. Endo Kittner
C. Harrington retractor
D. Schroeder tenaculum

274. Which of the following will be used in obstetrics and gynecology?
A. Hank dilators
B. Lacrimal probe
C. Ball Tip probe
D. Vascular dilators

275. Which of the following would be found in a gynecology instrument set?
A. Hulka tenaculum
B. Hegar dilators
C. Auvard speculum
D. All of the above

276. Which of the following can be used in ophthalmic and vascular procedures?
A. Tonometer
B. Serrefine Clamps
C. Strabismus scissors
D. Yasargil scissors

277. Which of the following is a hand held retractor?
A. Volkman retractor
B. Weitlaner retractor
C. Gelpi retractor
D. Barraquer eye speculum

278. Where would the shank of the instrument be located?
A. Between the tip and the jaws
B. Between the ratchet and the box lock
C. Between the finger rings and the ratchet
D. None of the above

279. Which part of the instrument is designed to lock it?
A. Jaws
B. Finger rings
C. Ratchet
D. Box lock

280. Which of the following are urethral instruments?
A. Vanburen sound
B. Hegar dilator
C. Heaney-Ballantine clamp
D. Raney clip

281. Which of the following is used to dilate the urethra in a TURP?
A. Hegar dilator
B. Penfield
C. Van Buren sound
D. None of the above

282. Which of the following are ophthalmic surgical forceps?
A. Pott-Smith and Cushing bayonet forceps
B. Colibri forceps and Bishop-Harmon forceps
C. Pott-Smith and Colibri forceps
D. Cushing bayonet and Bishop-Harmon forceps

283. Which of the following instruments would be used in a thyroidectomy?
A. Dennis clamp
B. Bipolar forceps
C. Bakes dilator
D. Doyen forceps

284. Which of the following would not be found in a typical dental set?
A. Iris scissors
B. McGill
C. Minnesota retractor
D. Gingival probe

285. Which of the following will be needed when the surgical procedure calls for arch bar application?
A. Army-Navy retractor
B. Iris scissors
C. Midas drill
D. Wire cutters

286. Which of the following is **NOT** a gynecologic instrument?
A. Minnesota retractor
B. Auvard weighted speculum
C. Luikart forceps
D. Sims curettes

287. What are Hegar uterine dilators use for?
A. Dilation of the uterus
B. Dilation of vessels
C. Dilation of the cervix
D. Dilation of the aorta

288. What procedure is a uterine sound used in?
A. Hysterectomy
B. Rectocele
C. Cesarean section
D. Dilation and curettage

289. Which of the following is used in a cholecystectomy?
A. Gall stone scoop
B. Bone rasp
C. Lung retractor
D. Lacrimal probe

290. Which of the following would be used in a craniotomy?
A. Lung retractor
B. Raney clips
C. Iris scissors
D. Lacrimal probe

291. Which of the following would be used to cut suture?
B. Jorgenson scissors
C. Wire cutters
D. Iris scissors
A. Straight Mayo scissors

292. Which of the following would be used in peripheral vascular surgery?
A. Corneal knife
B. Lid retractor
C. Hemoclip appliers
D. Penetrating clamp

293. When performing an aortic aneurysm procedure, which of the following would be used?
A. Aortic clamp
B. Intestinal clamp
C. Non-penetrating clamp
D. Heaney clamp

294. Which of the following instrument is used in neurosurgery?
A. Burr
B. Nerve retractor
C. Rongeur
D. All of the above

295. Which knife blade is used to make the initial oblique incision for an inguinal herniorrhaphy?
A. #3 handle
B. #7 handle
B. #10 blade
C. #11 blade
D. #25 blade

296. What instrument would be used to retract the liver during a Nissan Fundoplication?
A. Liver retractor
B. Army-Navy retractor
C. Hohmann retractor
D. Ribbon Retractor

297. Which instrument would be used to grasp the appendix during an appendectomy?
A. Allis
B. Babcock
C. Backhaus clamp
D. Pean hemostat

298. Which instrument is used to explore the common bile duct?
A. Van Buren sound
B. Baron suction
C. Bowman probe
D. Stone forceps

299. When the cervix needs to be dilated which instrument will the surgical technologist pass to the surgeon?
A. Lacrimal probe
B. Uterine dilator
C. Urethral sound
D. None of the above

300. Which blade is used when performing the incision for a mastoidectomy?
A. #10
B. #11
C. #15
D. #25

301. Which instrument would be used to hold the tonsil while it is removed from the mucosa?
A. Allis
B. Curette
C. Pean
D. Snare

302. Which of the following instruments would be needed during an immobilization of a jaw and arch bar application?
A. Wire cutters
B. Cheek retractor
C. Hohmann retractor
D. Both A and B
E. Both A and C

303. What instrument is used to lift the periosteum from the bone during a mandibular fracture repair?
A. Minnesota retractor
B. Periosteum elevator
C. Hohmann retractor
D. Curette

304. Which of the following is used in a dilation and curettage procedure?
A. Uterine sound
B. Dilator
C. Curette
D. None of the above
E. All of the above

305. Which of the following would be found in a major laparotomy set?
A. Poole suction tip, Mayo-Hagar needle holder, Potts-Smith scissors, Lahey forceps, Goelet retractor, Adson forceps
B. Poole suction tip, Mayo-Hagar needle holder, Metzenbaum scissors, Lahey forceps, Adson forceps
C. Poole suction tip, Metzenbaum scissors, Baron suction, Lahey forceps, Goelet retractor, Adson forceps
D. Poole suction tip, Mayo-Hagar needle holder, Metzenbaum scissors, Lahey forceps, Goelet retractor, Adson forceps

306. Which of the following would be used in a posterior vitrectomy procedure?
A. Oscillating saw
B. Ocutome
C. Reciprocating saw
D. Gigli saw

307. What is used to keep the skin graft flat so it will pass through the mesh device evenly?
A. Telfa
B. Raytec
C. Derma-carrier
D. The graft can be placed in the mesh device by itself.

308. What is used to create burr holes in the cranium?
A. Gigli saw
B. Trephine
C. Midas Rex
D. Chisel

309. Which of the following is a device used to replace a body structure like a foot or arm?
A. Prosthesis
B. Quarks
C. Parostosis
D. Prostatitis

310. What is used to cut a circular piece of bone?
A. Sagittal saw
B. Trephine
C. Reciprocating saw
D. Gigli saw

311. Venous compression device:
A. A device used in surgery to assist arterial blood return to assist in preventing Thrombophlebitis.
B. A device used in surgery to assist arterial blood pooling in the extremities.
C. A device used in surgery to assist lymphatic drainage.
D. A device used in surgery to assist venous blood return to assist in the prevention of thrombophlebitis.

312.Which one of the following four surgical instruments is identified in figure 6-1?
A. Metzenbaum scissors
B. Mayo scissors
C. Utility scissors
D. Jorgenson scissors

313. Which one of the following four surgical instruments is identified in figure 6-2?
A. Intestinal clamp
B. Aortic clamp
C. Peripheral vascular clamp
D. None of the above

314. Which one of the following four surgical instruments is identified in figure 6-3?
A. Balfour
B. Deaver
C. Richardson
D. Goelet

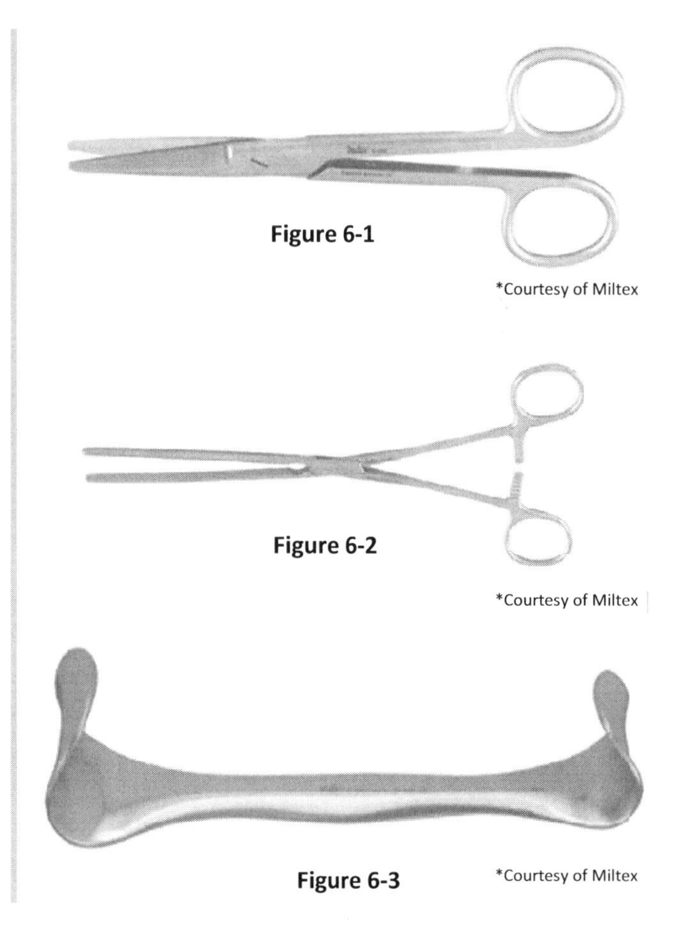

Figure 6-1

*Courtesy of Miltex

Figure 6-2

*Courtesy of Miltex

Figure 6-3

*Courtesy of Miltex

315. Which one of the following four surgical instruments is identified in figure 6-4?
A. Cottle hook
B. Frazier hook
C. Meyerding hook
D. Dandy hook

316. Which one of the following four surgical instruments is identified in figure 6-5?
A. Coneal knife
B. Seldin elevator
C. Gallstone scoop
D. Osteotome

317. Which one of the following four surgical instruments is identified in figure 6-6?
A. Pole suction
B. Poole suction
C. Yankauer suction
D. Baron suction

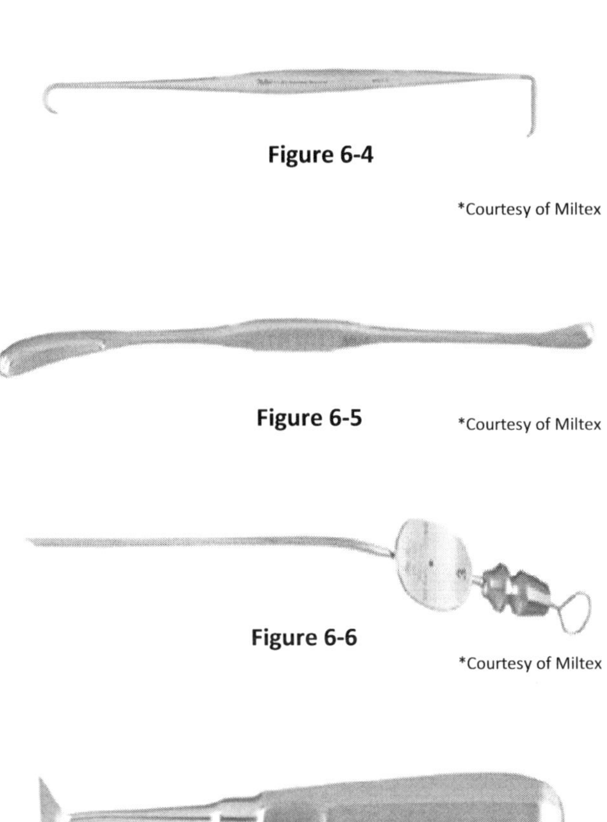

Figure 6-4

*Courtesy of Miltex

Figure 6-5 *Courtesy of Miltex

Figure 6-6

*Courtesy of Miltex

318. Which one of the following four surgical instruments is identified in figure 6-7?
A. Osteotome
B. Seldin elevator
C. Freer elevator
D. File

Figure 6-7 *Courtesy of Miltex

319. Which one of the following four surgical instruments is identified in figure 6-8?
A. Tubing
B. Magnifying loope
C. Spagmagnometer
D. Glasses

Figure 6-8 *Courtesy of Miltex

320. Which one of the following four surgical instruments is identified in figure 6-9?
A. Tissue forceps
B. Jewwler forceps
C. Potts-Smith forceps
D. Bayonett forceps

Figure 6-9

*Courtesy of Miltex

*Images are provided courtesy of Miltex. Permission granted by Integra Miltex, a business of Integra Life Sciences Corporation, Plainsboro, New Jersey, USA.

321. Which one of the following four surgical instruments is identified in figure 6-10?
A. Volkman retractor
B. Hohmann retractor
C. Scapula retractor
D. Balfour retractor

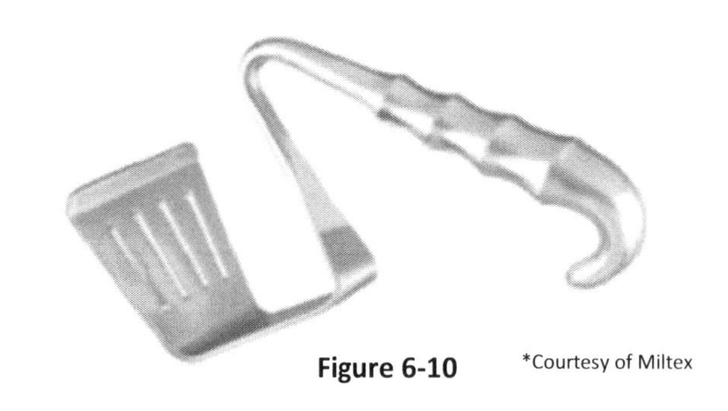

Figure 6-10 *Courtesy of Miltex

322. Which one of the following four surgical instruments is identified in figure 6-11?
A. O'Sullivan-O'Connor retractor
B. Balfour retractor
C. Bookwalter retractor
D. Volkman retractor

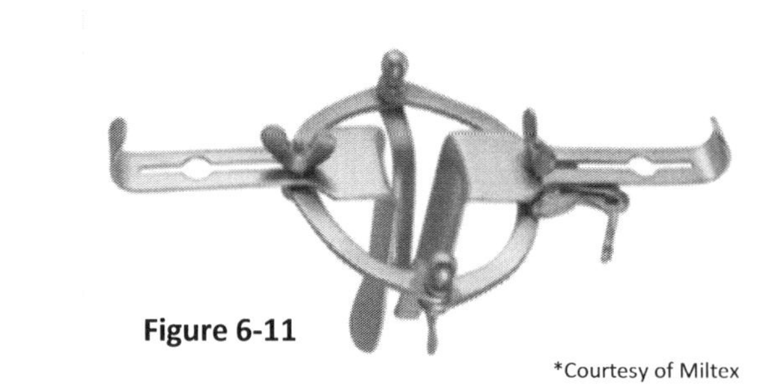

Figure 6-11 *Courtesy of Miltex

323. Which one of the following four surgical instruments is identified in figure 6-12?
A. Hibbs retractor
B. Lid retractor
C. Cast spreader
D. Weitlaner retractor

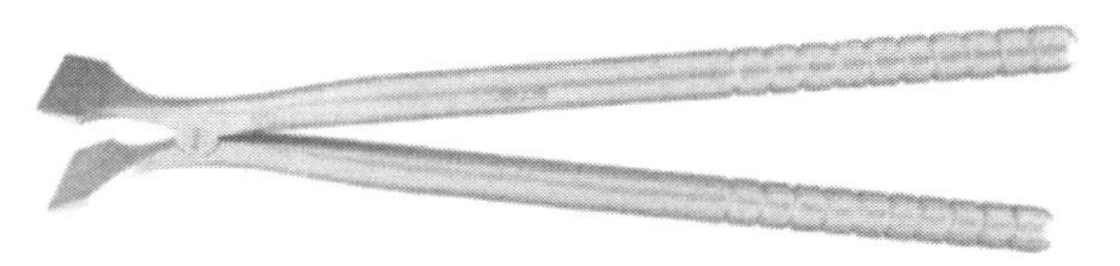

Figure 6-12 *Courtesy of Miltex

324. Which one of the following four surgical instruments is identified in figure 6-13?
A. Lancaster speculum
B. Septum speculum
C. Barraquer speculum
D. Vaginal speculum

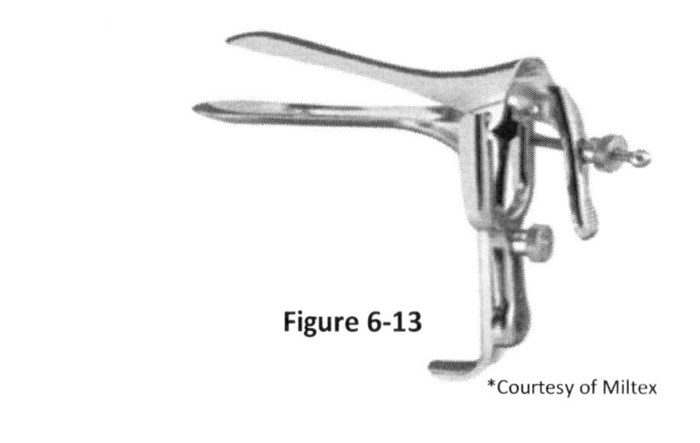

Figure 6-13 *Courtesy of Miltex

325. Which one of the following four surgical instruments is identified in figure 6-14?
A. Iris scissors
B. Tenotomy scissors
C. Corneal scissors
D. Bandage scissors

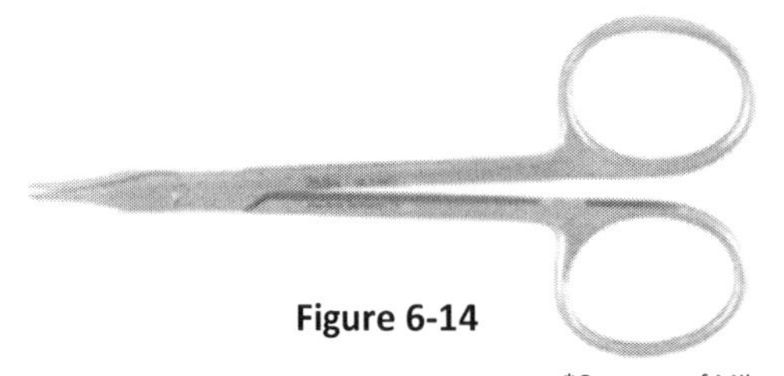

Figure 6-14 *Courtesy of Miltex

*Images are provided courtesy of Miltex. Permission granted by Integra Miltex, a business of Integra Life Sciences Corporation, Plainsboro, New Jersey, USA.

326. Which one of the following four surgical instruments is identified in figure 6-15?
A. Eleven blade
B. Ten blade
C. Twelve blade
D. Twenty blade

Figure 6-15 *Courtesy of Miltex

327.Which one of the following four surgical instruments is identified in figure 6-16?
A. Babcock forcep
B. Allis forcep
C. Bullet Nose forcep
D. Scissors

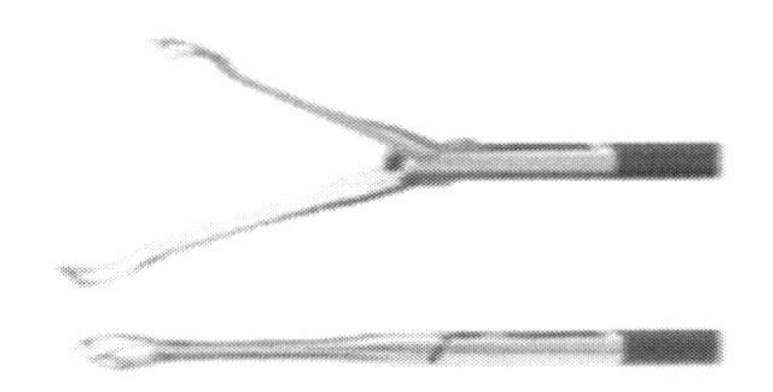

Figure 6-16 *Courtesy of Miltex

328. Which one of the following four surgical instruments is identified in figure 6-17?
A. Suction
B. Dilator
C. Probe
D. Scope

Figure 6-17 *Courtesy of Miltex

329. Which one of the following four surgical instruments is identified in figure 6-18?
A. Brown-Adson forceps
B. Russian forceps
C. Potts-Smith forceps
D. Jeweler forceps

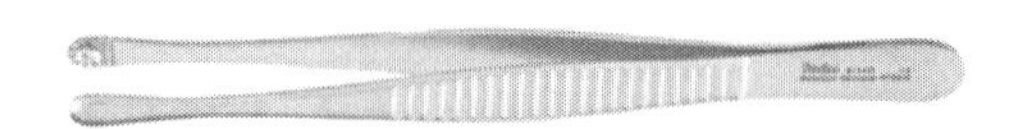

Figure 6-18 *Courtesy of Miltex

330. Which one of the following four surgical instruments is identified in figure 6-19?
A. Urethral sound
B. Hank dilator
C. Bowman probe
D. None of the above

Figure 6-19

*Courtesy of Miltex

331. Which one of the following four surgical instruments is identified in figure 6-20?
A. Listen amputating knife
B. Myringotomy knife
C. Miller bone file
D. Saw

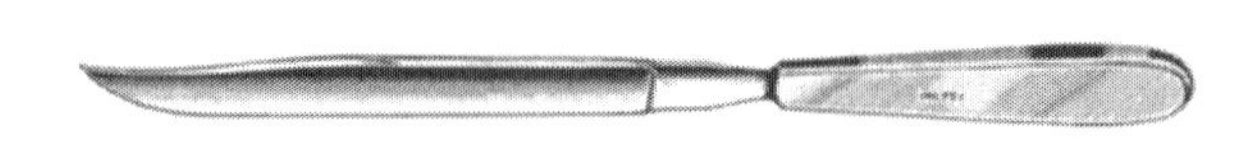

Figure 6-20

*Courtesy of Miltex

*Images are provided courtesy of Miltex. Permission granted by Integra Miltex, a business of Integra Life Sciences Corporation, Plainsboro, New Jersey, USA.

332. Which one of the following four surgical instruments is identified in figure 6-21?
A. Babcock
B. Heaney
C. Allis
D. Mixter

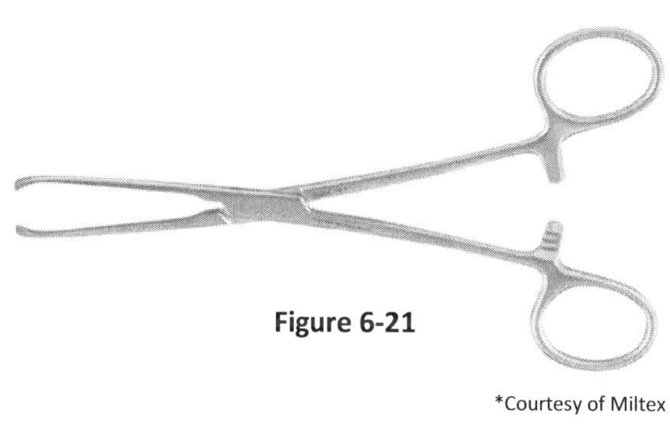

Figure 6-21

*Courtesy of Miltex

333. Which one of the following four surgical instruments is identified in figure 6-22?
A. Pin puller
B. Needle holder
C. Crile-Wood needle holder
D. Wire twister

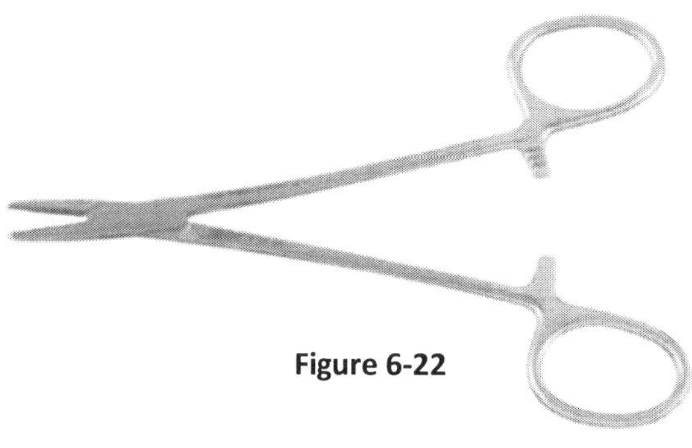

Figure 6-22

*Courtesy of Miltex

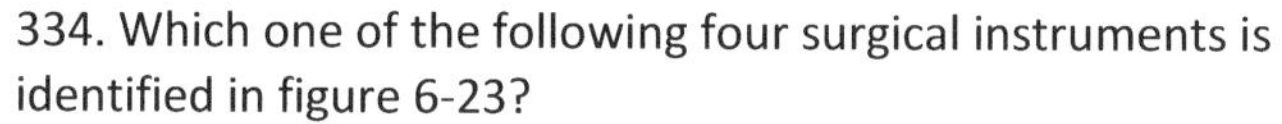

334. Which one of the following four surgical instruments is identified in figure 6-23?
A. Volkman retractor
B. Hibbs retractor
C. Senn retractor
D. Parker retractor

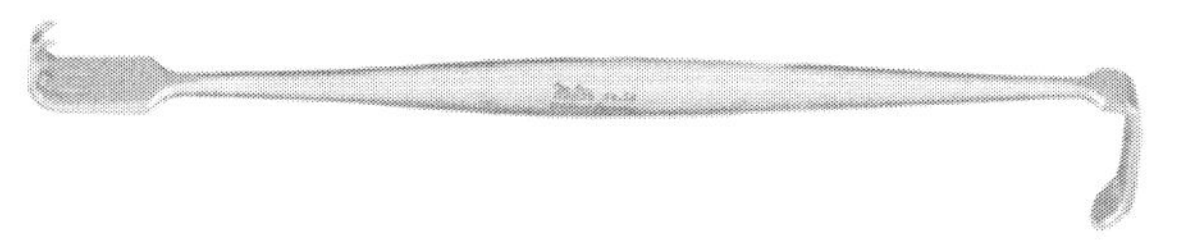

Figure 6-23 *Courtesy of Miltex

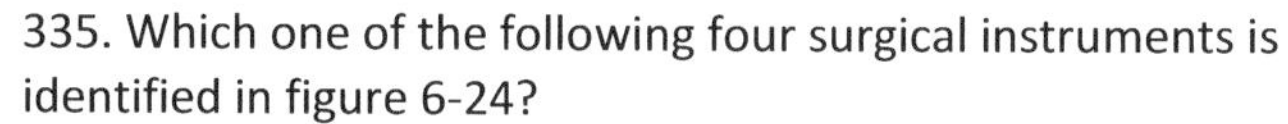

335. Which one of the following four surgical instruments is identified in figure 6-24?
A. Bookwalter retractor
B. Weitlaner retractor
C. Gelpi retractor
D. Balfour retractor

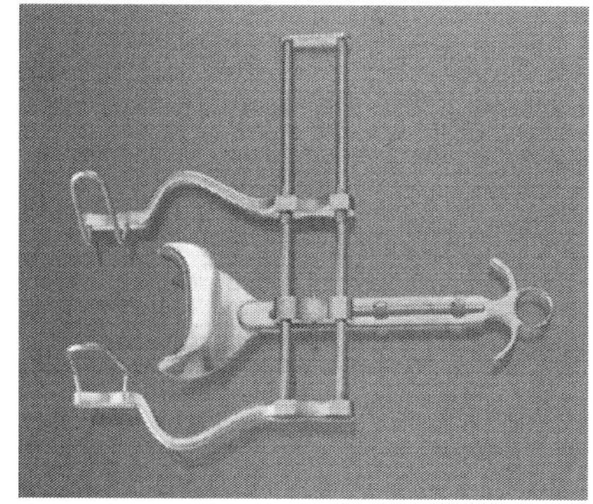

Figure 6-24 *Courtesy of Miltex

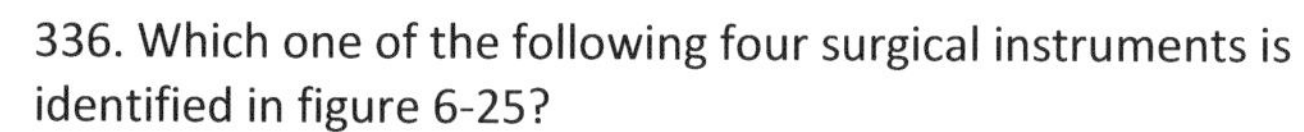

336. Which one of the following four surgical instruments is identified in figure 6-25?
A. Lacrimal probe
B. Poole suction
C. Yankauer suction
D. Baron suction

Figure 6-25

*Courtesy of Miltex

*Images are provided courtesy of Miltex. Permission granted by Integra Miltex, a business of Integra Life Sciences Corporation, Plainsboro, New Jersey, USA.

337. Which one of the following four surgical instruments is identified in figure 6-26?
A. #3 handle
B. #4 handle
C. #7 handle
D. #9 handle

Figure 6-26 *Courtesy of Miltex

338. Which one of the following four surgical instruments is identified in figure 6-27?
A. Gallbladder retractor
B. Liver retractor
C. Lung retractor
D. None of the above

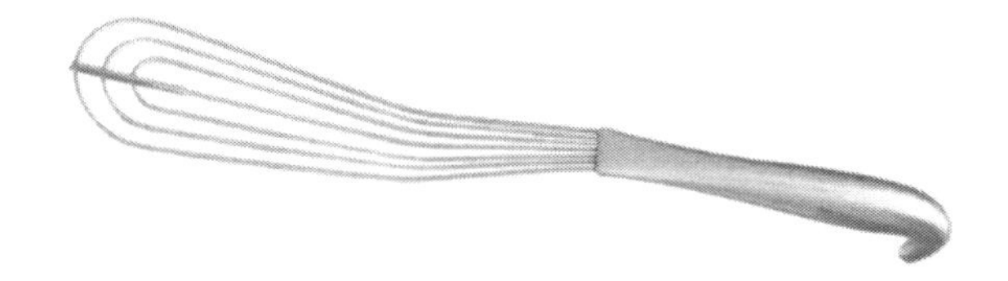

Figure 6-27 *Courtesy of Miltex

339. Which one of the following four surgical instruments is identified in figure 6-28?
A. Volkman retractor
B. Myeriding hook
C. Osteotome
D. Dura Hook

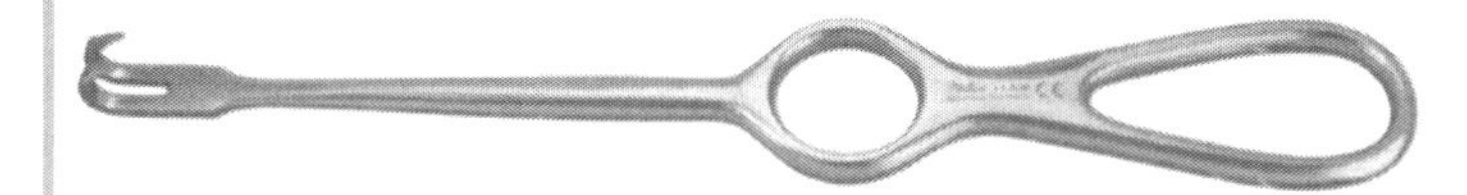

Figure 6-28 *Courtesy of Miltex

340. Which one of the following four surgical instruments is identified in figure 6-29?
A. Skin hook
B. Lid retractor
C. Rake
D. Elevator

Figure 6-29 *Courtesy of Miltex

341. Which one of the following four surgical instruments is identified in figure 6-30?
A. Dura retractor
B. Gallbladder scoop
C. Enucleation spoon
D. Osteotome

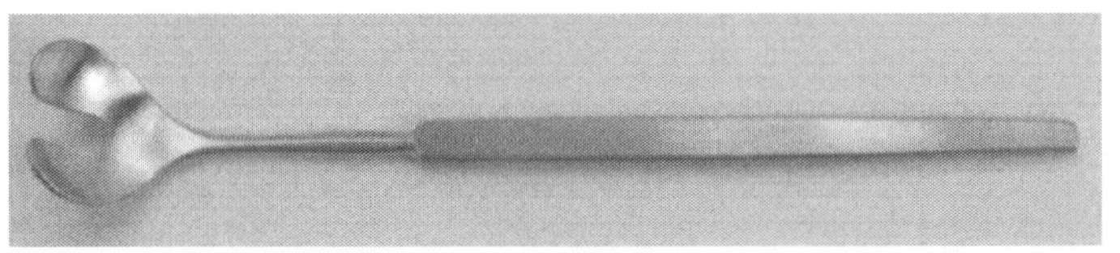

Figure 6-30 *Courtesy of Miltex

342. Item A in figure 6-31 is which of the following?
A. Jorgenson scissors
B. Mayo scissors
C. Babcock
D. Bandage scissors

343. Item B in figure 6-31 is which of the following?
A. Bandage scissors
B. Mayo scissors
C. Jorgenson scissors
D. Babcock

344. Item C in figure 6-31 is which of the following?
A. Wire cutter
B. Jorgenson scissors
C. Bandage scissors
D. Mayo scissors

345. Item D in figure 6-31 is which of the following?
A. Babcock
B. Jorgenson scissors
C. Bandage scissors
D. Wire cutters

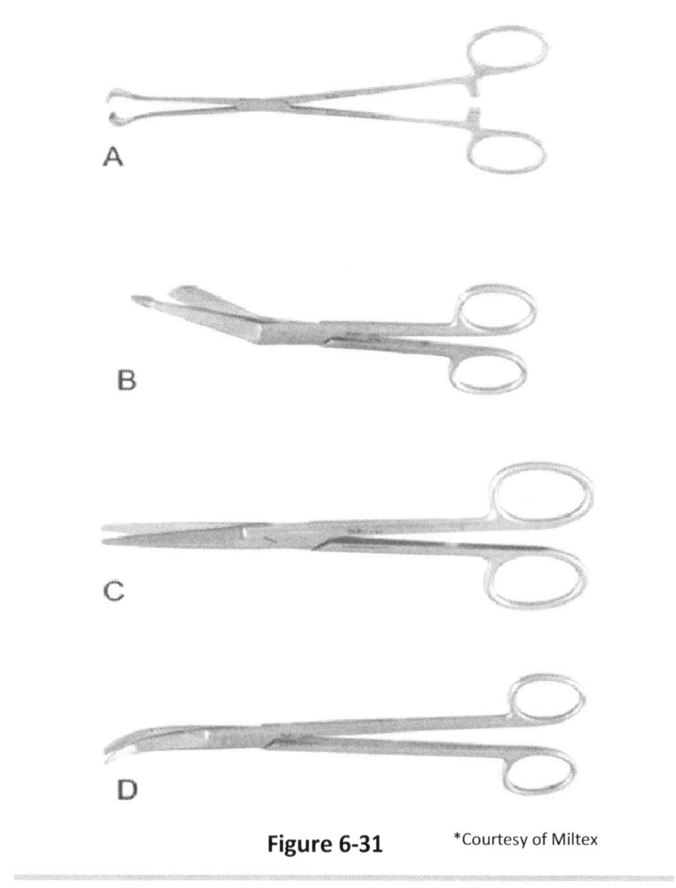

Figure 6-31 *Courtesy of Miltex

346. Item A in figure 6-32 is which of the following?
A. Pliers
B. Wire cutter
C. Rib shear
D. Pin and wire puller

347. Item B in figure 6-32 is which of the following?
A. Rib shear
B. Wire cutter
C. Mayo scissors
D. Bandage scissors

348. Item C in figure 6-32 is which of the following?
A. Wire cutter
B. Pin and wire puller
C. Bandage scissors
D. Pliers

349. Item D in figure 6-32 is which of the following?
A. Metzenbaum scissors
B. Wire cutter
C. Rib shear
D. Pliers

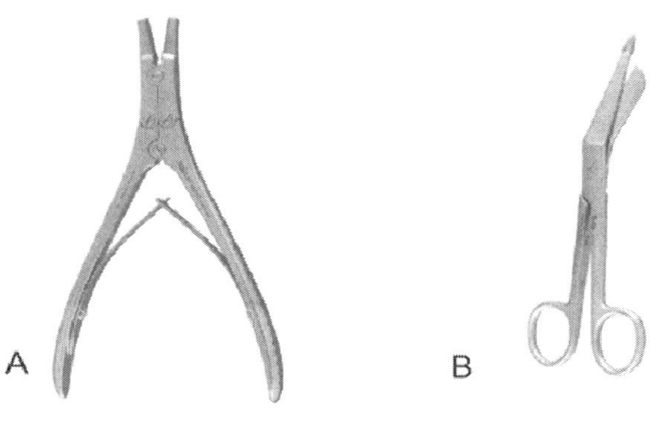

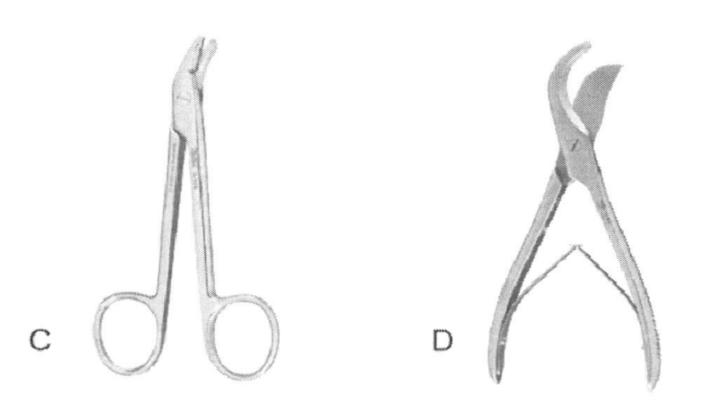

Figure 6-32 *Courtesy of Miltex

*Images are provided courtesy of Miltex. Permission granted by Integra Miltex, a business of Integra Life Sciences Corporation, Plainsboro, New Jersey, USA.

350. Item A in figure 6-33 is which of the following?
A. Russian forceps
B. Ferris-Smith forceps
C. Bayonett forceps
D. Adson tissue forceps
E. Hemostat

351. Item B in figure 6-33 is which of the following?
A. Tissue forceps
B. Clamp
C. Ferris-Smith forceps
D. Adson forceps
E. Bayonett forceps

352. Item C in figure 6-33 is which of the following?
A. Bayonett forceps
B. Clamp
C. Hemostat
D. Tissue forceps
E. Adson forceps

353. Item D in figure 6-33 is which of the following?
A. Russian forceps
B. Tissue forceps
C. Ferris forceps
D. Hemostat
E. Bayonett forceps

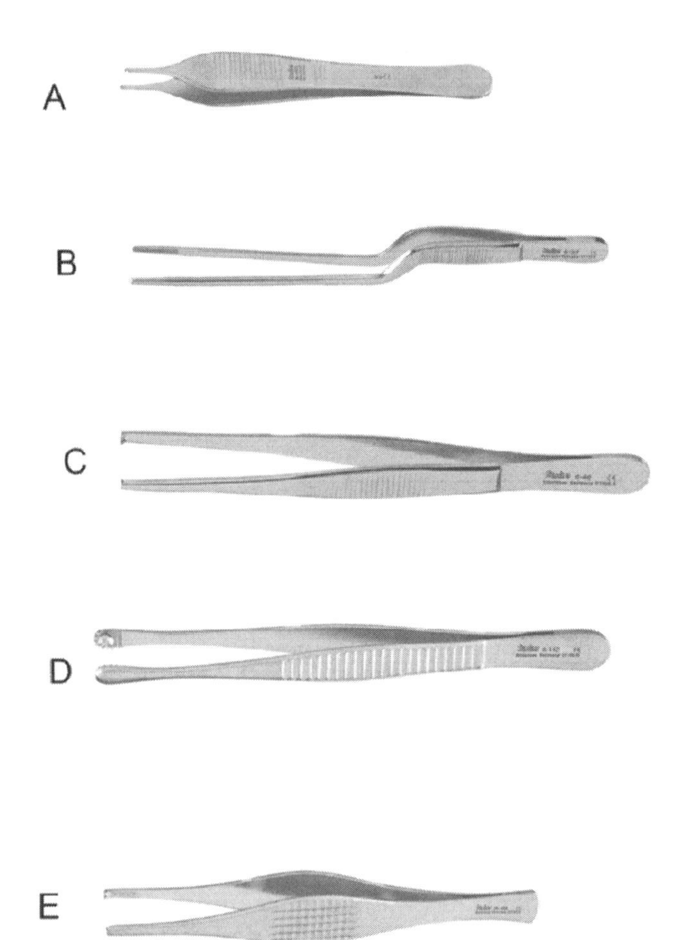

Figure 6-33 *Courtesy of Miltex

*Images are provided courtesy of Miltex. Permission granted by Integra Miltex, a business of Integra Life Sciences Corporation, Plainsboro, New Jersey, USA.

354. Item A in figure 6-34 is which of the following?
A. Iris scissors
B. Serrefine
C. Towel clamp
D. Babcock
E. Debakey forceps

355. Item B in figure 6-34 is which of the following?
A. Serrefine
B. Towel clamp
C. Iris scissors
D. Babcock
E. Debakey forceps

356. Item C in figure 6-34 is which of the following?
A. Debakey forceps
B. Babcock hemostat
C. Serrefine
D. Towel clamp
E. Iris scissors

357. Item D in figure 6-34 is which of the following?
A. Metzenbaum scissors
B. Serrefine
C. Debakey forceps
D. Iris scissors
E. Towel clamp

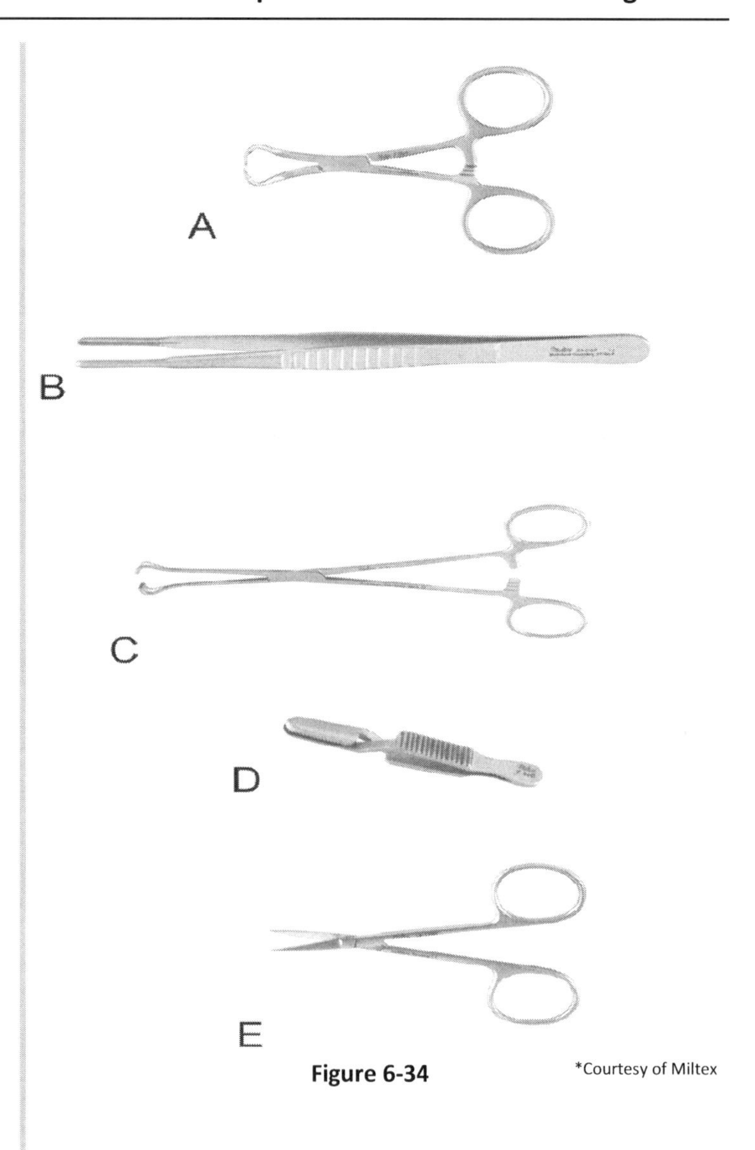

Figure 6-34 *Courtesy of Miltex

358. Item A in figure 6-35 is which of the following?
A. Allis forceps
B. Army-Navy retractor
C. Nerve hook
D. Kelly forceps

359. Item B in figure 6-35 is which of the following?
A. Army-Navy retractor
B. Kelly forceps
C. Nerve hook
D. Allis forceps

360. Item C in figure 6-35 is which of the following?
A. Army-Navy retractor
B. Nerve hook
C. Kelly forceps
D. Allis forceps

361. Item D in figure 6-35 is which of the following?
A. Dandy nerve hook
B. Allis forceps
C. Kelly forceps
D. Army-Navy retractor

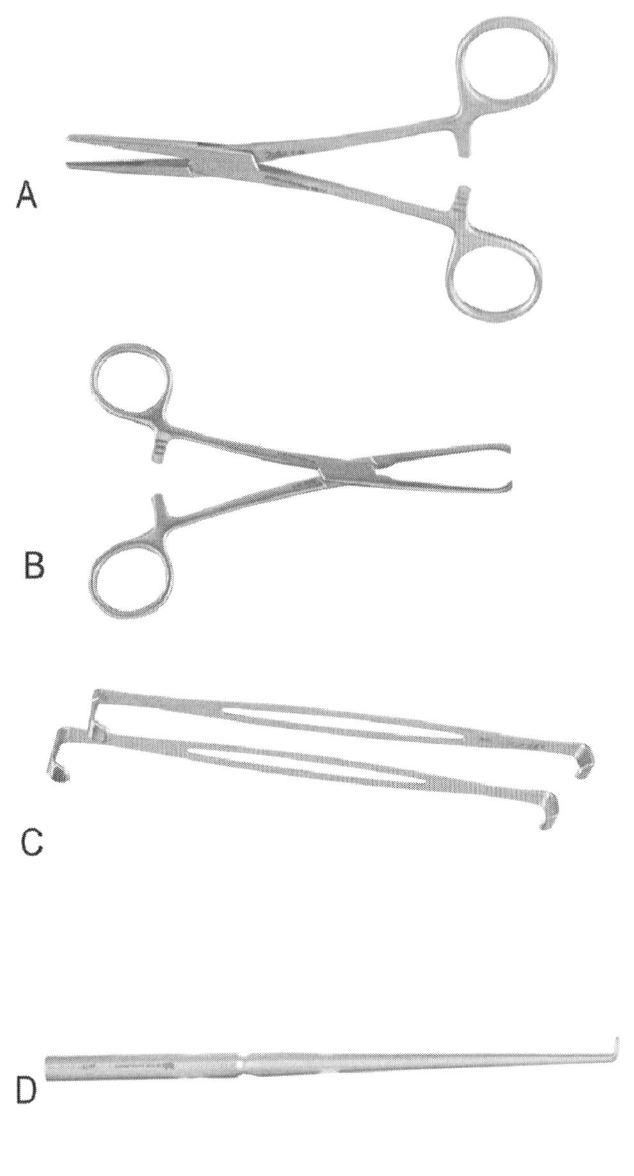

Figure 6-35 *Courtesy of Miltex

*Images are provided courtesy of Miltex. Permission granted by Integra Miltex, a business of Integra Life Sciences Corporation, Plainsboro, New Jersey, USA.

362. Item A in figure 6-36 is which of the following?
A. Gelpi retractor
B. Army-Navy retractor
C. Weitlaner retractor
D. Senn retractor

363. Item B in figure 6-36 is which of the following?
A. Rake retractor
B. Castroviejo needle holder
C. Weitlaner retractor
D. Senn retractor

364. Item C in figure 6-36 is which of the following?
A. Army-Navy retractor
B. Castroviejo needle holder
C. Weitlaner retractor
D. Senn retractor

365. Item D in figure 6-36 is which of the following?
A. Army-Navy retractor
B. Castroviejo needle holder
C. Senn retractor
D. Weitlaner retractor

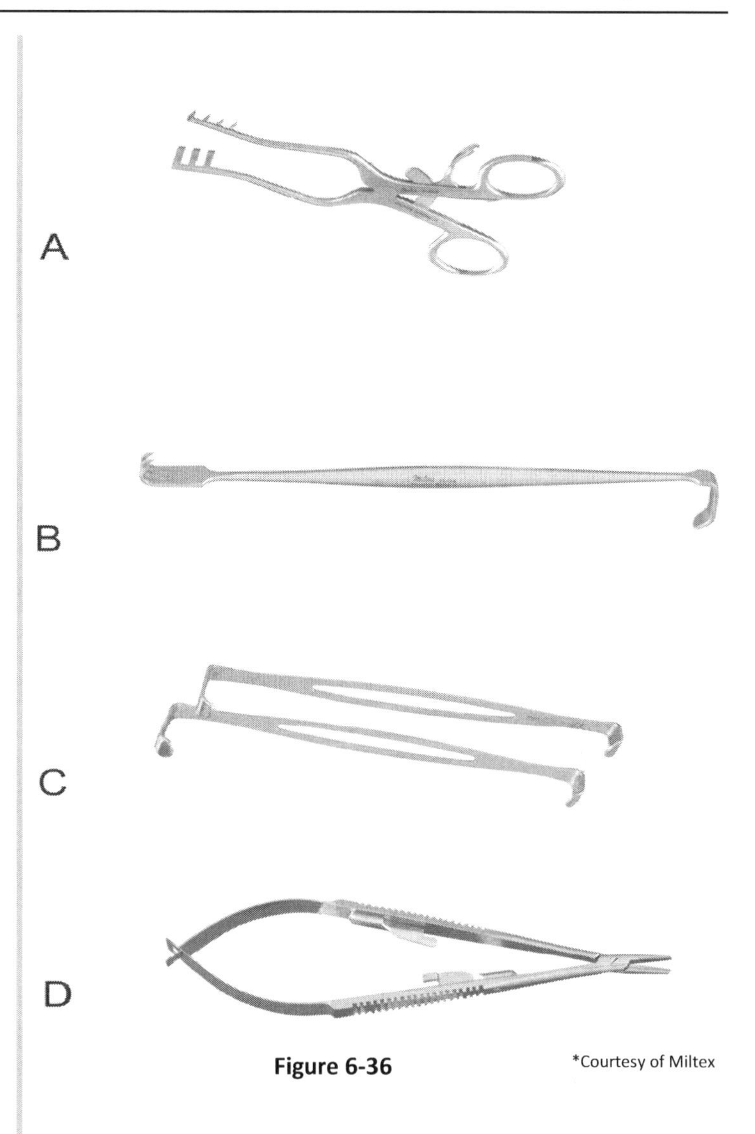

Figure 6-36 *Courtesy of Miltex

*Images are provided courtesy of Miltex. Permission granted by Integra Miltex, a business of Integra Life Sciences Corporation, Plainsboro, New Jersey, USA.

366. Item A in figure 6-37 is which of the following?
A. Ryder needle holder
B. Volkman retractor
C. Senn retractor
D. Skin hook

367. Item B in figure 6-37 is which of the following?
A. Volkman retractor
B. Skin hook
C. Senn retractor
D. Ryder needle holder

368. Item C in figure 6-37 is which of the following?
A. Volkman retractor
B. Ryder needle holder
C. Skin hook
D. Senn retractor

369. Item D in figure 6-37 is which of the following?
A. Volkman retractor
B. Ryder needle holder
C. Skin hook
D. Senn retractor

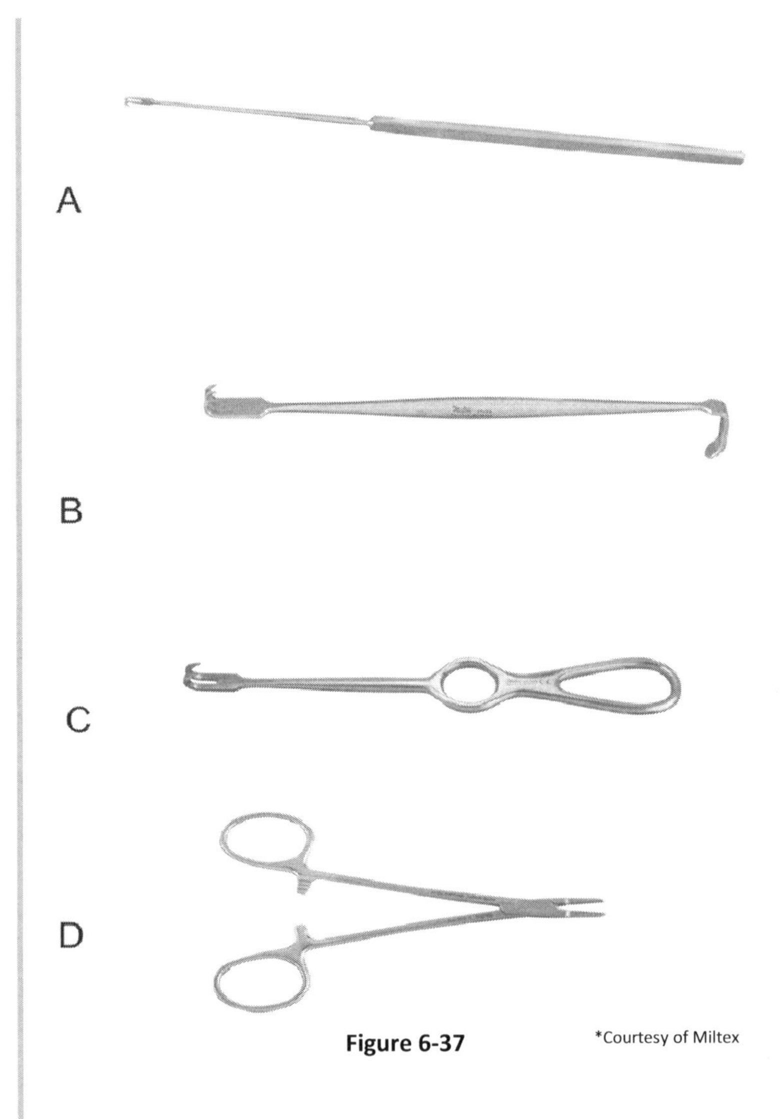

Figure 6-37 *Courtesy of Miltex

*Images are provided courtesy of Miltex. Permission granted by Integra Miltex, a business of Integra Life Sciences Corporation, Plainsboro, New Jersey, USA.

370. Item A in figure 6-38 is which of the following?
A. Poole suction
B. Hohmann retractor
C. DeLee retractor
D. Graves speculum

371. Item B in figure 6-38 is which of the following?
A. Hohmann retractor
B. DeLee retractor
C. Graves speculum
D. Poole suction

372. Item C in figure 6-38 is which of the following?
A. Poole suction
B. DeLee retractor
C. Hohmann retractor
D. Graves speculum

373. Item D in figure 6-38 is which of the following?
A. Graves speculum
B. Pool suction
C. Hohmann retractor
D. DeLee retractor

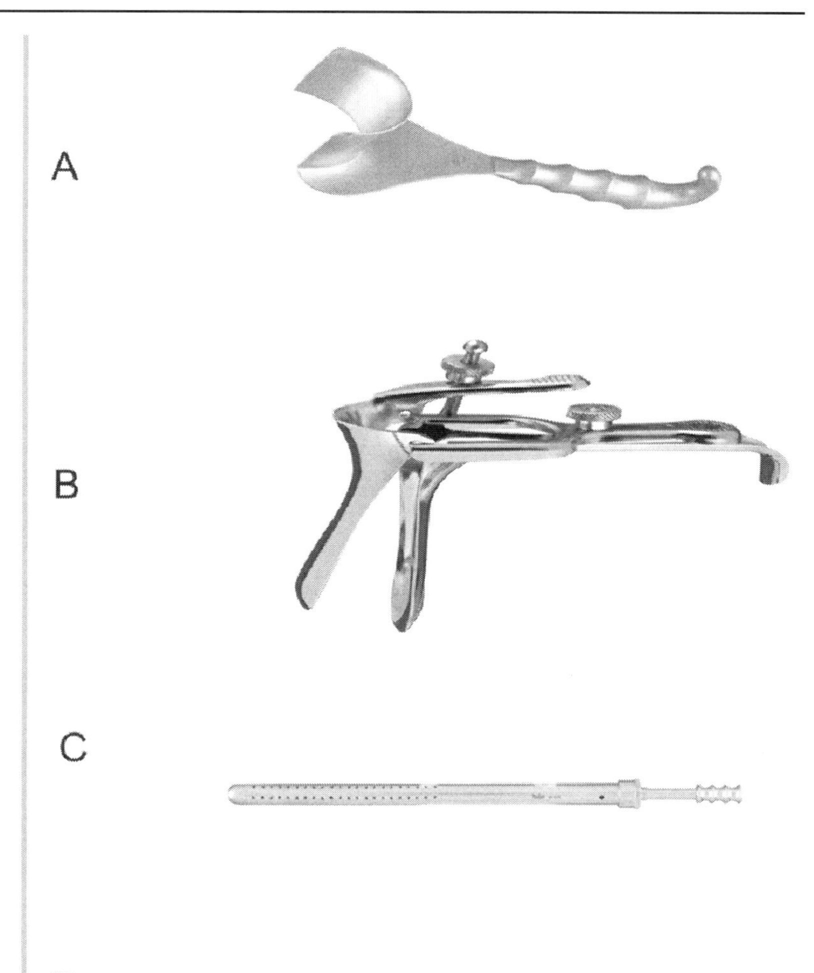

Figure 6-38 *Courtesy of Miltex

*Images are provided courtesy of Miltex. Permission granted by Integra Miltex, a business of Integra Life Sciences Corporation, Plainsboro, New Jersey, USA.

374. Item A in figure 6-39 is which of the following?
A. Satterlee saw
B. Rasp
C. Chisel
D. Lambotte osteotome

375. Item B in figure 6-39 is which of the following?
A. Chisel
B. Satterlee saw
C. Lambotte osteotome
D. Rasp

376. Item C in figure 6-39 is which of the following?
A. Rasp
B. Satterlee saw
C. Chisel
D. Rasp

377. Item D in figure 6-39 is which of the following?
A. Rasp
B. Lambotte osteotome
C. Satterlee saw
D. Chisel

A

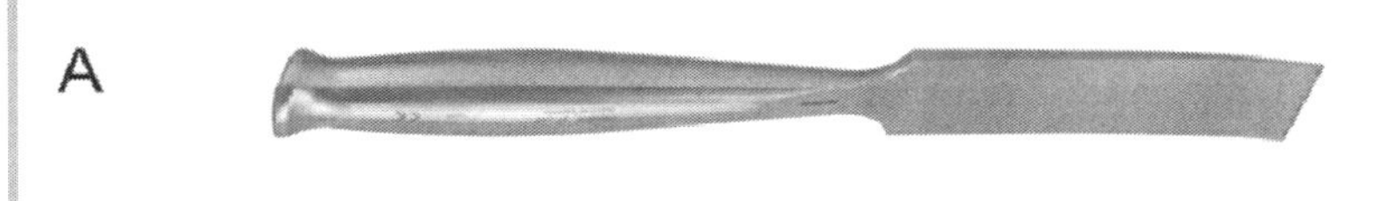

B

C

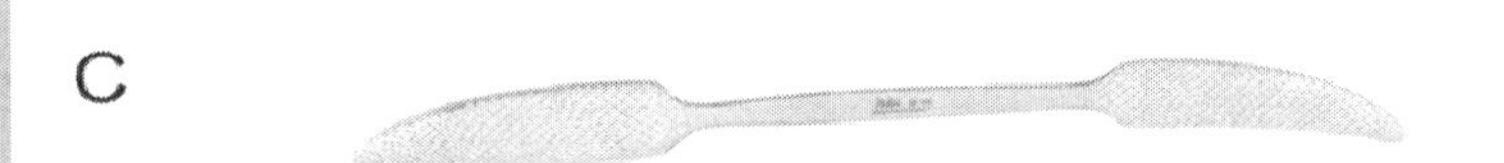

D

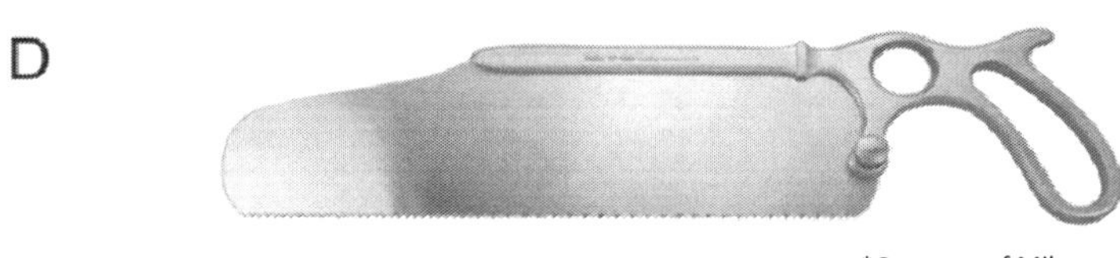

Figure 6-39 *Courtesy of Miltex

*Images are provided courtesy of Miltex. Permission granted by Integra Miltex, a business of Integra Life Sciences Corporation, Plainsboro, New Jersey, USA.

378. Item A in figure 6-40 is which of the following?
A. Gallstone scoop
B. Lacrimal probe
C. Hank dilator
D. Common duct dilator

379. Item B in figure 6-40 is which of the following?
A. Lacrimal probe
B. Hank dilator
C. Common duct dilator
D. Lacrimal probe

380. Item C in figure 6-40 is which of the following?
A. Gallstone scoop
B. Lacrimal probe
C. Hank dilator
D. Common duct dilator

381. Item D in figure 6-40 is which of the following?
A. Common duct probe
B. Hank dilator
C. Lacrimal probe
D. Gallstone scoop

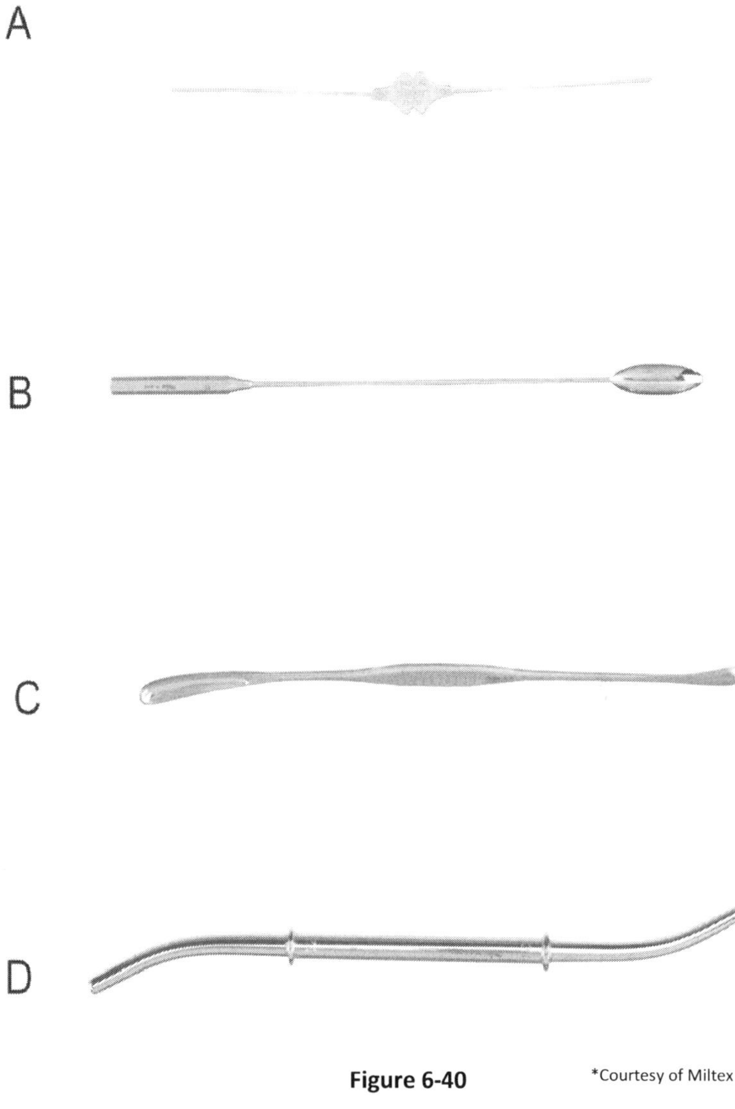

Figure 6-40 *Courtesy of Miltex

*Images are provided courtesy of Miltex. Permission granted by Integra Miltex, a business of Integra Life Sciences Corporation, Plainsboro, New Jersey, USA.

382. Item A in figure 6-41 is which of the following?
A. Scalpel handle
B. Yankauer suction
C. Poole suction
D. Baron suction

383. Item B in figure 6-41 is which of the following?
A. Scalpel handle
B. Baron suction
C. Yankauer suction
D. Poole suction

384. Item C in figure 6-41 is which of the following?
A. Baron suction
B. Poole suction
C. Scalpel handle
D. Yankauer suction

385. Item D in figure 6-41 is which of the following?
A. Knife handle
B. Scalpel handle
C. Baron suction
D. Poole suction

A

B

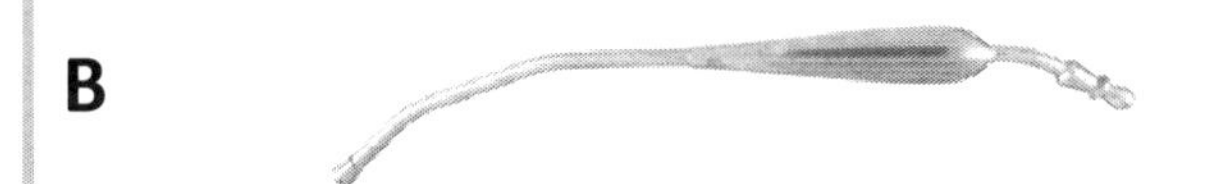

C

D

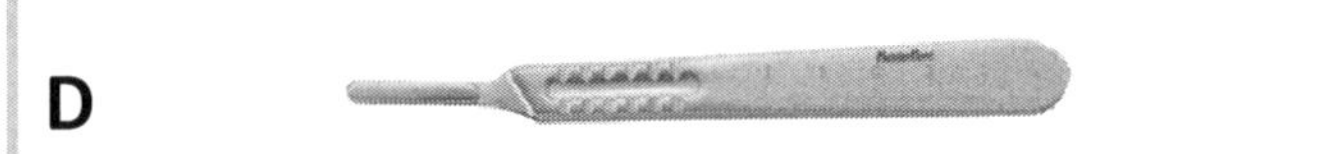

Figure 6-41 *Courtesy of Miltex

386. Item A in figure 6-42 is which of the following?
A. Corneal knife
B. Amputation knife
C. Myringotomy knife
D. Chisel

387. Item B in figure 6-42 is which of the following?
A. Myringotomy knife
B. Gallstone scoop
C. Probe
D. Corneal knife

388. Item C in figure 6-42 is which of the following?
A. Amputation knife
B. Scalpel
C. Myringotomy knife
D. Chisel

389. Item D in figure 6-42 is which of the following?
A. Corneal knife
B. Myringotomy knife
C. Probe
D. Chisel

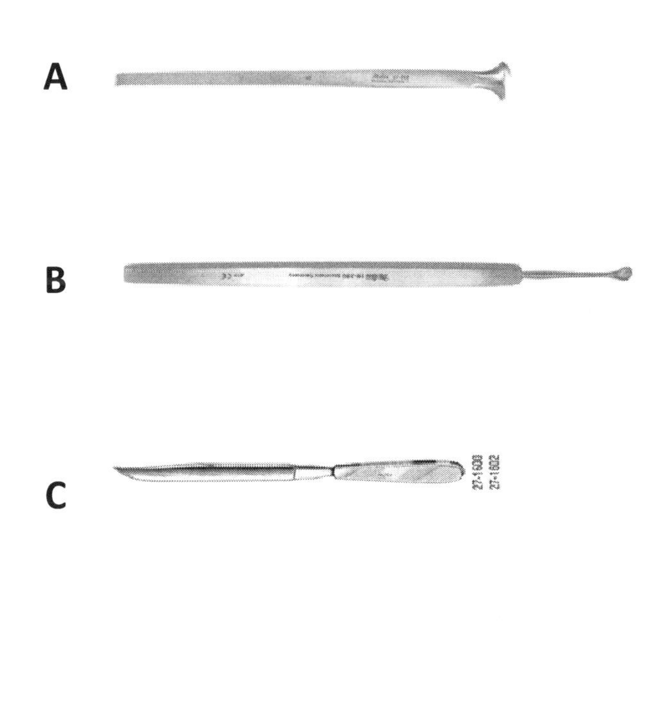

Figure 6-42 *Courtesy of Miltex

390. Item A in figure 6-43 is which of the following?
A. Nerve hook
B. IM pin
C. Duct dilator
D. Lacrimal probe

391. Item B in figure 6-43 is which of the following?
A. IM pin
B. Lacrimal probe
C. Duct dilator
D. Nerve hook

392. Item C in figure 6-43 is which of the following?
A. Duct dilator
B. Nerve hook
C. IM pin
D. Lacrimal probe

393. Item D in figure 6-43 is which of the following?
A. IM pin
B. Lacrimal probe
C. Duct dilator
D. Nerve hook

A

B

C

D

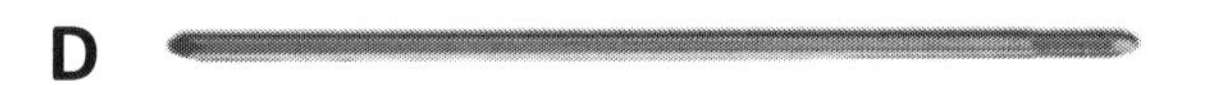

Figure 6-43 *Courtesy of Miltex

394. Item A in figure 6-44 is which of the following?
A. Rongeur
B. Caliper
C. Periosteal elevator
D. Enucleation spoon

395. Item B in figure 6-44 is which of the following?
A. Enucleation spoon
B. Rongeur
C. Caliper
D. Periosteal elevator

396. Item C in figure 6-44 is which of the following?
A. Enucleation spoon
B. Periosteal elevator
C. Rongeur
D. Caliper

397. Item D in figure 6-44 is which of the following?
A. Enucleation spoon
B. Caliper
C. Rongeur
D. Periosteal elevator

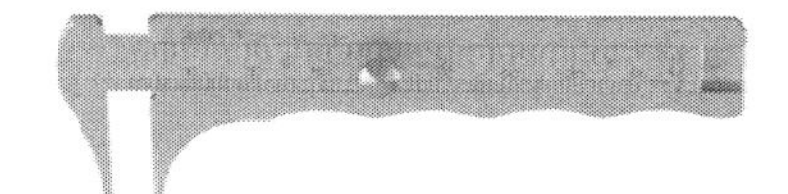

B

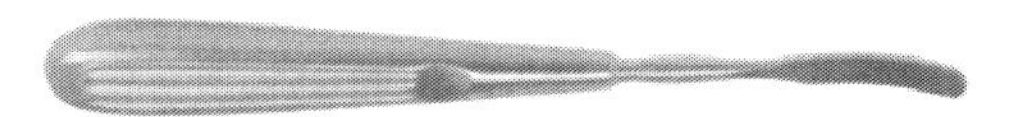

C

D

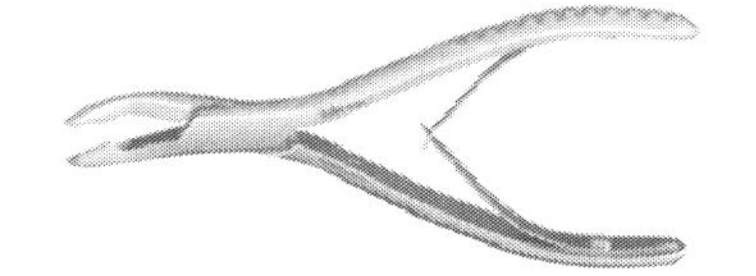

Figure 6-44 *Courtesy of Miltex

398. Item A in figure 6-45 is which of the following?
A. Castroviejo needle holder
B. Duval lung forceps
C. Micro-Bull dog
D. Mosquito forceps

399. Item B in figure 6-45 is which of the following?
A. Micro-Bull dog
B. Duval Lung forceps
C. Castroviejo needle holder
D. Mosquito forceps

400. Item C in figure 6-45 is which of the following?
A. Duval lung forceps
B. Mosquito forceps
C. Caliper
D. Castroviejo needle holder

401. Item D in figure 6-45 is which of the following?
A. Micro-Bulldog
B. Caliper
C. Duval lung forceps
D. Castroviejo needle holder

A

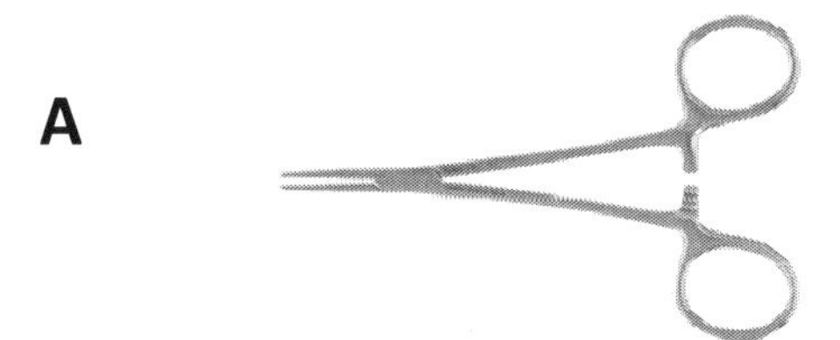

B

C

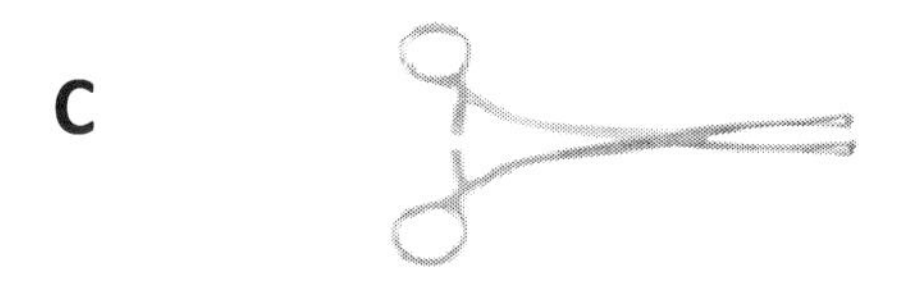

D

Figure 6-45 *Courtesy of Miltex

402. Item A in figure 6-46 is which of the following?
A. Placenta forceps
B. Alligator ear forceps
C. Corneal knife
D. Adenoid curette

403. Item B in figure 6-46 is which of the following?
A. Alligator ear forceps
B. Adenoid curette
C. Corneal knife
D. Placenta forceps

404. Item C in figure 6-46 is which of the following?
A. Alligator ear forceps
B. Corneal knife
C. Placenta forceps
D. Adenoid curette

405. Item D in figure 6-46 is which of the following?
A. Corneal knife
B. Placenta forceps
C. Adenoid curette
D. Alligator ear forceps

A

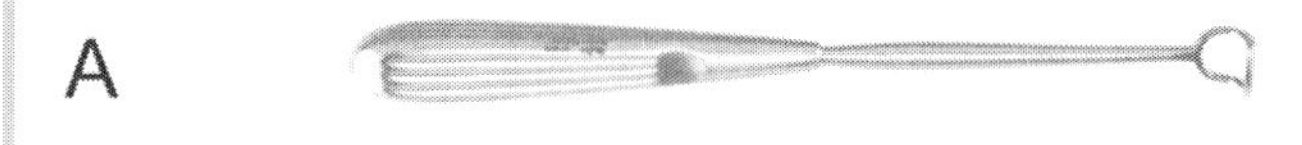

B

C

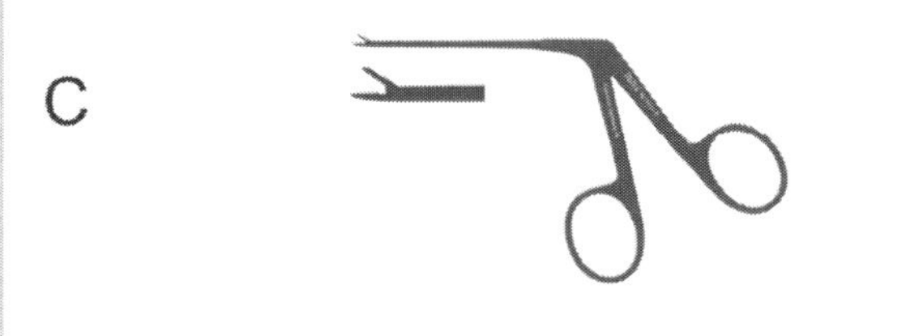

D

Figure 6-46 *Courtesy of Miltex

406. Item A in figure 6-47 is which of the following?
A. Laminectomy spreader
B. Amputation knife
C. Gigli saw
D. Bone saw

407. Item B in figure 6-47 is which of the following?
A. Bone saw
B. Amputation knife
C. Laminectomy spreader
D. Gigli saw

408. Item C in figure 6-47 is which of the following?
A. Gigli saw
B. Laminectomy spreader
C. Bone saw
D. Amputation knife

409. Item D in figure 6-47 is which of the following?
A. Bone saw
B. Laminectomy spreader
C. Gigli saw
D. Amputation knife

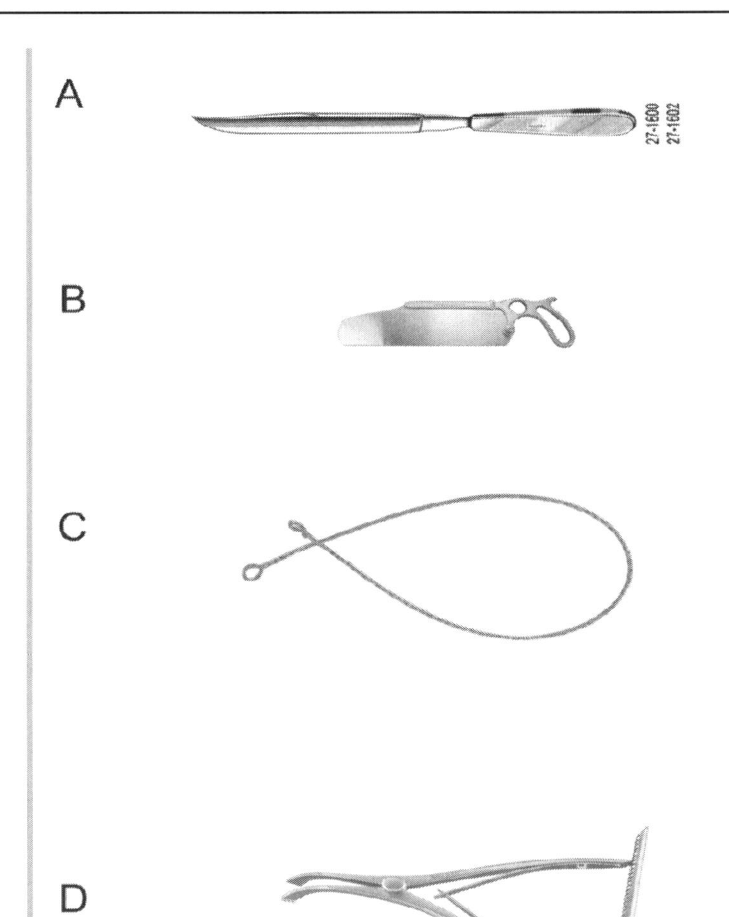

Figure 6-47 *Courtesy of Miltex

410. Item A in figure 6-48 is which of the following?
A. Scapula retractor
B. Lung retractor
C. Ribbon retractor
D. Israel retractor

411. Item B in figure 6-48 is which of the following?
A. Lung retractor
B. Israel retractor
C. Ribbon retractor
D. Scapula retractor

412. Item C in figure 6-48 is which of the following?
A. Lung retractor
B. Ribbon retractor
C. Israel retractor
D. Scapula retractor

413. Item D in figure 6-48 is which of the following?
A. Ribbon retractor
B. Israel retractor
C. Scapula retractor
D. Lung retractor

A

B

C

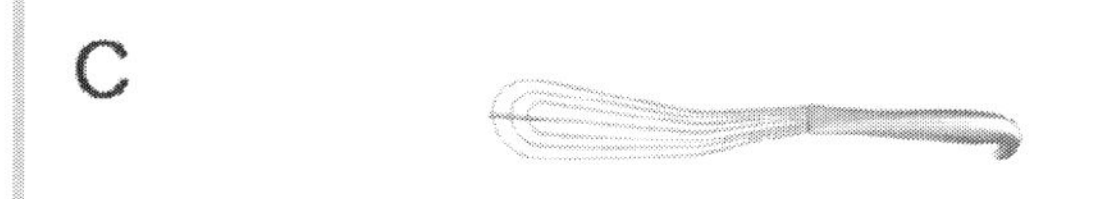

D

Figure 6-48 *Courtesy of Miltex

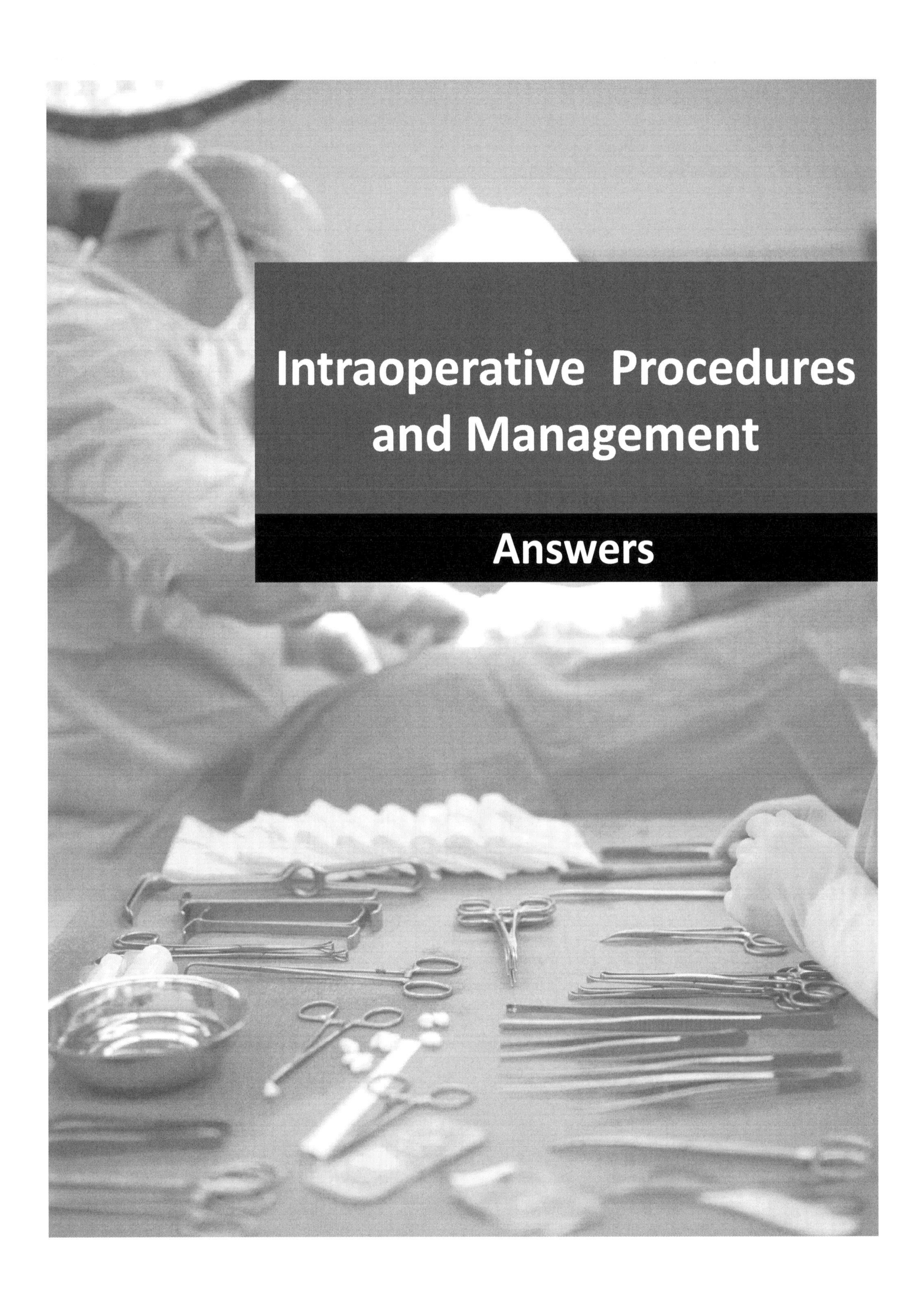
Intraoperative Procedures
and Management
Answers

Supplies

1. Which of the following are used to immobilize, absorb drainage, reduce edema, and eliminate dead space?
B. Pressure dressing - A pressure dressing assists in eliminating dead space, absorb drainage, immobilize, reduce hematoma and edema, and distributes even pressure across the wound.

2. What is used to inflate a Foley catheter?
C. Sterile water - Sterile water is used to fill the Foley catheter balloon to retain it.

3. Which surgery would polymethyl methacrylate be used?
B. Orthopedic - Polymethyl Methacrylate is bone cement used in orthopedic implant surgery.

4. How much Sterile water is used to fill a 5 cc catheter balloon?
D. 8-10 cc - A 5cc catheter balloon uses 8-10cc of sterile water to fill it. There is fluid that remains in the catheter lumen between the syringe port and the balloon so 8-10 cc are needed to compensate for that.

5. What are cervical cone biopsy samples placed on?
A. Telfa - Telfa is used to place biopsies on.

6. Which of the following catheters are referred to as a "red rubber"?
C. Robinson - A Robinson catheter is also called a "red rubber" or an "in and out" catheter. A Coudé is a non retaining catheter that has a rigid curved tip. A Foley is a self-retaining catheter used to measure output of urine and decompress the bladder. The Tenckhoff catheter is used to place dialysis fluid into the body (abdominal cavity).

7. How many cc's does an asepto syringe hold?
C. 120 cc - An asepto syringe holds about 120 cc's of fluid.

8. Which of the following would be needed for a thoracoscopy procedure?
D. Trocars, water-seal drainage system, lens defogger, chest tube drain - Trocars, water-seal drainage system, lens defogger, and chest tube drains are used in a thoracoscopy procedure. Stents are used to increase the lumen size of vessels therefore they are not needed in a thoracoscopy procedure.

9. What supplies will the surgical technologist need to gather and place in the operating room when a cast will be applied during a surgical procedure?
D. Lukewarm water, Webril, stockinette, plaster casting, and heavy scissors - The supplies needed to apply a cast include: lukewarm water, Webril, stockinette, plaster casting, and heavy scissors.

10. When performing a carpal tunnel release procedure, what equipment may be used to provide a blood free surgical site?
A. Tourniquet - A tourniquet will provide a blood free surgical site during extremity procedures like a carpal tunnel release. The Esmarch bandage is used to exsanguinate the extremity prior to inflating the tourniquet. Traction would be used to assist aligning a fracture and positioning allows access to the surgical site.

11. What is needed when repairing a Colles fracture?
D. Lead aprons - When fluoroscopy is used to repair Colles fracture lead aprons will need to be added to the surgical teams PPE.

12. Which suture would be used to repair an Achille's tendon tear?
B. Tycron - Tycron or Ethibon is used to repair Achille's tendon tears. Ethilon is used in skin closure. Monocryl is used in soft tissue and subcuticular closure. Plain gut is used in superficial hemostasis or in tissue that heals quickly.

13. What kind of dressing could be used with nasal procedures?
C. Mustache dressing - A mustache dressing is placed under the nose and secured to the head either tied behind the head or taped to the face. A Queen Ann's collar is used on the neck.

14. When using a laryngoscope what should be available?
A. Defogger - When a laryngoscope is used, defogger is needed to keep the camera fog free. An Esmarch bandage is used for exsanguination of an arm or a leg for application of a tourniquet and a tourniquet is to provide a blood free surgical site.

15. Identify the materials from which vascular stents are made.
D. All of the above - Polypropylene, titanium, stainless steel mesh, and other inert materials are all substances that stents can be fabricated from.

16. Which graft does not need to be pre-clotted?
A. Woven polyester - Knit polyester grafts need to be pre-clotted because they are porous which allows blood to seep through the material. The porous nature of this graft allows for excellent tissue ingrowth.

17. What is used to reinforce the anastomosis in vascular surgery?
D. Pledgets - Pledgets are used to reinforce the anastomosis of vessels. Methyl methacrylate is used in orthopedic surgery. Stents are used to assist in keeping the lumen of a vessel open. Grafts are used to bypass blocked vessels.

18. Which of the following drain might be used in a rhytidectomy?
B. Jackson-Pratt - The Jackson-Pratt drain can be used to reduce dead space after a face lift, Rhytidectomy, procedure. The Hemovac drain is typically used in orthopedic procedures. The cyctostomy tube is used to drain urine from the bladder. The Fogarty catheter is a balloon tipped catheter used to remove obstructions from veins, arteries, or ducts.

19. Which of the following supplies should be available but not opened until needed in a groin hernia repair?
B. Mesh - Mesh should be available but not opened unless the surgeon requests it because it is expensive.

20. What is meant by the term *monofilament* when speaking of suture?
A. Single thread - Single thread suture is referred to as monofilament.

21. What is the diameter of a suture called?
B. Gauge - Suture gauge is the diameter of the suture.

22. When discussing suture, what is capillarity?
C. The ability of multifilament to move fluid down the suture - Multifilament has capillarity which moves fluid down the suture. This is not optimal because infection can move down the suture into the wound too.

23. What material is used for natural suture?
D. All of the above - Cellulose, silk, and gut are all natural materials for suture.

24. Which of the following is the largest gauge suture?
B. #2 - The largest suture gauge is #5. The middle gauge range is 0 to 4-0, and the smallest is 10-0. Therefore out of the available answer, #2 is the largest gauge suture.

25. Which suture gauge is the most commonly used to close subcuticular skin layer?
C. 3-0 - 3-0 and 4-0 gauge suture is most common for subcuticular skin closure. 6-0 is used with vessel anastomosis. 0 is used for abdominal fascia closures. #3 is used in orthopedic procedures.

26. Which of the following is used on peritoneum, fascia, or contaminated areas?
B. Chromic gut - Chromic gut is commonly used to close fascia, urinary tracts, biliary tract, or infected tissue. Polyglyconate (Maxon) is used with vascular tissue. Stainless steel is used in sternal closure, tendon repair, and bone repair. Ethicon is used in neurosurgical closures.

27. Which is a non-absorbable suture?
D. Prolene - Maxon, Vicryl, and Dexon are all absorbable suture. Prolene is not absorbable.

28. What are strands called that are precut, not attached to a needle, and are placed into the opened hand of the surgeon?
A. Free-tie - The free-tie is a suture that is not attached to a needle, is precut and is placed into the open hand of the surgeon. A stick tie has a non-traumatic needle swaged to it. The ligature reel is a reel that has suture wound onto it. Tie on a pass is a suture that is needle free and placed at the tip of an instrument.

29. How many cutting needles are there?
B. 3 - There are three types of cutting needles: conventional cutting needle, reverse cutting needle, and side cutting needle.

30. Which of the following would be used in a thoracoscopy procedure?
D. Water-seal drainage system - A water-seal drainage system is used in thoracoscopy procedures. An osteotome is used in orthopedic procedures. A septum speculum assists in visualization in nasal procedures Penfield dissectors are used in neurosurgery.

31. What is used to filter blood, deoxygenate blood, oxygenate blood and return it to the circulatory system during a CABG?
B. Pump oxygenator - A pump oxygenator is a machine used during a CABG (Coronary Artery Bypass Graft). It deoxygenates the blood, filters the blood, and oxygenates the blood then sends it back into the system. A pulse oximeter is a device placed on the finger, ear lobe, or toe to measure the blood oxygen levels. Pulse generator is a part of a pacemaker device. It controls heart rate, and energy output. A ventilator is a mechanical device used to assist the patient in breathing.

32. Which of the following refers to suture type that can be broken down by the tissues and fluids of the body?
A. Absorbable suture - Sutures that can be broken down by the tissues and fluids of the body are referred to as absorbable sutures. Non-absorbable suture has to be removed after the incision heals because it is not absorbed by the body. Monofilament is a type of suture made of one strand of material.

33. Which of the following is a suture that is braided or twisted together?
C. Multifilament suture - Multifilament suture is made of more than one strand that is twisted or braided together. Suture is the material that is used to close wounds. Absorbable suture is a material that is used to close wounds and it is broken down and absorbed by the body. Monofilament suture is a single strand of material used to close wounds.

34. What supply is the term 'swaged' associated with?
C. Suture - Swaged refers to how the suture material is attached to the needle. The needle does not have an eye for the suture to feed through the suture is continuous with the needle.

35. What term is defined as: the amount of pull a suture strand can take before it breaks?
A. Tensile strength - Tensile strength is the amount of stress a suture strand can withstand before is breaks. It is measured in pounds.

36. Which type of surgery would a pledget most likely be used?
B. Peripheral vascular surgery - Pledgets are used in peripheral vascular surgery. It is a Teflon square that is used to promote clotting by putting pressure on vessels.

37. Venous compression device:
D. A device used in surgery to assist venous blood return to assist in the prevention of thrombophlebitis. - The venous compression device helps the venous blood movement by inflating and deflating intermittently throughout surgery, which helps prevent thrombophlebitis.

Diagnostics

38. Which of the following diagnostic tool is used to check for calculi within the common bile duct?
C. Cholangiography - Cholangiography is a diagnostic tool used under fluoroscopy to check for calculi within the common bile duct. A cholangiogram is the film that is produced from the cholangiography. Fluoroscopy is a 'real time' x-ray.

39. What is used to keep the skin graft flat so it will pass through the mesh device evenly?
B. Derma-carrier - A derma-carrier is used to keep the skin graft flat so it will pass through the mesh device evenly. Biopsy specimens can be placed on telfa pads then passed to the circulator for the pathology department. Raytec sponges are used to absorb fluid or blood in smaller procedures.

40. Which of the following records the electric activity of the brain?
C. EEG - An EEG is and electroencephalography and measures the electric activity in the brain. An ECG and EKG, electrocardiograph, records the electric activity in the heart. An ESU is an electrosurgical unit that is used in surgery to cut or coagulate by using heat.

41. What does the term LASER stand for?
A. Light amplification by stimulated emission of radiation - LASER: Light amplification by stimulated emission of radiation

42. Which of the following is used to measure the oxygen levels in blood?
B. Pulse oximeter - A pulse oximeter is a device placed on the finger, ear lobe, or toe to measure the blood oxygen levels. A pump oxygenator is a machine used during a CABG (coronary artery bypass graft). It deoxygenates the blood, filters the blood, and oxygenates the blood then sends it back into the system. Pulse is what is felt at the arteries caused by the blood flowing through the vessel with each contraction of the heart. Pulse generator is a part of a pacemaker device. It controls heart rate, and energy output.
A ventilator is a mechanical device used to assist the patient in breathing.

43. Which device is used to measure left atrial and left ventricular pressures?
B. Swan-Ganz catheter - The Swan-Ganz catheter is used to measure left atrial and left ventricular pressures. The Tenckoff catheter is used to infuse dialysis fluid. The Foley catheter is used to decompress the bladder or measure urinary output. The Robinson is also called the "red rubber" is used to decompress the bladder

44. Which of the following uses electrons colliding with a metal target in an x-ray tube to produce an image for the radiologist to use to diagnose a condition?
D. Both A and B - An x-ray is the production of high-energy electromagnetic radiation that is formed by the collision of a metal target in an X-ray tube with a beam of electrons. CAT Scan also utilize an X-ray tube that moves in a circular motion around the patient.

45. What device will the operating staff use to view x-rays?
A. Viewing box - An x-ray box or viewing box is used to look at CT Scans, MRI Scans, and X-rays.

46. NPO means:
C. Both A and B - NPO is an abbreviation for nil per os, nothing by mouth.

Procedures

47. What is a lumpectomy?
B. It is a breast procedure that removes a mass and not the entire breast. - A lumpectomy is usually used for diagnostic purposes. It is a procedure that removes a mass from the breast without removing any tissue around the mass.

48. Which of the following incisions would be used for a cesarean section?
B. Pfannenstiel - Cesarean sections use a midline or Pfannenstiel incision. Thoracolumbar incision is used to access the pleural and peritoneal spaces, midline incisions are used to access the abdominal cavity, and McBurney's is used for appendectomies.

49. Where is the reservoir for ventriculoperitoneal shunt placed?
C. Behind and above the ear - The reservoir is used to test the patency of the shunt system and it is used to flush the system if it gets obstructed. It is placed behind and just above the ear.

50. What has to be repaired for a digit re-plantation to be viable?
C. One artery and two veins - For a digit re-plantation to be successful one artery and two veins must be repaired.

51. Which of the following terms are defined as a joint that is surgically fused?
C. Arthrodesis - Arthrodesis: the surgical fusion of a joint. Laminectomy: surgical removal of the lamina. Arthrocentesis: removing synovial fluid from a joint with a needle for diagnostic purposes.

52. The procedure is a Cesarean section. What suture is used to close the uterine incision?
A. 2-0 absorbable suture - The uterus is usually closed with 2-0 or 0 absorbable suture.

53. What condition is corrected with a Nissen fundoplication?
B. Hiatal hernia - A hiatal hernia is corrected with a Nissen fundoplication.

54. What is the skin graft called when it is harvested from a cadaver and used on a person?
D. Homograft - A homograft comes from a cadaver or another person (the same species). Heterograft and xenograft is harvested from a different species, i.e. pig. An autologous graft is one that the patient donates for themselves.

55. When can traction be used to align fractures?
D. All of the above - Traction (manual, skin, and skeletal) can be used preoperatively, intraoperatively, and postoperatively to reduce a fracture, realign anatomy, or immobilize a joint.

56. Which of the following is not a gynecologic incision?
A. Gibson - Pfannestiel, Maylard, and Cherney incisions are used in gynecologic surgery. Gibson incision is used in genitourinary surgery.

57. When the retina is detached which of the following could be used?
B. Cryotherapy unit - Cryotherapy unit is used for retinal detachment procedures by sealing the tears and holes. Bulldogs and Potts scissors are found in a Dietrich coronary set for vascular procedures, a bowman probe is used to probe the lacrimal duct.

58. Which of the following are options for genitourinary incisions?
D. All of the above - Gibson, scrotal, inguinal, abdominal, flank, and lumbar are the incisions options for genitourinary surgery.

59. Which of the following are used for ACL grafts?
D. All of the above - ACL auto grafts can be harvested from the patella tendon, hamstrings, and quadriceps tendon. Allografts can be harvested from patella, Achilles, and anterior tibialis tendons.

60. What is connected when a femorofemoral bypass is performed?
C. Common femoral arteries - The common femoral arteries are connected when there is an iliac artery occlusion to restore blood flow to the extremity.

61. Which of the following techniques are used in scar revision?
D. A, B, and C - The most used technique form scar revision is the Z-plasty, but M-plasty, W-plasty, and Y-V-plasty are also used.

62. Which of the following procedures would use a needle to evaluate the fluid in the intrapleural space of the lungs?
A. Thoracentesis - Thoracentesis is the procedure used to evaluate the fluid in the intrapleural space of the lung. Thoracoscopy is used to evaluate and biopsy lung masses. Mediastinoscopy (Chamberlin procedure) is used to evaluate mediastinal masses. Bronchoscopy is a diagnostic lung procedure.

63. Which of the following category of instruments will be used to excise an appendix?
B. Cutting - Cutting and dissecting instruments are used to make an incision, increase the size of the incision, excise, or separate structures from each other. Grasping and holding instruments are used to move tissues and structures away or to hold them out of the way so the surgeon can see the operative site.
Suturing instruments are used to close the wound.

64. Which of the following breaks up the lens while it irrigates and aspirates simultaneously?
C. Phacoemulsification - Phacoemulsification breaks up the lens while it irrigates and aspirates. A vitrectomy is a procedure that repairs disorders of the retina. Keratoplasty is a cornea transplant procedure. Dacryocystitis is when the lacrimal sac becomes irritated and inflamed.

65. What does the graft connect in an axillofemoral bypass?
C. Axillary artery to the femoral artery - The axillofemoral bypass connects the axillary artery to the femoral artery to return blood flow to the lower extremity.

66. Which approach should be used when accessing the lower ureter?
D. Gibson incision - The Gibson incision is usually used when the lower ureter is accessed.

67. When the STSR sets up for a trabeculectomy and iridectomy she should be sure to have which of the following instruments, equipment, and supplies?
D. All of the above - BSS is basic salt saline for irrigation and keeping the eyeball moist during surgery. Weck sponges are for removing fluid from the eye. The loupe is used by the surgeon to magnify the eye where he is performing the surgery to see better.

68. Which of the following is not used to occlude a vessel?
A. Stapler - Staplers are used to close skin tissue.

69. What position is the patient placed for a transurethral resection of the prostate?
A. Lithotomy - The lithotomy position is used to perform a TURP.

70. When reducing a fracture in the operating room which piece of equipment would be used to check alignment?
B. Fluoroscopy - The C-arm fluoroscopy is used during surgery to be sure the fractured bones are aligned properly. The Hohmann retractor is used to retract bone. The bone holding clamp is used to hold a bone in position.

71. What is it called when the nose is operated on for aesthetic purposes?
A. Rhinoplasty - Rhinoplasty is the surgical procedure that aesthetically changes the look of the nose. Cheiloplasty is the surgical procedure to repair a cleft lip. Palatoplasty is the surgical procedure to repair a cleft palate. Abdominoplasty is a surgical procedure to flatten/tighten the abdominal wall.

72. Which of the following are the factors that affect digit replantation?
B. Type and location of amputation, extent of damage, elapsed time between injury and surgery, and how well the severed digit is preserved - To replant an amputated digit depends on the type of injury, location of the amputation, how much damage the digit has endured, how long the digit has been severed from the hand, and how well the severed digit is preserved prior to re-plantation.

73. Which of the following will be needed when the surgical procedure calls for arch bar application?
B. Wire cutters - When arch bar application is performed the wire cutters will be necessary to cut the wire to proper length and trim the wire once installed.

74. Which of the following is used for blunt dissection during laparoscopic procedures?
C. Cone tip dissector - Cone tip dissector is used for blunt dissection during laparoscopic procedures. Endo harmonic scalpel is used to cut and coagulate tissue simultaneously. The blunt grasper is used to hold and manipulate tissue during laparoscopic procedures.

75. What procedure is a uterine sound used in?
C. Dilation and curettage - A uterine sound is used to measure the uterine depth during a dilation and curettage procedure.

76. What condition is being repaired when the eyelid is elevated and the surgeon creates an upper fold in the eyelid?
B. Ptosis - When the upper eyelid droops causing the lid crease to be absent or reduced is Ptosis and is corrected by creating an upper fold in the eyelid. Cataract is the clouding of the lens. Glaucoma is pressure on the optic nerve. Entropion is when the lower eyelid turns inward and the eyelashes brush against the eyeball.

77. What information needs to be documented when implants are used?
B. Number of implants used, type of implant, size of implant, serial number - When implants are used the following information has to be placed in the patient's chart: number of implants used, type of implant, size of implant, serial number.

78. Which of the following can be used in ophthalmic and vascular procedures?
D. Serrefine clamps - Serrefine clamps are used with ophthalmic and vascular procedures. The eyeball's intraocular pressure is measured with a tonometer. Yasargil scissors are used in vascular procedures to extend an arteriotomy. Strabismus scissors are used in resection eye procedures.

79. Which of the following is used to dilate the urethra in a TURP?
A. Van Buren sound - The Van Buren sound is used to dilate the urethra for a TURP. Hegar dilators are used in gynecology procedures and the Penfield is used for blunt dissection.

80. Which of the following are ophthalmic surgical forceps?
A. Colibri forceps and Bishop-Harmon forceps - Colibri forceps hold corneal and sclera incision edges. Bishop-Harmon forceps are used to hold the delicate tissues of the eye. Pott-Smith forceps are used in cardiothoracic surgery and Cushing bayonet forceps are used in neurosurgery.

81. Which of the following would be used for a nephrectomy?
A. Flank incision - To access the kidney a flank incision would be used.

82. When a bone graft is performed, which of the following is the best donor sit for cancellous bone?
D. Iliac crest - The iliac crest and the iliac spine are excellent donor sites for cancellous and cortical bone graft.

83. Which of the following instruments would be used in a thyroidectomy?
D. Bipolar forceps - Bipolar forceps are used in a thyroidectomy. The Dennis clamp and Doyen forceps are used in intestinal surgery, and Bakes dilator is used in gallbladder surgery.

84. Which of the following procedures would be done for a lung biopsy?
D. Thoracoscopy - Thoracoscopy and thoracotomies are used to evaluate and biopsy lung masses. Mediastinoscopy (Chamberlin procedure) is used to evaluate mediastinal masses. Electrocardiography is a diagnostic test to check for cardiac disease.

85. Which of the following would be used to immobilize the lumbar vertebrae and lower thoracic vertebrae?
C. Body jacket - A body jacket immobilizes the lumbar and lower thoracic vertebrae. It is applied from the axillae to the hip. The spica cast immobilizes the shoulder or the hip in a particular position. Minerva jacket immobilizes the cervical and upper thoracic vertebrae. It runs from the head to the hip.

86. What are Hegar uterine dilators use for?
C. Dilation of the cervix - Hegar dilators are used to dilate the cervix.
87. Which of the following is **NOT** used as a blunt dissector during surgery?
A. Lap sponge - Kitners, peanuts, and cherries are used for blunt dissection.

88. Which of the following is used with a pneumothorax?
D. Chest tube - Chest tubes are used to remove air from the pleural space. Endotracheal tubes are used in the trachea. Penrose drains are used to drain wounds. Fogarty catheters are used to remove obstructions from arteries, veins, and ducts.

89. A splenectomy is being performed on the patient. What incision will most likely be used?
B. Subcostal - A subcostal incision will give access to the spleen.

90. Which of the following would be needed for neurosurgery?
D. All of the above - A headlight with light source, microscope, and burrs are a few items needed for neurosurgery.

91. Which of the following is **NOT** a treatment for Atheroma?
B. Pacemaker - A stent, percutaneous transluminal coronary angioplasty, and intracoronary thrombolysis are all treatments for an atheromas. A pacemaker is used to help regulate the electric impulses of the heart for proper contractions.

92. What is the surgical approach for a pediatric atrial septal defect?
A. Median sternotomy - Atrial septal defects and ventricle septal defects in pediatric patients are approached through a median sternotomy.

93. Which of the following is **NOT** an approach for a prostatectomy procedure?
C. Scrotal - Transurethral, perineal, retropubic and suprapubic are all approaches for a prostatectomy procedure.

94. Which of the following is defined as a joint that is reconstructed or completely replaced to allow for normal function?
B. Arthroplasty - Arthroplasty is done to restore function are movement to a joint. Osteogenesis is bone formation or generation. Arthroscopy is a procedure to look into a joint with a scope. Arthrodesis is a surgical fusion of a joint.

95. Which of the following is a treatment for hydrocephalus?
D. All of the above - Hydrocephalus can be treated with ventriculoperitoneal shunt, ventriculoatrial shunt, or ventriculoscopy. These are procedures that place a catheter draining system between the lateral ventricle into either the peritoneal cavity or into the right atrium of the heart.

96. What does a commissurotomy separate?
B. Mitral valve commissura - A commissurotomy is performed to treat mitral valve stenosis by separating the fused leaflets (valves commissures).

97. Which of the following is not a sterile procedure?
A. Bronchoscopy - Bronchoscopy is a procedure where the scope is passed through the mouth making it a non-sterile procedure. Thoracoscopy is where a scope is placed inside the thoracic cavity to evaluate the space. Cardiac catheterization is a surgical procedure where a stent is placed inside a vessel to compress plaque and create a larger lumen. Mediastinoscopy (Chamberlin procedure) is used to evaluate mediastinal masses through a suprasternal notch incision.

98. What structure is cut to relieve carpal tunnel symptoms?
D. Transverse carpal ligament - The transverse carpal ligament is cut to alleviate the signs and symptoms of carpal tunnel syndrome.

99. Which of the following is **NOT** a surgical patient position for an intrathoracic procedure?
D. Prone with Trendelenburg - The typical positions for intrathoracic procedure include anterolateral, posterolateral, and supine.

100. Which of the following are adult cardiac surgical procedures?
A. Pericardectomy, aortocoronary bypass, valve replacements, heart transplants, coronary angioplasty, and pacemaker implants - Pericardectomy, aortocoronary bypass, valve replacements, heart transplants, coronary angioplasty, and pacemaker implants are adult cardiac surgical procedures. Peripheral vessel angioplasty is a balloon dilation procedure done on the peripheral artery not the heart. Endarterectomy is where plaque and atheromatous tunica intima of the artery are excised from the artery(ies). Aortofemoral bypass is done when an artery is blocked from atherosclerosis.

101. Which of the following is used to oxygenate and filter blood during a cardiopulmonary bypass?
C. Pump oxygenator - The pump oxygenator (perfusion system) is used to oxygenate and filter blood during a cardiopulmonary bypass. A closed-seal drainage unit is used to drain air and or fluid from the pleural space. Defibrillator unit is used to start the heart.

102. During cardiopulmonary bypass how is the myocardium protected?
B. Hypothermia - Hypothermia, lowering body temperature, is used to protect the myocardium during a cardiopulmonary bypass. Hyperthermia is the raising of body temperature and it is not used to protect the myocardium. Stenting is used to open the lumen of vessels.

103. Which procedure would use a figure-eight suture technique?
A. Simple nephrectomy - A simple nephrectomy wound is closed using a figure-eight suture technique and the skin can be closed with staples.

104. Which of the following is the position used for a Marshall-Marchetti-Krantz procedure ?
B. Supine with Trendelenburg - The supine Trendelenburg position is used to perform the Marshall-Marchetti-Krantz procedure.

105. What is the name of the procedure where the prepuce is removed?
A. Circumcision - Circumcision is the removal of the prepuce on the head of the glands penis.
Reconstruction of the urethra is called urethroplasty. TURP is where part of the prostate is removed. An orchiectomy is the removal of the testicle (s).

106. What is the maximum time the tourniquet should be used on an upper extremity before deflating the tourniquet?
A. One hour - The tourniquet time is 1 hour for the upper extremities and 1 1/2 hours for the lower extremities. At this time the doctor should be notified of tourniquet time and every 15 minutes after. The doctor may choose deflate the tourniquet for a period of time then re-inflate it during long procedures.

107. In which procedure would Hesselbach's triangle be encountered?
C. Groin hernia surgery - Hesselbach's triangle is located in the groin area. Therefore, a groin hernia repair surgery would allow the Hesselbach's triangle to be exposed/encountered.

108. Tetany and death can be caused by the removal of what structure(s)?
B. Parathyroid glands - Removing all the parathyroid glands can cause tetany and death.

109. Which of the following are options for a coronary bypass graft?
D. B and C - The saphenous vein and the internal mammary arteries are appropriate grafts for a CABG.

110. Which of the following is used in aortic valve replacement?
D. All of the above - Human cadaver valves, pig valves and cow pericardium are all possible options for aortic valve replacement .

111. What structure will the pacemaker electrode pass through to get placed into the heart?
A. Subclavian vein - The pacemaker electrode will be inserted and passed through the subclavian vein to reach the heart.

112. When performing a pediatric cardiac procedure, what will be used to cut the sternum?
A. Mayo scissors - The pediatric sternum is softer than an adult's sternum so Mayo scissors will be enough to cut through the sternum.

113. Which of the following is a concern for the surgical team with a pediatric patient?
C. Hypothermia so the OR temperature should be raised prior to patient arrival - The pediatric patient has a high risk for hypothermia so the surgical team should raise the OR temperature to accommodate the patient.

114. What makes up a full thickness skin graft?
B. The dermis, the epidermis and sometimes the subcutaneous tissue - A full thickness skin graft (FTSG) is made up of the epidermis, dermis and sometimes the subcutaneous tissue. FTSG is usually used for small areas. A split-thickness skin graft (STSG) is composed of the epidermis and half of the dermis. It is used for large areas that need to be grafted.

115. What dressing would be used for a thyroidectomy?
D. Queen Ann's collar - A Queen Ann's collar is the dressing used for a thyroidectomy. It circumferentially wraps the neck. A bolster dressing is held in place with sutures. It is usually used for skin grafts. A wet to dry dressing is usually used with debridement wounds. It is applied wet and removed once it dries. A rigid dressing prevents movement and is usually in the form of a cast or splint.

116. When doing a simple nephrectomy what can be used for the blunt dissection of the renal pedicle?
C. A and B - When dissecting the renal pedicle the surgeon might use the finger, peanut sponge or a sponge stick.

117. Kidneys are harvested from which of the following?
E. All of the above - Kidneys harvested for transplant can come from living relatives, unrelated living donors and cadavers.

118. When performing a GU endoscopy what position is used?
A. Lithotomy - A lithotomy position is used when performing a GU endoscopy.

119. What is a skin graft called when it is harvested from a pig or a calf and used on a person?
B. Xenograft - Heterograft and xenograft is harvested from a different species, i.e. pig. An autologous graft is one that the patient donates for themselves. A homograft comes from a cadaver or another person (the same species).

120. What incision is used in an Abdominoplasty?
D. Low transverse incision - A low transverse incision is made that can extend the width of the patient.

121. What structures are removed in a male radical cystectomy?
A. Bladder, prostate, seminal vesicles - The bladder, prostate and seminal vesicles are removed in a male radical cystectomy.

122. What is transplanted in a keratoplasty surgery?
B. Cornea - Keratoplasty surgery is a corneal transplant.

123. What PPE should be worn during a total knee arthroplasty to assist in preventing infection?
C. Body exhaust system - As a more stringent surgical site infection prevention, a body exhaust system should be worn.

124. Which of the following is the correct order of a TKA?
C. Femoral preparation, alignment, resection, sizing; tibial preparation, resection, sizing; patellar preparation; trial reduction; implant placement - The correct order for a TKA: femoral preparation, alignment, resection, sizing; tibial preparation, resection, sizing; patellar preparation; trial reduction; implant placement

125. Which of the following is the closing order for a laparotomy procedure?
A. Peritoneum, Scarpa's fascia, subcuticular layer, skin - The order for a laparotomy closure is peritoneum, fascia, subcuticular layer and skin.

126. What is the name of the procedure that incises the tympanic membrane?
C. Myringotomy - Myringotomy is when an incision is placed into the tympanic membrane. Mastoiditis is a condition where the middle ear is inflamed. A stapedotomy is a procedure where a small opening is placed into the stapes. Stapectomy is the removal of the stapes.

127. Which of the following can repair female incontinence?
D. Marshall-Marchetti-Krantz procedure - The Marshall-Marchetti-Krantz procedure is used to repair female incontinence. When there is a tumor in the bladder a cystectomy is performed. A TURP is a transurethral resection of the prostate is the removal of all or part of the prostate. Marsupialization is the procedure to drain a cyst in the Bartholin's gland in the vagina.

128. What eye structure is adjusted to correct strabismus?
B. Eye muscles - Strabismus is when the eyes are misaligned or one is deviated. To correct this the muscles of the eye are adjusted so the eyes can tract simultaneously for binocular vision. Different forms of strabismus include esotropia ("cross eyed"), exotropia (both eyes are pointed away from midline or "wall eyes"), comitant (eye distance remains constant), incomitant (eye distance changes as the eyes move to focus), and diplopia (double vision).

129. What are the prep parameters for a rotator cuff procedure?
C. Wrist to shoulder and chest on affected side - The prep parameters for a rotator cuff repair is from the wrist to the shoulder and the chest on the affected side.

130. What is considered the safest method to remove foreign bodies from the throat?
A. Rigid bronchoscopy - The rigid bronchoscope is the method that is thought to be the safest.

131. Once the skin has been harvested where should it go while waiting to be meshed prior to being transplanted?
A. Body temperature sterile saline - The harvested skin should be placed in body temperature sterile saline while waiting to be meshed and transplanted.

132. What equipment is used to help position the patient in a knee to chest position for surgery?
C. Andrew's frame - The Andrew's frame is used when positioning a patient in the knee to chest position for surgery. The Wilson frame is used to position the patient in the prone and lateral positions. The Fracture table is used for hip procedures and femoral nailing.

133. When performing an above the knee amputation, where will the femur be resected?
B. 4-6" proximal to the knee joint - The femur will be resected about 4-6" proximal to the knee joint in an above the knee amputation. The goal of the surgery is to allow enough stump to fit a prosthesis.

134. What is used to prevent the drill from overheating and causing thermal necrosis of the bone?
C. Irrigation fluid dripped onto the drill bit - To prevent over heating irrigation fluid is dripped onto the drill bit in the surgical site.

135. When using the reamers in a total hip arthroplasty what order should they be passed to the surgeon?
B. Smallest to largest - The STSR should pass the smallest reamer to the surgeon first and progress to the next larger size until the canal is the correct diameter for the prosthesis .

136. What does ORIF stand for?
C. Open reduction internal fixation - Open reduction internal fixation, ORIF, is when a fracture is reduced and secured with K-wires, screws, and/or plates through an incision.

137. When performing a rotator cuff repair what position will the patient be placed?
B. Semi-Fowler's position - The patient should be put into the Semi-Fowler's position for a rotator cuff repair procedure.

138. What instrument will be used when removing the femoral head in a total hip arthroplasty procedure?
B. Oscillating saw - The oscillating saw will be used to remove the femoral head during a total hip arthroplasty procedure.

139. Which procedure is done for cosmetic purposes?
D. Rhinoplasty - Rhinoplasty is a procedure to change how the nose looks. It is a cosmetic procedure. The turbinectomy removes part of the turbinate. Polypectomy removes polyps and the Caldwell-Luc is a procedure that removes part of the antral wall because it is diseased.

140. What instrument will be used to begin the opening in the femur for the femoral component of the hip prosthesis?
C. T-handle reamer - The T-handle intramedullary canal reamer is used to begin the opening and a power reamer is used to continue the process. The rasp is used to enlarge the femoral space.

141. What are the procedural steps for peripheral artery angioplasty?
A. Arterial needle/cannula punctures artery, guide wire placed, balloon catheter placed, balloon inflated, optional stent placed. - Procedural steps for peripheral artery angioplasty: Arterial needle/cannula punctures artery, guide wire placed, balloon catheter placed, balloon inflated, optional stent placed

142. What areas are used for skin graft donor sites?
D. All of the above - The areas used for skin graft donor sites include the back, thigh, abdomen, and chest.

143. What procedure is done to remove part of the bony portion of the mastoid air cells?
B. Mastoidectomy - When a patient has mastoiditis, a mastoidectomy may be performed. This procedure removes part of the bony sections of the mastoid air cells. A myringotomy is an incision into the tympanic membrane to relieve fluid build-up. A stapedotomy is a procedure that places an opening at the footplate of the stapes. Otosclerosis is a condition where the stapes become immobile because of a bone overgrowth.

144. What is removed during a T & A procedure?
B. Palatine and adenoid tonsils - The T & A procedure is a palatine and adenoid tonsil removal.

145. Which laser is commonly used for larynx and oropharynx surgeries?
D. Carbon dioxide laser - Carbon dioxide laser is the one that is used with surgeries of the larynx and oropharynx. The Argon laser is used in diabetic retinopathy procedures. YAG laser is used with orthopedic procedures. Krypton laser is used in ophthalmology procedures.

146. Which of the following is **NOT** a common peripheral vascular surgery?
D. Coronary angioplasty - Coronary angioplasty is a treatment for the coronary (heart) arteries not peripheral vascular conditions.

147. What is used to maintain the lumen of a vessel after an angioplasty procedure?
B. Stent - A stent is placed within the lumen after balloon angioplasty to keep the vessel open. Balloon angioplasty is the procedure that compresses the plaque to open the vessel. Endarterectomy is the surgical removal of plaque and cholesterol buildup within a vessel.

148. When using an autogenous vein for a bypass procedure, what needs to happen to the vein?
C. The valves need to be stripped from the vein - The autogenous vein for a bypass procedure needs to have the valves removed prior to being anastomosed.

149. Which of the following defines rhytidectomy?
A. Face lift - A rhytidectomy is a face lift. An eyelift is a blepharoplasty and mentoplasty is the procedure to fix an underdeveloped jaw.

150. What is the procedure that removes excess fat and skin from the upper or lower eyelid?
D. Blepharoplasty - Blepharoplasty is the procedure that removes excess fat and skin from the eyelids. Rhytidectomy is a face lift and mentoplasty is the procedure that fixes an underdeveloped jaw line.

151. Which of the following procedures would an umbilical template be used?
C. Abdominoplasty - Abdominoplasty uses an umbilical template to be sure the umbilical incision is a perfect circle but remains attached to its pedicle and the incision that is made to replace the umbilicus is the proper size and shape.

152. What is it called when a patient donates their own skin for their skin graft?
A. Autologous - An autologous graft is one that the patient donates for themselves. A homograft comes from a cadaver or another person (the same species). Heterograft and xenograft is harvested from a different species, i.e. pig.

153. What procedure is done to prevent spontaneous abortion?
D. A and C - Cervical cerclage, AKA Shirodkar's procedure, is used to correct an incompetent cervix to prevent spontaneous abortion. It is usually done in the second or third trimester.

154. What order will the digit re-plantation be performed?
B. Bones, Tendons, blood vessels, then nerves - To replant a severed digit the bones need to be connected, then the tendons, blood vessels, and lastly the nerves.

155. Which of the following is used to irrigate the vessels to prepare them for anastomosis?
A. Heparin - Heparin is used to irrigate the vessels for anastomosis. To prevent the vessels from spasming Papaverine is used.

156. Which of the following is a surgical procedure that would use a periareolar line incision or an inframammary fold incision?
B. Augmentation mammoplasty - When augmentation mammoplasty is performed the periareolar line or an inframammary fold incision would be used. A keyhole incision would be utilized in reduction mammoplasty. Abdominoplasty is performed with a low transverse incision. The TRAM is the transverse rectus abdominis musculocutaneous flap procedure and uses a transverse abdominal incision.

157. Which of the following is used in a TRAM?
D. Rectus abdominis muscle - Tissue from the rectus abdominis us used in a TRAM.

158. What incision would be used for an appendectomy?
C. McBurney's - An oblique or transverse incision would be used for an appendectomy. Oblique lateral, Kocher, and McBurney's are oblique, transverse incisions.

159. Which hernia is more likely seen in a female?
C. Femoral hernias - Because of the differences between female and male femoral areas, women are more prone to femoral hernias.

160. When performing a gastrectomy, which incision would **NOT** be used?
A. Pfannenstiel - A Pfannenstiel incision gives access to the pelvic region and the upper midline, bilateral subcostal and thoracoabdominal incisions allow access to the abdominal region.

161. The Whipple procedure is done for which organ?
D. Pancreas - A Whipple procedure is performed when the head of the pancreas has a tumor.

162. What is the name of the procedure that removes the entire mammary gland?
A. Mastectomy - A mastectomy is the procedure that removes the entire mammary gland. A lumpectomy removes only a mass with no surrounding tissue removed, and mammoplasty is a procedure for breast reconstruction.

163. During cranial procedures saline irrigation should be:
B. Body temperature - Irrigation fluid needs to be body temperature in a cranial procedure.

164. When a bone flap is removed where will it be placed?
C. It is placed on the back table soaking in normal saline and antibiotic - When a bone flap is removed it is placed in a moist laparotomy sponge and put on the back table until it is time to be put back into place toward the end of the procedure.

165. Where is the distal drain tube placed in hydrocephalus treatment?
B. Right atrium of the heart, peritoneal cavity - The distal drain tube can be placed either in the peritoneal cavity or the right atrium of the heart in the hydrocephalus procedure.

166. When a patient has a pituitary gland tumor which procedure is used to remove it?
D. Transphenoidal hypophysectomy - Pituitary gland tumors are usually removed with a transphenoidal hypophysectomy procedure. Ventriculoscopy is a procedure to treat hydrocephalus and a laminectomy removes the lamina from the vertebrae.

167. What is the most common cause for a Cesarean section to be performed?
C. Labor failing to progress - The most common cause for Cesarean sections to be performed is failure of labor progressing.

168. Which of the following correctly describes an episiotomy?
A. An episiotomy in an incision made in the perineum to ease the process of delivering babies and to prevent tearing of the perineum during delivery. - An episiotomy is an incision made in the perineum during delivery to prevent the perineum from tearing and make the delivery process easier.

169. Which of the following procedures would use Mersilene tape?
C. Answer A and B - Cervical cerclage, also known as the Shirodkar's procedure, is where Mersilene tape is placed around the cervix to prevent loss of the pregnancy, spontaneous abortion.

170. What is called when the uterus, both fallopian tubes and ovaries are removed through the abdomen?
D. Total abdominal hysterectomy with bilateral salpingo-oophorectomy - A total abdominal hysterectomy with bilateral salpingo-oophorectomy is the excision of the uterus, both ovaries and fallopian tubes.

171. What organs are excised in a total pelvic exenteration?
D. Vagina, uterus, cervix, fallopian tubes, ovaries, bladder, and rectum - Total pelvic exenteration is a radical cancer surgery where the vagina, uterus, cervix, fallopian tubes, ovaries, bladder, and rectum are removed.

172. Which of the following needles would be used on thick tough tissue?
C. Cutting - A cutting needle is used on thick, tough tissue.

173. What suture is used for an appendectomy?
A. Purse string suture - The purse string suture is used for an appendectomy. Traction sutures are used to hold a structure that would be difficult to retract with instruments. Primary suture is used to approximate wound edges.

174. What is used to prevent the suture from cutting into tissue?
B. Bolsters - Bolsters are used to prevent the suture from cutting into tissue. Vessel loops are used to retract vessels, nerves and ducts. Adhesive is used to close skin and is applied topically.

175. Which gauge suture would be used to close the fascia in an abdominal procedure?
B. #2 - Abdominal fascia would be closed with a #2 or #1 gauge suture.

176. Which of the following is used for blunt dissection during laparoscopic procedures?
A. Cone tip dissector - Cone tip dissector is used for blunt dissection during laparoscopy. Endo harmonic scalpel is used to cut and coagulate tissue simultaneously. The blunt grasper is used to hold and manipulate tissue during laparoscopic procedures.

177. Which of the following surgical techniques utilizes heat to remove, erode or vaporize tissues?
B. Ablation - The surgical technique that utilizes heat to remove, erode, or vaporize tissues is ablation. Cryotherapy uses cold to kill cells/tissue. Fluoroscopy uses x-rays to visualize the surgical area in 'real time'.

178. Which of the following procedures refers to the surgical removal of the adrenal gland?
D. Adrenalectomy - An adrenalectomy is the surgical procedure that removes the adrenal gland. A stapedectomy is the surgical removal of the stapes in the ear. An odontectomy is surgical removal of a tooth/teeth. A splenectomy is the surgical removal of the spleen.

179. Which of the following refers to a surgically made connection between adjacent blood vessels or parts of the intestine?
B. Anastomosis - When adjacent blood vessels or parts of the intestine are joined it is called anastomosis. A fistula is a connection via an opening between two structures that should be separate.
A fenestration is an opening.

180. Which of the following is a surgical procedure utilized to reconstruct damaged blood vessels?
C. Angioplasty - Angioplasty is a surgical procedure utilized to reconstruct damaged blood vessels. Arthroscopy is the surgical procedure to view into the joints. Bronchoscopy is the surgical procedure used to view the airway. Mentoplasty is the surgical procedure to reconstruct the mandible.

181. Which of the following refers to the surgical fixation of a patient's joint in order to provide support and relieve pain?
B. Arthrodesis - The term arthrodesis refers to the surgical fixation of a patient's joint in order to provide support and relieve pain. A surgical procedure that utilizes an endoscope to visualize a patient's joint space is known as an arthroscopy. An arthroplasty is a surgical procedure utilized to reconstruct or replace a patient's joint. Arthrotomy is a joint incision.

182. Which of the following refers to the surgical reconstruction or replacement of a patient's joint?
C. Arthroplasty - An arthroplasty is a surgical procedure utilized to reconstruct or replace a patient's joint. A surgical procedure that utilizes an endoscope to visualize a patient's joint space is arthroscopy.
Arthrotomy is a joint incision.

183. Which of the following refers to a surgical procedure that utilizes an endoscope to visualize a patient's joint space?
A. Arthroscopy - Arthroscopy is a surgical procedure that utilizes an endoscope to visualize a patient's joint space. An arthroplasty is a surgical procedure utilized to reconstruct or replace a patient's joint. Arthrotomy is a joint incision. The term arthrodesis refers to the surgical fixation of a patient's joint in order to provide support and relieve pain.

184. Which of the following refers to the surgical opening of a joint?
C. Arthrotomy - The term arthrotomy refers to the surgical opening of a joint. A surgical procedure that utilizes an endoscope to visualize a patient's joint space is known as an arthroscopy. An arthroplasty is a surgical procedure utilized to reconstruct or replace a patient's joint.

185. Which of the following refers to a plastic reconstructive surgical procedure that is used to increase the size of the breasts?
D. Augmentation mammoplasty - Augmentation mammoplasty is a plastic reconstructive surgical procedure used to increase the size of the breasts. Augmentation is the procedure on increasing size of something. Mammoplasty is the reconstruction of the breast. Mentoplasty is the surgical procedure to alter the chin.

186. What procedure is used to remove foreign objects that are lodged in the airway?
C. Bronchoscopy - Bronchoscopy is the procedure used to remove foreign objects from the airway and to evaluate the throat for damage and disease. A tracheostomy is an incision that is placed in the trachea so that an indwelling tube can be placed. It is usually done as an emergency measure. Endoscopy is a procedure to visualize the interior of the body.

187. Define *cystoscopy*.
C. This is a procedure where a scope is passed through the urethra into the bladder to perform diagnostic tests and or to treat the bladder. - Cystoscopy is a procedure where a scope is passed through the urethra into the bladder to perform diagnostic tests and /or to treat the bladder.

188. What is the definition of *cystectomy*?
D. Surgical removal of the bladder - Cystectomy is the surgical removal of the bladder. (Cyst=bladder, ectomy=removal) Hysterectomy is the surgical removal of the uterus. Nephrectomy is the surgical removal of the kidney. Gastrectomy is the surgical removal of the stomach.

189. What is the name of the procedure that will repair a cleft lip?
D. Cheiloplasty - Cheiloplasty is the surgical repair of a cleft lip. Cheiloschisis is the term used for cleft lip. Chelation is the process of cleaning instruments while preventing the deposit of iron and magnesium onto the instruments.

190. In which of the following procedures would cannulation need to be used?
C. Coronary artery bypass graft - A coronary artery bypass graft is a procedure where cannulation would be needed. Cannulation is the process of placing a cannula into the ventricle of the heart to pump the blood into a pump oxygenator and back into the aorta.

191. When a surgeon separates tissue with a sponge stick what is it called?
B. Blunt dissection - When a surgeon separates tissue with a sponge stick he is using blunt dissection. Sharp dissection is when the surgeon separates tissue with a scalpel or scissors. Dissection is the method of separating tissue layers.

192. When a surgical wound opens partially or totally:
D. Dehiscence - Dehiscence happens when a surgical wound opens partially or totally. Rupture is a tearing of intact tissue. An avulsion is when a structure is torn off partially or completely.

193. What term is used when an injury needs to have necrotic tissue and or debris removed from it?
A. Debridement - Debridement is when a wound is cleaned and necrotic tissue and foreign objects are removed. Decontaminate is when instruments and equipment have organic debris and body fluids removed. Antisepsis is the method of removing microbial flora from a person's skin. Dehiscence is when a surgical closure of a wound separates.

194. When something is exsanguinated it:
C. Has all the blood removed - To be exsanguinated all the blood is removed from a structure, organ, or space completely.

195. When a total pelvic exenteration procedure is done on a female patient which of the following is not removed?
D. Cecum - When a female pelvic exenteration procedure is performed the vagina, cervix, uterus, fallopian tubes, ovaries, bladder, and rectum are all removed.

196. What supply would be used to exsanguinate an extremity prior to tourniquet application?
C. Esmarch bandage - An Esmarch bandage is used to exsanguinate an extremity prior to tourniquet application.

197. During labor and delivery what will the doctor do to prevent tearing of the perineum?
A. Episiotomy - During labor and delivery the doctor will do an episiotomy, put an incision into the perineum, to prevent the perineum from tearing. A Pfannenstiel incision is a transverse incision to give access to the pelvic cavity.

198. When a tissue is completely removed to be transplanted (usually on the chest):
B. Free flap reconstruction - Free flap reconstruction is usually completed on chest procedures. The tissue is completely removed from the harvest location to be placed on the transplant site.

199. When performing a laparoscopic procedure, what term is used to place air/gas into the abdominal cavity for visualization purposes?
C. Insufflation - Insufflation is the method of instilling gas or vapor into a cavity, as in laparoscopic procedures.

200. What structure can be ligated?
A. Blood vessels - Blood vessels are ligated to control hemorrhaging.

201. What term means: to wash out?
C. Lavage - Lavage means to wash out. Lysis means destruction. Suction is mechanically drawing fluid out of something.

202. What dressing would be used on the top lip?
B. Mustache dressing - A mustache dressing is used on the upper lip. A Queen Ann's collar is used on the neck.

203. What is the safest method for passing scalpels?
A. Neutral zone - The safest method of passing sharps is to use a neutral zone. This is a space or place designated where the sharps will be placed and picked up from instead of passing from hand to hand.

204. In which of the following procedures is the lung surgically removed?
D. Pneumonectomy - Pneumonectomy is a procedure where the lung is excised. Pneumothorax is a condition where there is an accumulation of air in the pleural cavity. Pneumatic is a term that refers to the word air. Pleurectomy is the surgical removal of the pleura.

205. The definition of phacoemulsification:
D. The process of breaking up and aspirating the lens from the eye that uses ultrasonic energy. - Phacoemulsification is the process that uses ultrasonic energy to break up the lens of the eye and at the same time irrigating and aspirating the fragments from the eye.

206. Which of the following is a procedure where tissue remains attached to its blood supply and is relocated through a tunneling procedure under the skin?
C. Pedicle flap reconstruction - Pedicle flap reconstruction is a mammoplasty procedure where the tissue that is being transplanted stays attached to the blood supply and is brought to its location through a tunnel under the skin. Free flap reconstruction is a mammoplasty procedure where the transplant tissue is detached from the original site.

207. Which of the following is a treatment of a condition or disease that is not a cure but allows the patient to be more comfortable by reducing the symptoms?
A. Palliative - Palliative treatment is one that allows the patient to have less severe signs and symptoms. It does not cure the disease or the condition. Enteral is a route of drug administration: oral or rectal. Parenteral is a route of drug administration: include intradermal, subcutaneous, intramuscular, intravenous, intra-articular, intrathecal, and intracardiac. Buccal is an area of the mouth between the cheek and the gum.

208. What procedure 'lifts' the face and removes wrinkles?
B. Rhytidectomy - Rhytidectomy is the surgical procedure that lifts the face. Mentoplasty is the surgical procedure to reconstruct the chin. Rhinoplasty is the surgical procedure to reconstruct the nose. Acromioplasty is the surgical procedure to repair shoulder impingement.

209. The patient is being treated for malignant neoplasms. What treatment would be used?
C. Radiation therapy - Radiation therapy is a treatment option for malignant neoplasms. Antibiotic therapy is a treatment for a bacterial infection. Radiculopathy is a condition of numbness in the extremity.

210. Which procedure removes the prostate gland?
A. Suprapubic prostatectomy - Suprapubic prostatectomy is the removal of the prostate through a suprapubic incision. Suprapubic vesicourethral suspension is a procedure that elevates the bladder to relieve stress incontinence. A suprapubic cystostomy is a method used to drain the bladder when the urethra is blocked or cannot be penetrated.

211. Which procedure is used to drain the bladder when the urethra is blocked or cannot be penetrated?
C. Suprapubic cystostomy - A suprapubic cystostomy is a method used to drain the bladder when the urethra is blocked or cannot be penetrated. Suprapubic prostatectomy is the removal of the prostate through a suprapubic incision. Suprapubic vesicourethral suspension is a procedure that elevates the bladder to relieve stress incontinence.

212. The patient's comes in to repair esotropia. What procedure will he have done?
C. Strabismus correction - Strabismus correction surgery repairs esotropia ("crossed eyes") and exotropia ("wall eyes"). Sclera buckle repairs retinal detachments. Keratoplasty is a corneal transplant procedure. Cataract extraction is a procedure that removes cataract.

213. What term refers to the spleen being removed?
A. Splenectomy - When the spleen is removed the procedure is called a splenectomy. Splenomegaly is the term used when the spleen has enlarged.

214. The procedure is a mastectomy with a breast reconstruction because of cancer. The mastectomy is complete and the reconstruction is underway. The surgical technologist passes a Crile to the surgeon to use in the reconstruction procedure that was used during the mastectomy. What possible problem did the surgical technologist do?
B. The surgical technologist possibly allowed seeding to take place. - Seeding is the process of implanting cancer cells from one part of a patient into the other.

215. What is it called when the rectus abdominis muscle is used in breast reconstruction surgery?
C. TRAM - TRAM- transverse rectus abdominis musculocutaneous flap- is when the rectus abdominis muscle is used in breast reconstruction surgery. The muscle is pushed through a tunnel under the skin and placed to construct a new breast. TURP- Transurethral resection of the prostate- is the procedure that removes all or part of the prostate gland through the urethra. TIA is a transient ischemic attack. It is when the blood cannot flow through an artery properly because of a blockage; plaque.

216. Which of the following is an examination of the thoracic cavity with a scope?
A. Thoracoscopy - Thoracoscopy is the process of examining the thoracic cavity through a rigid scope. Thoracocentesis is the process of inserting a needle into the pleural space to analyze pleural effusion. A thorascope is the instrument that is used to examine the thoracic cavity.

217. Which of the following is the definition of Thoracocentesis?
D. The process of inserting a needle into the pleural space to analyze pleural effusion - Thoracocentesis is the process of inserting a needle into the pleural space to analyze pleural effusion. A thorascope is the instrument that is used to examine the thoracic cavity. Thoracoscopy is the process of examining the thoracic cavity through a rigid scope.

218. When two granulated surfaces are approximated it is called:
C. Third intention - Third intention is when a wound needs to have primary closure delayed because of necrosis or because it is a Class III or Class IV wound. It is when two granulated surfaces are approximated. First intention is when healing occurs from side to side. Second intention is when the wound heals from inside out because primary union fails, when infection sets in, or when the wound had necrotic tissue removed.

219. Which of the following is a suture technique?
A. Pursestring suture - Pursestring suture is used to close a wound circumferentially. Sutura is a joint located in the skull. Blanket suture is not a technique in surgery.

220. When an abdominal hysterectomy is being performed, what instrument would be used to assist in manipulating the uterus?
B. Tenaculum - A single or multi toothed tenaculum is used to manipulate the uterus during an abdominal hysterectomy.

221. Which instrument is used to cut the cornea during a Keratoplasty procedure?
A. Trephine - The trephine is used to cut the cornea during a keratoplasty procedure (corneal transplant).

222. What will the doctor use to redirect body fluid to another part of the body?
B. Shunt - Shunts redirect fluid in the body. Stents open lumens for the flow of fluid. Catheters are used to insert fluid, drain fluid, or remove objects from the body. Syringe is used to insert fluid, remove fluid from the body or irrigate the wound.

223. What is retracted with a vessel loop?
D. All of the above - Vessels, nerves, and ducts can all be retracted with a vessel loop.

224. Which type of surgery would a pledget most likely be used?
C. Peripheral vascular surgery - Pledgets are used in peripheral vascular surgery. It is a teflon square that is used to promote clotting by putting pressure on vessels.

Instruments

225. What instrument would be used to harvest a skin graft?
D. A and B - Both the Ferris-Smith, Watson, Weck, and Padgett and Reese dermatomes are used to harvest skin grafts free hand. In addition to hand held, there are power operated dermatomes that use oscillating blades and nitrogen, air, or electricity to power them.

226. Which of the following are urethral instruments?
B. Vanburen sound - The Vanburen sound is used in urethral surgery to dilate the urethra. The Hegar dilator and Heaney-Ballantine clamp are used in gynecologic surgery. The Raney clip is used in neurosurgery.

227. Which instrument finish is used in laser procedures?
A. Ebony - An ebony finish on instruments is preferred for laser procedures to prevent reflection/glare. A mirror finish is used to prevent corrosion. The gold plating lets you know tungsten carbide was used to make the instrument which gives the instrument the ability to remain sharp.

228. Which of the following category of instruments will be used to stop the flow of fluid/blood?
C. Clamping - To stop the flow or slow the flow of fluid clamping and occluding instruments should be used. Cutting and dissecting instruments are used to make an incision, increase the size of the incision, excise, or separate structures from each other. Grasping and holding instruments are used to move tissues and structures away or to hold them out of the way so the surgeon can see the operative site. Suctioning instruments are used to remove fluid from an area not to stop the flow of the fluid.

229. Which of the following would be found in a gynecology instrument set?
D. All of the above - All of the instruments would be found in a gynecology instrument set.

230. Which part of the instrument is designed to lock it?
A. Ratchet - The ratchet of the instrument is designed to lock the instrument to hold tissue firmly.

231. What is used to expand the harvested skin for grafting purposes?
D. Mesh graft device - Once the skin has been harvested it has to be stretched to fit the graft sight. This is done with a mesh graft device. The skin is placed on a Derma-carrier and then it is 'run' through the mesh graft device where diamond shape slits are put into the skin that will allow the skin to stretch to fit the grafting sight.

232. Which of the following is a grasping/holding instrument?
C. Ferris-Smith tissue forceps - Ferris-Smith forceps are used to grasp and hold thick tissue like muscle or tendon. Crile forceps are used to clamp/occlude bleeding vessels.
Skin hooks and Gelpi retractors are used to expose the surgical site.

233. Which of the following would be found in a general instrument set?
B. Harrington retractor - The Harrington Retractor is used to retract the liver or intestines in general surgery. The intraluminal stapler is used in gastrointestinal procedures but it is not in a general instrument set. The endo kittner is used to bluntly dissect tissue during laparoscopic procedures. The Schroeder tenaculum is used in obstetric and gynecology procedures to grasp and hold thick fibrous tissue

234. Which of the following will be used in obstetrics and gynecology?
A. Hank dilators - Hank dilators are used to dilate the cervical os. Lacrimal probes are used to dilate the lacrimal duct and the salivary duct. The ball tip probe is used to manipulate vessels and nerves. Vascular dilators gradually dilate vessels and are used in cardiovascular thoracic procedures.

235. Which of the following is a hand held retractor?
C. Volkman retractor - The Volkman retractor is a handheld retractor. The Weitlaner and Gelpi retractors are self-retaining because they are ratcheted. The Barraquer eye speculum is a self-retaining and holds the eyelids open.

236. Where would the shank of the instrument be located?
C. Between the ratchet and the box lock - The shank of the instrument is located between the ratchet and the box lock of the instrument.

237. What type of instrument can be used to retract the tongue during an adenoidectomy?
B. Wieder tongue depressor - A Wieder tongue depressor is used to retract the tongue during tonsillectomy and adenoidectomy surgeries.

238. Which of the following would be found in a plastic surgery instrument set?
D. All of the above - The basic plastic set has an assortment of instruments - these are just a few.

239. Which of the following would not be found in a typical dental set?
A. Iris scissors - Iris scissors are found in a plastic set.

240. Which of the following is not a gynecologic instrument?
B. Minnesota retractor - The Minnesota retractor is used in oral and maxillofacial surgeries. The Auvard speculum, Luikart forceps, and Sims curettes are used in gynecological surgeries.

241. Which of the following is used to make a sponge stick?
B. Raytec sponge - A raytec sponge is folded around the end of a Foerster sponge forceps. Tonsil sponges are used to pack the area where the tonsil is removed. Laparotomy sponges are used in laparotomy procedures. Kitner's are use for blunt dissection.

242. Which instrument would be used to pull the ribs back together after a rib retraction?
A. Rib contractor - A rib contractor will be used to pull the ribs back together after a rib retraction.

243. Which of the following would **NOT** be used in ophthalmic surgery?
C. Raney clip - The Raney clip is used in neurosurgery to retain the scalp. The scleral hook retracts the scleral of the eye, Graefe knife is used in cataract surgery, and Westcott scissors are used when performing strabismus and conjunctiva procedures.

244. What instrument is used to cut the cornea in a keratoplasty surgery?
C. Trephine - A trephine is an instrument that cuts the central portion of the cornea in a circle shape to be removed so the transplant can be put into place.

245. What suture would be used to close the cornea incision in a cataract extraction procedure?
D. 10-0 - 10-0 and 11-0 suture are used in microvascular and eye surgeries. 4-0 and 5-0 suture are used with aorta anastomosis surgeries. 6-0 and 7-0 suture are used with vessel anastomosis.

246. What instruments need to be added to the set up when an internal fixation of the femoral shaft is performed?
A. Power reamer - The Hohmann retractor, Lowman bone holding clamp and bone rongeur are already in the instrument set. The power reamer, drill, and guide wires should be added to the set up.

247. What is used to prepare the acetabulum for the prosthesis?
C. Acetabular reamer - The acetabular cartilage is removed with an acetabular reamer to prepare the space for the prosthesis.

248. Which of the following knife blades are popular in oropharyngeal surgery?
C. #12 - #12 Blades are popular in oropharyngeal surgery because of it's shape. The cutting edge is on the inside curve of the blade.

249. Which of the following instruments are used to excise the tonsil?
B. Sage tonsil snare - The Sage tonsil snare, as well as the Bovie can excise the tonsil.

250. Which of the following is not a peripheral vascular instrument?
D. Raney clip appliers - Raney clip appliers are used in neurosurgery to retain the scalp tissue.

251. What instrument would be used to make the tunnel for a bypass surgery?
A. Tunneler - A tunneler along with blunt instrument or finger dissection is used to form the tunnel between the two sites to perform a bypass procedure.

252. What instrument could be used to remove the plaque from the carotid artery during an endarterectomy?
C. Freer elevator - The freer elevator is an instrument used to remove plaque during an endarterectomy. A key elevator is used to cut or dissect hard tissues. Diethrich scissors are used to extend an incision.

253. Which is used to anastomose the femoral artery in an artery bypass procedure?
A. 5-0, 6-0 Prolene, double armed - 3-0 and 4-0 gauge suture are used for subcuticular skin closure, 4-0 and 5-0 gauge are used for Aortic anastomosis, 5-0, 6-0, and 7-0 gauge are used in vessel anastomosis, 8-0 through 11-0 gauge suture are used in microvasular and eye surgery.

254. Which of the following is not needed for an aneurysmectomy procedure?
B. Raney clips - Raney clips are used in neurosurgery to retract scalp tissue.

255. Which of the following would be added to the set up for a rhytidectomy procedure?
D. All of the above - The following instruments would be added to a rhytidectomy set up: Westcott scissors, Tenotomy scissors, Jeweler's forceps, Bishop-Harmon iris forceps, Castroviejo needle holder, caliper, cotton tip applicators, and ophthalmic antibiotic ointment.

256. Which of the following are used for a skin graft harvest procedure?
D. Dermatome, mineral oil, sterile tongue blades, derma-carrier, mesh graft device - When setting up for a skin graft harvest the STSR needs to be sure there is a dermatome, mineral oil, sterile tongue blades, a derma-carrier, mesh graft device, and thrombin or adrenalin on the back table.

257. Which of the following would **NOT** be found in a laparotomy set?
A. Army Navy retractor and O'Sullivan- O'Conner retractor - O'Sullivan -O'Connor retractors are abdominal retractors for gynecological surgeries and would not be found in a laparotomy set.

258. What is used to retract the spermatic cord during a herniorrhaphy?
C. Penrose drain - A Penrose drain is soaked in saline and passed to the surgeon when the spermatic cord has been exposed and needs to be retracted during a herniorrhaphy.

259. When performing a gastrectomy, which of the following instruments might be used?
B. Bookwalter - A Bowman probe is used in ophthalmic surgery, Heaney forceps are used in gynecological surgery, and a Minnesota retractor is used in oral surgery. The Bookwalter is a self retaining retractor used for abdominal surgery.

260. When a laparoscopic cholecystectomy is being done, which of the following will be needed?
D. All of the above - Equipment needed for a laparoscopic cholecystectomy are laparoscope, two 5 mm trocars, two 10 mm trocars, #11 blade, endoscopic instruments, laparoscopic tower an monitor, camera, light cord, CO2, and insufflator tubing along with the traditional supplies for a cholecystectomy.

261. Which of the following is a cranial immobilizer?
C. A three pin fixation system - A fracture table is used in orthopedic hip procedures. Beanbags help position and support the body; they do not immobilize. A three pin fixation device is used to immobilize the head in a cranial procedure.

262. What instrument is used to clip a cranial aneurysm?
A. Aneurysm clips - Aneurysm clips are applied to treat cerebral aneurysms. They come in different configurations to accommodate different placement options of the clip.

263. Which of the following can be used to cut the cranium between the bur holes during a craniotomy?
D. All of the above - When cutting the cranium a Gigli saw, air powered craniotome saw, and the electric craniotome saw all can be used.

264. When performing a tuboplasty what instruments should be added to the set up?
C. Microsurgical instruments - Microsurgical instruments are necessary because the fallopian tubes are so small. A Minnesota retractor is used in oral and maxillofacial surgeries. The Toomey syringe is used in genitourinary surgery. The Lambotte osteotome is used in orthopedic surgery.

265. What instrument is used to grasp the cervix during a vaginal hysterectomy?
B. Tenaculum - The cervix is held and manipulated with a tenaculum or a Vulsellum forceps during a vaginal hysterectomy.

266. How is the needle placed into the needle holder?
A. One third the distance between the swage and the needle tip - The needle is placed one third the distance between the swage and the needle tip.

267. What direction should the needle point be directed when passing the needle to the surgeon?
B. Toward the surgeon - The needle should point toward the surgeon when passing the needle.

268. Which of the following staples and cuts?
D. Linear cutter - Linear cutters staple and transect tissue. Linear stapler places two parallel rows of staples. Ligating clips are used to occlude vessels. Intraluminal staplers are used to anastomose tubular structures.

269. Which of the following category of instruments will be used to stop the flow of fluid/blood?
A. Clamping - To stop the flow or slow the flow of fluid clamping and occluding instruments should be used. Cutting and dissecting instruments are used to make an incision, increase the size of the incision, excise, or separate structures from each other. Grasping and holding instruments are used to move tissues and structures away or to hold them out of the way so the surgeon can see the operative site. Suctioning instruments are used to remove fluid from an area not to stop the flow of the fluid.

270. Which of the following category of instruments will be used to excise an appendix?
B. Cutting - Cutting and dissecting instruments are used to make an incision, increase the size of the incision, excise, or separate structures from each other. Grasping and holding instruments are used to move tissues and structures away or to hold them out of the way so the surgeon can see the operative site. Suturing instruments are used to close the wound.

271. Which of the following is a grasping/holding instrument?
D. Ferris-Smith tissue forceps - Ferris-Smith forceps are used to grasp and hold thick tissue like muscle or tendon. Crile forceps are used to clamp/occlude bleeding vessels. Skin hooks and Gelpi retractors are used to expose the surgical site.

272. Which of the following is not used to occlude a vessel.
A. Stapler - Staplers are used to close skin tissue.

273. Which of the following would be found in a general instrument set?
C. Harrington retractor - The Harrington retractor is used to retract the liver or intestines in general surgery. The intraluminal stapler is used in gastrointestinal procedures but it is not in a general instrument set. The endo Kittner is used to bluntly dissect tissue during laparoscopic procedures. The Schroeder tenaculum is used in obstetric and gynecology procedures to grasp and hold thick fibrous tissue.

274. Which of the following will be used in obstetrics and gynecology?
A. Hank dilators - Hank dilators are used to dilate the cervical os. Lacrimal probes are used to dilate the lacrimal duct and the salivary duct. The ball tip probe is used to manipulate vessels and nerves. Vascular dilators gradually dilate vessels and are used in cardiovascular thoracic procedures.

275. Which of the following would be found in a gynecology instrument set?
D. All of the above - All of the instruments would be found in a gynecology instrument set.

276. Which of the following can be used in ophthalmic and vascular procedures?
B. Serrefine Clamps - Serrefine Clamps are used in ophthalmic and vascular procedures. The eyeball's intraocular pressure is measured with a tonometer. Yasargil scissors are used in vascular procedures to extend an arteriotomy. Strabismus scissors are used in resection eye procedures.

277. Which of the following is a hand held retractor?
A. Volkman retractor - The Volkman retractor is a handheld retractor. The Weitlaner and Gelpi retractors are self-retaining because they are ratcheted. The Barraquer eye speculum is a self-retaining and holds the eyelids open.

278. Where would the shank of the instrument be located?
B. Between the ratchet and the box lock - The shank of the instrument is located between the ratchet and the box lock of the instrument.

279. Which part of the instrument is designed to lock it?
C. Ratchet - The ratchet of the instrument is designed to lock the instrument to hold tissue firmly.

280. Which of the following are urethral instruments?
A. Vanburen sound - The Vanburen sound is used in urethral surgery to dilate the urethra. The Hegar dilator and Heaney-Ballantine clamp are used in gynecologic surgery. The Raney clip is used in neurosurgery.

281. Which of the following is used to dilate the urethra in a TURP?
C. Van Buren sound - The Van Buren Sound is used to dilate the urethra for a TURP. Hegar dilators are used in gynecology procedures and the Penfield is used for blunt dissection.

282. Which of the following are ophthalmic surgical forceps?
B. Colibri forceps and Bishop-Harmon forceps - Colibri forceps hold corneal and sclera incision edges. Bishop-Harmon forceps are used to hold the delicate tissues of the eye. Pott-Smith forceps are used in cardiothoracic surgery and Cushing bayonet forceps are used in neurosurgery.

283. Which of the following instruments would be used in a thyroidectomy?
B. Bipolar forceps - Bipolar forceps are used in a thyroidectomy. The Dennis clamp and Doyen forceps are used in intestinal surgery, and Bakes dilator is used in gallbladder surgery.

284. Which of the following would not be found in a typical dental set?
A. Iris scissors - Iris scissors are found in a plastic set.

285. Which of the following will be needed when the surgical procedure calls for arch bar application?
D. Wire cutters - When arch bar application is performed the wire cutters will be necessary to cut the wire to proper length and trim the wire once installed.

286. Which of the following is **NOT** a gynecologic instrument?
A. Minnesota retractor - The Minnesota retractor isused in oral and maxillofacial surgeries. The Auvard speculum, Luikart forceps, and sims curettes are used in gynecological surgeries.

287. What are Hegar uterine dilators use for?
C. Dilation of the cervix - Hegar dilators are used to dilate the cervix.

288. What procedure is a uterine sound used in?
D. Dilation and curettage - A uterine sound is used to measure the uterine depth during a dilation and curettage procedure.

289. Which of the following is used in a cholecystectomy?
A. Gall stone scoop - A gallstone scoop is used to remove gallstones during a cholecystectomy. A lung retractor is used in cardiothoracic surgery. A bone rasp is used in orthopedic surgery. Lacrimal probes are used in ophthalmic procedures.

290. Which of the following would be used in a craniotomy?
B. Raney clips - Raney clips are used to retract the scalp during a craniotomy. Lung retractor is used during cardiothoracic procedures. Iris scissors and lacrimal probes are used during ophthalmic procedures

291. Which of the following would be used to cut suture?
A. Straight Mayo scissors - Straight Mayo scissors are used to cut suture. Jorgenson scissors are used in gynecological procedures. Wire cutters cut wire not suture. Iris Scissors are used to cut delicate eye tissue.

292. Which of the following would be used in peripheral vascular surgery?
C. Hemoclip appliers - Hemoclip appliers are used in peripheral vascular surgery. The corneal knife and lid retractor are used in ophthalmic surgery.

293. When performing an aortic aneurysm procedure, which of the following would be used?
A. Aortic clamp - Aortic clamp is used during an aortic aneurysm procedure. The intestinal clamp is used during intestinal surgery. Heaney clamp is used in Obstetric and Gynecological procedures.

294. Which of the following instrument is used in neurosurgery?
D. All of the above - A rongeur, burr, and nerve retractor are all found in a neurosurgery set.

295. Which knife blade is used to make the initial oblique incision for an inguinal herniorrhaphy?
B. #10 blade - The #10 blade is used to make the initial incision for many surgeries. Surgical blades are placed onto handles. Handles do not make incisions.

296. What instrument would be used to retract the liver during a Nissan Fundoplication?
A. Liver retractor - The liver retractor is used to retract the liver during a Nissan fundoplication procedure.

297. Which instrument would be used to grasp the appendix during an appendectomy?
B. Babcock - A Babcock is used to grasp the appendix during an appendectomy.

298. Which instrument is used to explore the common bile duct?
D. Stone forceps - Stone forceps are used to explore the common bile duct. Bowman probes are used in ophthalmic procedures. A Van Buren sound is used in genitourinary procedures. The Baron suction is used in ear procedures.

299. When the cervix needs to be dilated which instrument will the surgical technologist pass to the surgeon?
B. Uterine dilator - The uterine dilator is used to dilate the cervix. The urethral sound is used in genitourinary procedures. Lacrimal probes are used in eye procedures.

300. Which blade is used when performing the incision for a mastoidectomy?
C. #15 - The #15 blade is used to make the incision for a mastoidectomy.

301. Which instrument would be used to hold the tonsil while it is removed from the mucosa?
A. Allis - The Allis or a tonsil tenaculum would be used to hold the tonsil while it is cut from the mucosa.

302. Which of the following instruments would be needed during an immobilization of a jaw and arch bar application?
D. Both A and B - Wire cutters and cheek retractor are necessary during immobilization of a jaw and arch bar application.

303. What instrument is used to lift the periosteum from the bone during a mandibular fracture repair?
B. Periosteum elevator - The periosteal elevator is used to lift the periosteum from the bone during a mandibular fracture repair.

304. Which of the following is used in a dilation and curettage procedure?
A. Uterine sound - A uterine sound measures the depth of the uterus, the dilator dilates the cervix, and the curette is used to gather the specimen during a dilation and curettage procedure.

305. Which of the following would be found in a major laparotomy set?
D. Poole suction tip, Mayo-Hagar needle holder, Metzenbaum scissors, Lahey forceps, Goelet retractor, Adson forceps - Poole suction tip, Mayo-Hagar needle holder, Metzenbaum scissors, Lahey forceps, Goelet retractor, Adson forceps are found in a major laparotomy set.

306. Which of the following would be used in a posterior vitrectomy procedure?
B. Ocutome - Vitrectomy procedures use an ocutome to cut the vitreous and aspirate it out. Oscillating saw and reciprocating saw are used in orthopedic surgeries. Gigli saw is used in neurosurgery.

307. What is used to keep the skin graft flat so it will pass through the mesh device evenly?
C. Derma-carrier - A derma-carrier is used to keep the skin graft flat so it will pass through the mesh device evenly Biopsy specimens can be placed on Telfa pads then passed to the circulator for the pathology department. Raytec sponges are used to absorb fluid or blood in smaller procedures.

308. 308. What is used to create burr holes in the cranium?
C. Midas Rex - A Midas Rex is a powered drill that is used with a burr bit to crate burr holes during a craniotomy.

309. Which of the following is a device used to replace a body structure like a foot or arm?
A. Prosthesis - A prosthesis is a device used to replace a structure on the body for function and or aesthetics. Quarks is a component of nucleons. Parostosis is the condition where the outside of the bone, periosteum, ossifies. Prostatitis is the condition where the prostate becomes inflamed.

310. What is used to cut a circular piece of bone?
B. Trephine - To cut a circular piece of bone a trephine is used.

311. Venous compression device:
D. A device used in surgery to assist venous blood return to assist in the prevention of thrombophlebitis. - The venous compression device helps the venous blood movement by inflating and deflating intermittently throughout surgery, which helps prevent thrombophlebitis.

312. Which one of the following four surgical instruments is identified in figure 6-1?
B. Mayo scissors

313. Which one of the following four surgical instruments is identified in figure 6-2?
A. Intestinal clamp

314. Which one of the following four surgical instruments is identified in figure 6-3?
D. Goelet

315. Which one of the following four surgical instruments is identified in figure 6-4?
C. Meyerding hook

316. Which one of the following four surgical instruments is identified in figure 6-5?
C. Gallstone scoop

317. Which one of the following four surgical instruments is identified in figure 6-6?
D. Baron suction

318. Which one of the following four surgical instruments is identified in figure 6-7?
B. Seldin elevator

319. Which one of the following four surgical instruments is identified in figure 6-8?
B. Magnifying loope

320. Which one of the following four surgical instruments is identified in figure 6-9?
D. Bayonett forceps

321. Which one of the following four surgical instruments is identified in figure 6-10?
C. Scapula retractor

322. Which one of the following four surgical instruments is identified in figure 6-11?
A. O'Sullivan-O'Connor retractor

323. Which one of the following four surgical instruments is identified in figure 6-12?
C. Cast spreader

324. Which one of the following four surgical instruments is identified in figure 6-13?
D. Vaginal speculum

Which one of the following four surgical instruments is identified in figure 6-14?
B325. Tenotomy scissors

326. Which one of the following four surgical instruments is identified in figure 6-15?
A. Eleven blade

327. Which one of the following four surgical instruments is identified in figure 6-16?
A. Babcock forceps

328. Which one of the following four surgical instruments is identified in figure 6-17?
D. Scope

329. Which one of the following four surgical instruments is identified in figure 6-18?
B. Russian forceps

330. Which one of the following four surgical instruments is identified in figure 6-19?
B. Hank dilator

331. Which one of the following four surgical instruments is identified in figure 6-20?
A. Listen amputating knife

332. Which one of the following four surgical instruments is identified in figure 6-21?
C. Allis

333. Which one of the following four surgical instruments is identified in figure 6-22?
B. Needle holder

334. Which one of the following four surgical instruments is identified in figure 6-23?
C. Senn retractor

335. Which one of the following four surgical instruments is identified in figure 6-24?
D. Balfour retractor

336. Which one of the following four surgical instruments is identified in figure 6-25?
D. Baron suction

337. Which one of the following four surgical instruments is identified in figure 6-26?
A. #3 handle

338. Which one of the following four surgical instruments is identified in figure 6-27?
C. Lung retractor

339. Which one of the following four surgical instruments is identified in figure 6-28?
A. Volkman retractor

340. Which one of the following four surgical instruments is identified in figure 6-29?
B. Lid retractor

341. Which one of the following four surgical instruments is identified in figure 6-30?
C. Enucleation spoon

342. Item A in figure 6-31 is which of the following?
C. Babcock

343. Item B in figure 6-31 is which of the following?
A. Bandage scissors

344. Item C in figure 6-31 is which of the following?
D. Mayo scissors

345. Item D in figure 6-31 is which of the following?
B. Jorgenson scissors

346. Item A in figure 6-32 is which of the following?
D. Pin and wire puller

347. Item B in figure 6-32 is which of the following?
D. Bandage scissors

348. Item C in figure 6-32 is which of the following?
A. Wire cutter

349. Item D in figure 6-32 is which of the following?
C. Rib shear

350. Item A in figure 6-33 is which of the following?
D. Adson tissue forceps

351. Item B in figure 6-33 is which of the following?
E. Bayonett forceps

352. Item C in figure 6-33 is which of the following?
D. Tissue forceps

353. Item D in figure 6-33 is which of the following?
A. Russian forceps

354. Item A in figure 6-34 is which of the following?
C. Towel clamp

355. Item B in figure 6-34 is which of the following?
E. Debakey forceps

356. Item C in figure 6-34 is which of the following?
B. Babcock hemostat

357. Item D in figure 6-34 is which of the following?
B. Serrefine

358. Item A in figure 6-35 is which of the following?
D. Kelly forceps

359. Item B in figure 6-35 is which of the following?
D. Allis forceps

360. Item C in figure 6-35 is which of the following?
A. Army-Navy retractor

361. Item D in figure 6-35 is which of the following?
A. Dandy nerve hook

362. Item A in figure 6-36 is which of the following?
C. Weitlaner retractor

363. Item B in figure 6-36 is which of the following?
D. Senn retractor

364. Item C in figure 6-36 is which of the following?
A. Army-Navy retractor

365. Item D in figure 6-36 is which of the following?
B. Castroviejo needle holder

366. Item A in figure 6-37 is which of the following?
D. Skin hook

367. Item B in figure 6-37 is which of the following?
C. Senn retractor

368. Item C in figure 6-37 is which of the following?
A. Volkman retractor

369. Item D in figure 6-37 is which of the following?
B. Ryder needle holder

370. Item A in figure 6-38 is which of the following?
C. DeLee retractor

371. Item B in figure 6-38 is which of the following?
C. Graves speculum

372. Item C in figure 6-38 is which of the following?
A. Poole suction

373. Item D in figure 6-38 is which of the following?
C. Hohmann retractor

374. Item A in figure 6-39 is which of the following?
D. Lambotte osteotome

375. Item B in figure 6-39 is which of the following?
A. Chisel

376. Item C in figure 6-39 is which of the following?
A. Rasp

377. Item D in figure 6-39 is which of the following?
C. Satterlee saw

378. Item A in figure 6-40 is which of the following?
B. Lacrimal probe

379. Item B in figure 6-40 is which of the following?
C. Common duct dilator

380. Item C in figure 6-40 is which of the following?
A. Gallstone scoop

381. Item D in figure 6-40 is which of the following?
B. Hank dilator

382. Item A in figure 6-41 is which of the following?
C. Poole suction

383. Item B in figure 6-41 is which of the following?
C. Yankauer suction

384. Item C in figure 6-41 is which of the following?
A. Baron suction

385. Item D in figure 6-41 is which of the following?
B. Scalpel handle

386. Item A in figure 6-42 is which of the following?
D. Chisel

387. Item B in figure 6-42 is which of the following?
D. Corneal knife

388. Item C in figure 6-42 is which of the following?
A. Amputation knife

389. Item D in figure 6-42 is which of the following?
B. Myringotomy knife

390. Item A in figure 6-43 is which of the following?
D. Lacrimal probe

391. Item B in figure 6-43 is which of the following?
C. Duct dilator

392. Item C in figure 6-43 is which of the following?
B. Nerve hook

393. Item D in figure 6-43 is which of the following?
A. IM pin

394. Item A in figure 6-44 is which of the following?
B. Caliper

395. Item B in figure 6-44 is which of the following?
D. Periosteal elevator

396. Item C in figure 6-44 is which of the following?
A. Enucleation spoon

397. Item D in figure 6-44 is which of the following?
C. Rongeur

398. Item A in figure 6-45 is which of the following?
D. Mosquito forceps

399. Item B in figure 6-45 is which of the following?
C. Castroviejo needle holder

400. Item C in figure 6-45 is which of the following?
A. Duval lung forceps

401. Item D in figure 6-45 is which of the following?
A. Micro-Bulldog

402. Item A in figure 6-46 is which of the following?
D. Adenoid curette

403. Item B in figure 6-46 is which of the following?
D. Placenta forceps

404. Item C in figure 6-46 is which of the following?
A. Alligator ear forceps

405. Item D in figure 6-46 is which of the following?
A. Corneal knife

406. Item A in figure 6-47 is which of the following?
B. Amputation knife

407. Item B in figure 6-47 is which of the following?
A. Bone saw

408. Item C in figure 6-47 is which of the following?
A. Gigli saw

409. Item D in figure 6-47 is which of the following?
B. Laminectomy spreader

410. Item A in figure 6-48 is which of the following?
D. Israel retractor

411. Item B in figure 6-48 is which of the following?
D. Scapula retractor

412. Item C in figure 6-48 is which of the following?
A. Lung retractor

413. Item D in figure 6-48 is which of the following?
A. Ribbon retractor

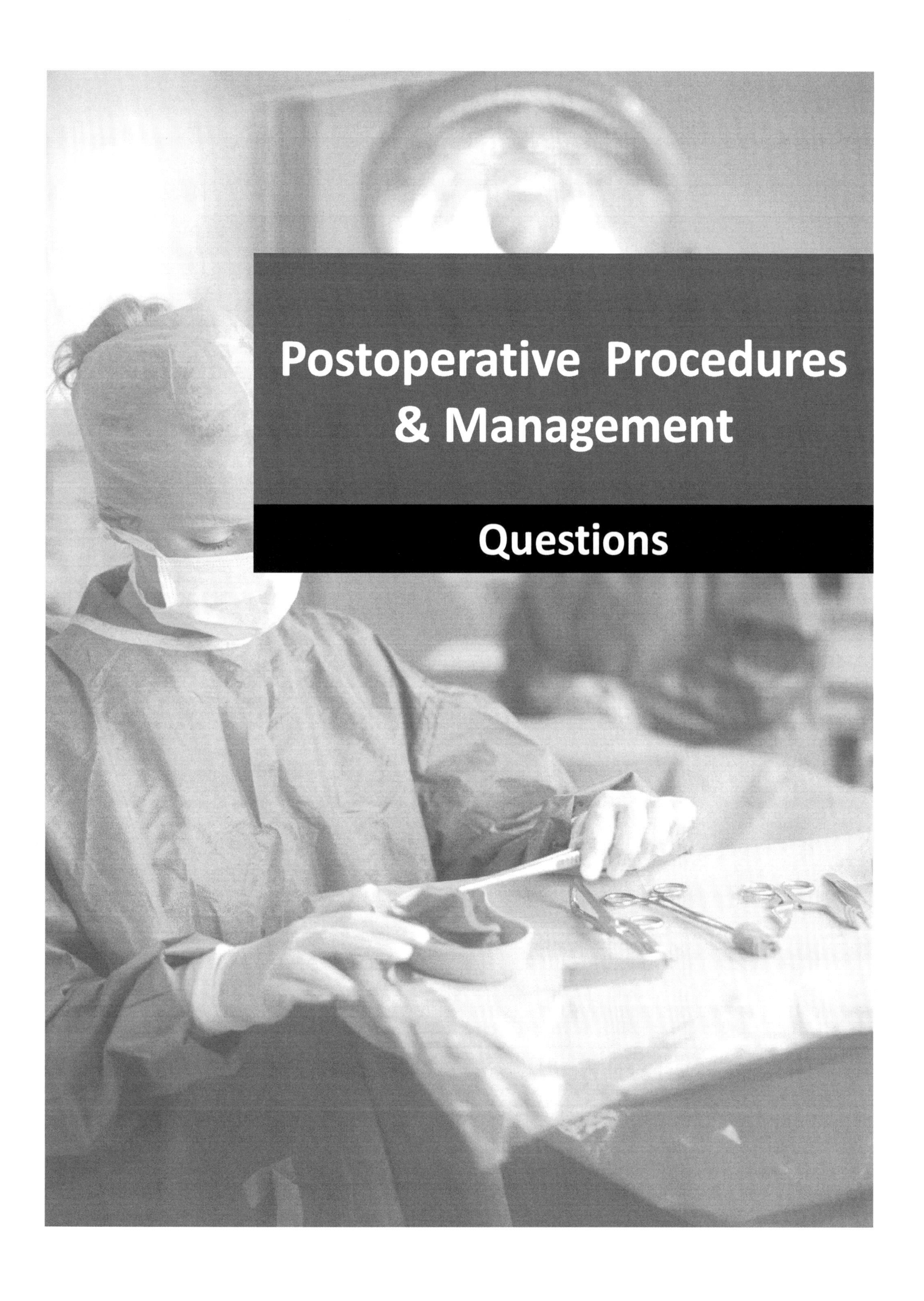

Postoperative Procedures & Management

Questions

Patient Care

1. Which of the following is **NOT** an immediate postoperative patient care task?
A. Extubate the patient
B. Foley catheter inserted
C. Remove the dispersive electrode
D. Remove prep solution from the patient's skin

2. Before the patient is transferred from the operating room table to the stretcher, what needs to be removed from their skin?
A. Blanket
B. IV needle
C. Gloves
D. Prep solution

3. When a dispersive electrode is used during surgery when should it be removed?
A. Preoperatively
B. Postoperatively
C. Perioperatively
D. None of the above
E. All of the above

4. Which of the following coordinates the transfer of the patient from the OR bed to the gurney?
A. Anesthesia provider
B. Circulator
C. STSR
D. Surgeon's assistant

5. How many team members are required to move the patient from the OR bed to the stretcher?
A. Two
B. Three
C. Four
D. Whoever is available

6. Which team member is responsible for coordinating the patient transfer to the stretcher from the operating room bed postoperatively?
A. Anesthesia provider
B. X-ray technician
C. Surgical technologist in the surgical role
D. Circulator

7. Once the patient is transferred from the operating room bed to the stretcher, what should be locked into place before the stretcher is moved?
A. Wheels
B. Side rails
C. Side rails and wheels
D. Nothing should be locked

8. What apparatus can be used to transfer the patient from the operating room bed to the stretcher?
A. Manpower
B. Back table cover
C. Transfer device
D. None of the above

9. Which of the following is the surgical technologist's role when the patient is being moved from the OR bed to the gurney?
A. Removes common gloves
B. Maintains sterile back table until patient leaves
C. Helps with patient transfer by holding patient's feet
D. Begins back table breakdown

10. What supplies must the surgical technologist be sure are removed from the drapes prior to the drape removal?
A. Disposable items
B. Sharps
C. Instruments
D. All sharps and non-disposable items

11. What PPE does the surgical technologist removed prior to drape removal?
A. Gown
B. Mask
C. Outer gloves
D. Nothing

12. What items must remain sterile while drapes are removed?
A. Mayo stand
B. Basin set
C. Back table
D. All of the above

13. What does the STSR hold in place while the drapes are removed?
A. Dressings
B. IV lines
C. Disposable supplies
D. None of the above

14. How are the drapes removed from the patient postoperatively?
A. The drape is pulled off as it is removed
B. The drape is folded as it is removed
C. The drape is rolled as it is removed
D. The drape is cut away

15. When are the towels and towel clips removed?
A. After the patient is extubated
B. Immediately after the drape is removed
C. After the prep solution has been removed from the patient's skin
D. Before the drape is removed

16. When a wound is not properly closed and a space forms between the tissues.
A. Infection
B. Necrosis
C. Dehiscence
D. Dead Space

17. What is the condition called when the suture has ruptured and the colon is protruding:
A. Evisceration
B. Exogenous
C. Fasciculation
D. Eversion

18. Which of the following healing process progresses from side to side with no dead space?
A. First intention
B. Second intention
C. Third intention
D. All of the above

19. Where will the patient be placed immediately after surgery before returning to her room?
A. Pre-Op
B. PACU
C. Post surgical care unit
D. None of the above

Operating Room Breakdown and Cleaning

20. Which of the following will cause pitting on the instrument?
A. Sterile water
B. Saline
C. Enzymatic solution
D. Proteolytic solution

21. Post-operatively, who is responsible for the breakdown of the back table?
A. Nurse
B. Anesthesiologist
C. Circulator
D. STSR

22. All of the following should be completed at the end of surgery **EXCEPT.**
A. Wipe down all furniture and lights
B. Remove linens and waste bags
C. Scrub walls down
D. Mop floor

23. Once the drape is removed from the patient where should it be placed?
A. On the back table
B. The circulator should take it
C. Biohazardous waste receptacle
D. None of the above

24. Where are contaminated sharps placed postoperatively?
A. In the trash can
B. In the red sharps container
C. In the red bag trashcan
D. Any of the above
E. None of the above

25. What should take place with the full sharps container in the operating room?
A. It should be set to the side and an empty one set out
B. STSR should inform the surgeon
C. The container should be closed and removed from the operating room
D. Nothing, let the night cleaning crew take care of it

26. What should the instruments be placed in when transferring them to the decontamination room?
A. Open table
B. Carried by hand
C. Case cart
D. Back table

27. Who is responsible for loading the case cart and returning dirty instruments to the central sterile department at the end of the surgical procedure?
A. Circulator
B. Surgeon
C. Nurse
D. STSR

28. What should the surgical technologist use to soak the dirty instruments in to prevent organic material from drying onto the instruments?
A. Tap water
B. Sterile water
C. Alcohol
D. Nothing

29. How should instruments with multiple parts be placed in the cart to be returned to the central sterile department?
A. None of the above
B. Assembled
C. In their respective cases
D. Disassembled

30. How should instruments be put back onto the stringer?
A. Unratcheted, like instruments together, curved instruments facing same direction
B. Like instruments together, ratchet locked, curves going in the same direction
C. Unratcheted, any order
D. Unratcheted, dirty instruments first

31. Which of the following aid in removing protein and fatty materials from the instruments? (i.e. blood and adipose tissue)
A. Sterile water
B. Enzymatic solution
C. Saline
D. Soapy water

32. When placing instruments on the trays which one should be placed on the bottom?
A. Wrapped supplies
B. Heavy instruments
C. Drapes
D. The order does not matter

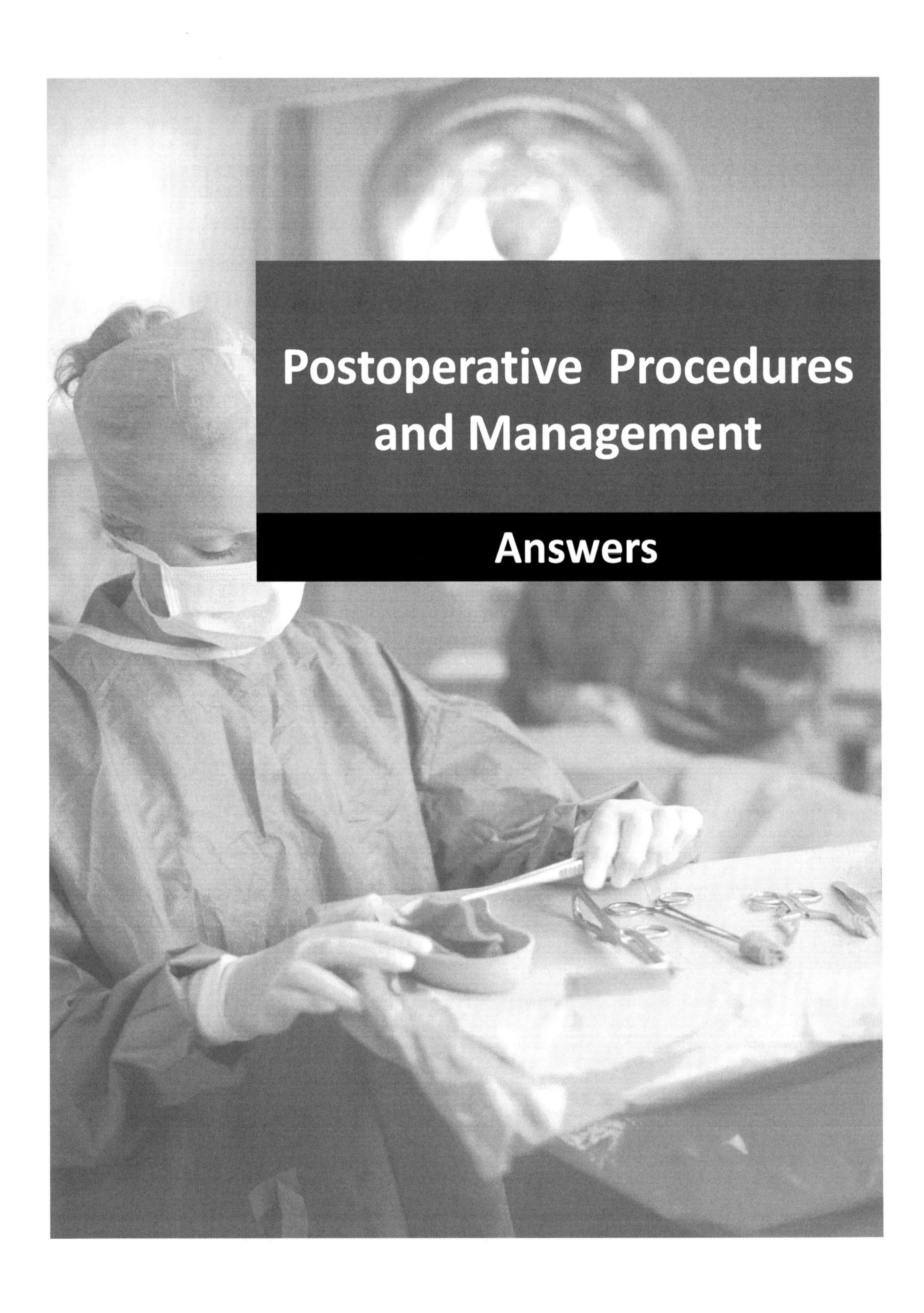
Postoperative Procedures and Management
Answers

Patient Care

1. Which of the following is **NOT** an immediate postoperative patient care task?
B. Foley catheter inserted - The following are immediate postoperative patient care procedures: Prep solution is removed from the patient's skin. The dispersive electrode, if used, is removed. The patient is extubated. Monitoring devices are removed.

2. Before the patient is transferred from the operating room table to the stretcher, what needs to be removed from their skin?
D. Prep solution - Excess prep solution should be removed from the patient's skin immediately after surgery.

3. When a dispersive electrode is used during surgery when should it be removed?
B. Postoperatively - The dispersive electrode is removed after surgery.

4. Which of the following coordinates the transfer of the patient from the OR bed to the gurney?
A. Anesthesia provider - The patient transfer from the OR bed to the gurney is coordinated by the anesthesia provider.

5. How many team members are required to move the patient from the OR bed to the stretcher?
C. Four - Four members transfer the patient to the stretcher from the operating room bed. One person at the head. One person at each side of the patient. One at the foot of the patient.

6. Which team member is responsible for coordinating the patient transfer to the stretcher from the operating room bed postoperatively?
A. Anesthesia provider - The anesthesia provider coordinates patient transfer from the operating room bed to the stretcher.

7. Once the patient is transferred from the operating room bed to the stretcher, what should be locked into place before the stretcher is moved?
B. Side rails - The side rail should be raised and locked into position to protect the patient from rolling off the stretcher.

8. What apparatus can be used to transfer the patient from the operating room bed to the stretcher?
C. Transfer device - There are transfer devices that are used to move patients to prevent injuries to the team members that are moving the patient.

9. Which of the following is the surgical technologist's role when the patient is being moved from the OR bed to the gurney?
B. Maintains sterile back table until patient leaves - The surgical technologist role when the patient is being moved from the operating room bed to the gurney is to maintain a sterile back table until the patient leaves the operating room.

10. What supplies must the surgical technologist be sure are removed from the drapes prior to the drape removal?
D. All sharps and non-disposable items - The surgical technologist should verify all sharps and non-disposable items are not on the drapes before removing the drapes.

11. What PPE does the surgical technologist removed prior to drape removal?
C. Outer gloves - The surgical technologist removes the outer pair of gloves prior to drape removal.

12. What items must remain sterile while drapes are removed?
D. All of the above - The back table, Mayo stand, and the basin set should remain sterile while the drapes are removed.

13. What does the STSR hold in place while the drapes are removed?
A. Dressings - The surgical technologist holds the dressing in place while the drapes are being removed.

14. How are the drapes removed from the patient postoperatively?
C. The drape is rolled as it is removed - The drape should be rolled as it is removed to contain any biohazardous material or disposable items.

15. When are the towels and towel clips removed?
B. Immediately after the drape is removed - The towels and towel clips are removed immediately after the drape.

16. When a wound is not properly closed and a space forms between the tissues.
D. Dead Space - Dead space is the space that forms between tissues when a wound is not properly closed.

17. What is the condition called when the suture has ruptured and the colon is protruding:
A. Evisceration - Evisceration is when a suture has ruptured or a traumatic injury has occurred and the organ is protruding from the wound.

18. Which of the following healing process progresses from side to side with no dead space?
A. First intention - First intention is a wound that heals with no dead space from side to side.

19. Where will the patient be placed immediately after surgery before returning to her room?
B. PACU - The PACU, postanesthesia care unit, is where the patient will go immediately following the procedure and prior to returning to the room.

Operating Room Breakdown and Cleaning

20. Which of the following will cause pitting on the instrument?
B. Saline - Saline contains salt and will pit instruments.

21. Post-operatively, who is responsible for the breakdown of the back table?
D. STSR - The STSR is responsible for the breakdown of the back table after the procedure is finished.

22. All of the following should be completed at the end of surgery **EXCEPT.**
C. Scrub walls down - At the completion of surgery, the OR furniture and lights need to be wiped down, linens and waste bags removed, floor is mopped, and the walls should be spot cleaned.

23. Once the drape is removed from the patient where should it be placed?
C. Biohazardous waste receptacle - Once the drape is removed from the patient it should be placed in the biohazardous waste receptacle.

24. Where are contaminated sharps placed postoperatively?
B. In the red sharps container - The sharps must be placed in the red sharps container postoperatively.

25. What should take place with the full sharps container in the operating room?
C. The container should be closed and removed from the operating room - The sharps container should never be allowed to overflow and it should be closed and removed from the operating room immediately when full.

26. What should the instruments be placed in when transferring them to the decontamination room?
C. Case cart - The instruments are transported to the decontamination room postoperatively in a case cart or on an open cart covered with plastic.

27. Who is responsible for loading the case cart and returning dirty instruments to the central sterile department at the end of the surgical procedure?
D. STSR - The surgical technician is responsible for loading the case cart and transferring it to the central sterile department postoperatively.

28. What should the surgical technologist use to soak the dirty instruments in to prevent organic material from drying onto the instruments?
B. Sterile water - The STSR should presoak the instruments in sterile water or enzymatic solution to prevent organic material from drying onto the instruments.

29. How should instruments with multiple parts be placed in the cart to be returned to the central sterile department?
D. Disassembled - Instruments with multiple parts should be disassembled and wiped down prior to being returned to the decontamination room.

30. How should instruments be put back onto the stringer?
A. Unratcheted, like instruments together, curved instruments facing same direction - The instruments need to be replaced onto the stringer unratcheted, keeping the curve of the instruments facing the same direction. Dirty instruments are not placed onto the stringer.

31. Which of the following aid in removing protein and fatty materials from the instruments? (i.e. blood and adipose tissue)
B. Enzymatic solution - Enzymatic solutions remove protein and fatty material from instruments.

32. When placing instruments on the trays which one should be placed on the bottom?
B. Heavy instruments - Heavy instruments are placed on the cart first to prevent damaging lighter instruments and equipment.

SECTION 3

Additional Responsibilities & Duties

Sterilization & Maintenance

Administrative & Personnel

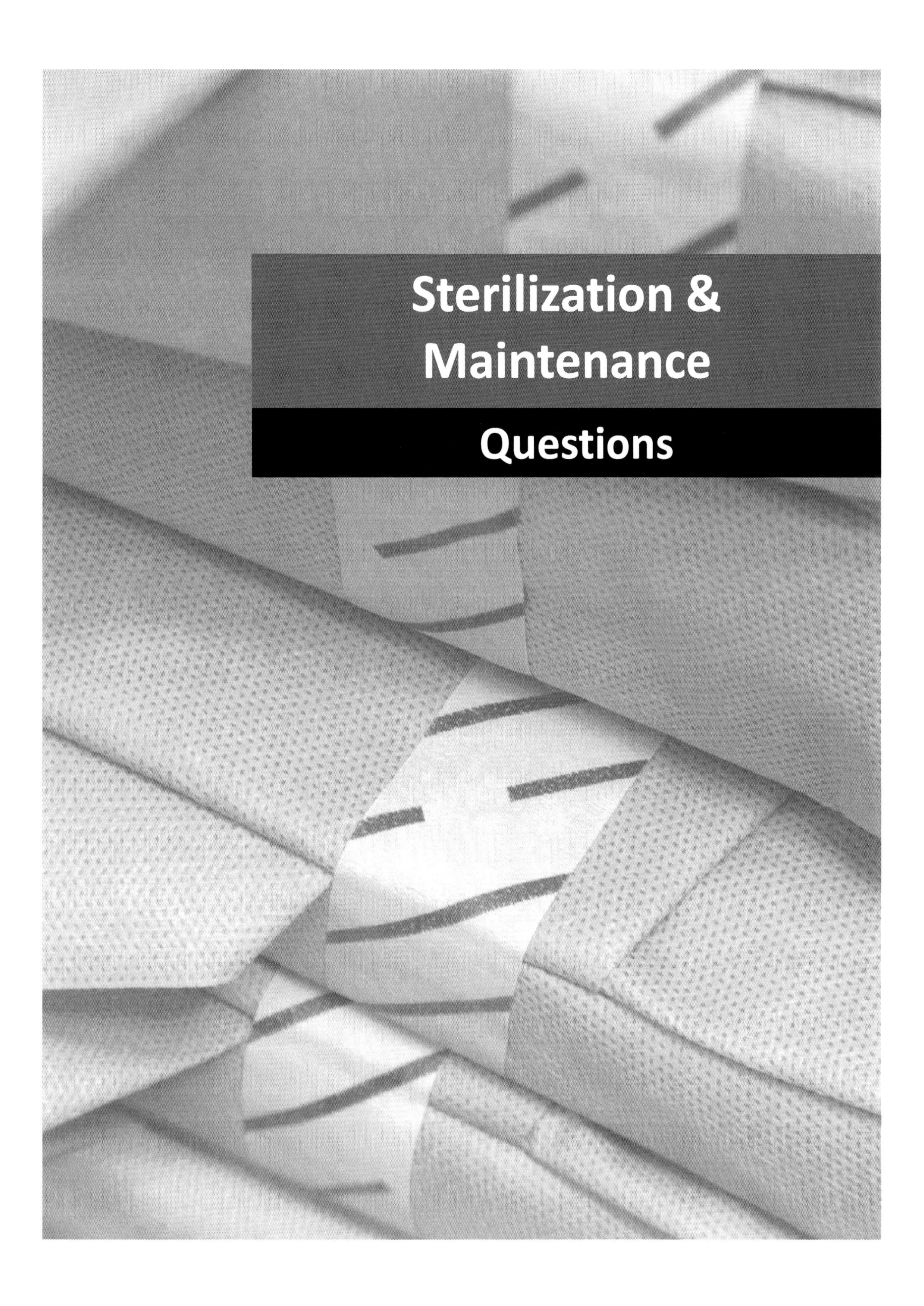
Sterilization &
Maintenance
Questions

1. Which of the following is a common time and temperature for the gravity displacement sterilizer?
A. 4 min.; 270°-276° F
B. 4 min.; 250°-254° F
C. 15 min.; 250°-254° F
D. 15 min.; 270°-276° F

2. What is the common time and temperature for pre-vacuum sterilizer?
A. 15 min.; 270°-276° F
B. 4 min.; 270°-276° F
C. 4 min.; 250°-254° F
D. 15 min.; 250°-254°F

3. Where does the air exit in a gravity displacement sterilizer?
A. Air exits from a vent in the top of the gravity displacement sterilizer
B. Air exits from a vent in the back of the gravity displacement sterilizer
C. Air exits a drain in the top of the gravity displacement sterilizer
D. Air exits from a drain in the bottom of the gravity displacement sterilizer

4. Which of the following is not sterilized in a high-speed gravity displacement sterilizer?
A. Ringed instruments
B. Power cords
C. Implants
D. Basic set

5. Which of the following uses cavitation for cleaning the instruments?
A. Ultrasonic cleaner
B. Washer-decontaminator
C. Washer-sterilizer
D. Steris

6. Who is responsible for presoaking used/dirty instruments once the procedure is completed?
A. Circulator
B. Surgeon
C. STSR
D. Central sterile employee

7. What motion should be used with the soft bristle brush when cleaning instruments?
A. Back-and-forth motion going against the grain of the instrument
B. Circular motion
C. Side to side motion going against the grain of the instrument
D. Back-and-forth motion following the grain of the instrument

8. When should the initial decontamination process begin?
A. When the patient is brought to PACU
B. In the central sterile department
C. At the completion of the surgical procedure
D. Any time the surgical technologist in the surgical role decides

9. How is the locking mechanism checked on a ratcheted instrument?
A. Tap the instrument lightly in the palm of the hand
B. Tap the instrument against the table
C. Tap the instrument against the thigh
D. Tap the instrument against anything

10. What is the lubrication process of instruments called?
A. Oiling
B. Greasing
C. Milking
D. Loosen

11. How are surgical scissors tested for sharpness?
A. Cut a lap sponge with little effort
B. Cut two 4X4 sponges with little effort
C. Cut a piece of paper with little effort
D. Cut a surgical towel with little effort

12. What is the maximum weight for a surgical instrument set?
A. 15 pounds
B. 25 pounds
C. 30 pounds
D. 40 pounds

13. Which of the following is the correct method for wrapping items for sterilization?
A. Item is placed diagonally in the center of the wrapper, the corner nearest the worker is placed over the item, the sides are placed over the item, the far corner is placed over the item, indicator tape secures the flaps
B. Item is placed diagonally in the center of the wrapper, the sides are placed over the item, the far corner placed over the item, the corner nearest the worker is placed over the item, indicator tape secures the flaps
C. Item is placed diagonally in the center of the wrapper the corner nearest the worker is placed over the item, the far corners placed over the item, the sides are placed over the item, indicator tape secures the flaps
D. Item is diagonally in the center of the wrapper, the corner nearest the worker is placed over the item, indicator tape secures the flap, the sides are placed over the item, the far corners placed over the item

14. Which of the following is NOT a performance characteristic of the material used to wrap instruments for the sterilization process?
A. The materials cover the contents completely
B. The material must allow air to be completely removed from the package
C. The material must be resistant to tears and punctures
D. Material should not allow gas and moisture to escape

15. Which of the following is **NOT** a factor in the steam sterilization process.
A. Length of time sterilant stays in contact with items
B. Temperature
C. Moisture
D. Type of antiseptic soap

16. Before a container is opened to the back table, which of the following do not need to be checked?
A. Integrity of the package
B. Weight of the package
C. Indicator tape is changed
D. Wrapping is free of holes

17. What do chemical indicators in the instrument sets ensure?
A. The item is sterile
B. The instruments have not been opened
C. The instrument has been exposed to the sterilization process
D. Item has been exposed to the decontamination process

18. How often should biologic testing be done on the steam sterilizers?
A. Daily
B. Monthly
C. Bimonthly
D. Every two months

19. Which of the following is used to test for the residual air in the pre-vacuum sterilizer?
A. Geobacillus stearothermophilus test
B. Chemical indicator test
C. Bauer-Dick test
D. Bowie-Dick test

20. Which of the following is **NOT** included in the load control number on items being sterilized?
A. Number of items sterilized in the load
B. Date of sterilization
C. Sterilizer used
D. Cycle\load number

21. What is included in the written record that is kept for each sterilization cycle?
A. Sterilizer number, cycle\load number, time and temperature of cycle, date of sterilization, load contents, and initials of the operator
B. Cycle\load number, time and temperature cycle, date of sterilization
C. Sterilizer number, date of sterilization, initials of the operator
D. Sterilizer number, cycle\load number, date of sterilization, load contents, initials of the operator

22. Which of the following refers to a substance that kills or inhibits the growth of microorganisms?
A. Sterilant
B. Soap
C. Antimicrobial
D. Disinfectant

23. What room will instruments and equipment be cleaned and decontaminated?
A. Decontamination
B. Decontamination room
C. Operating room
D. Sterilization room

24. Which of the following is a disinfectant and a sterilizing chemical?
A. Phenol
B. Sodium hypochlorite
C. Glutaraldehyde
D. Quaternary ammonium

25. What is the term used when an instrument is free from all microorganisms but is not sterile?
A. Sterilized
B. Surgically clean
C. Ultrasonic cleaner
D. Chelation

26. Which machine is used when manual or mechanical cleaning is not adequate to remove minute organic particles from instruments?
A. Autoclave
B. Dishwasher
C. Ultrasonic washer
D. None of the above

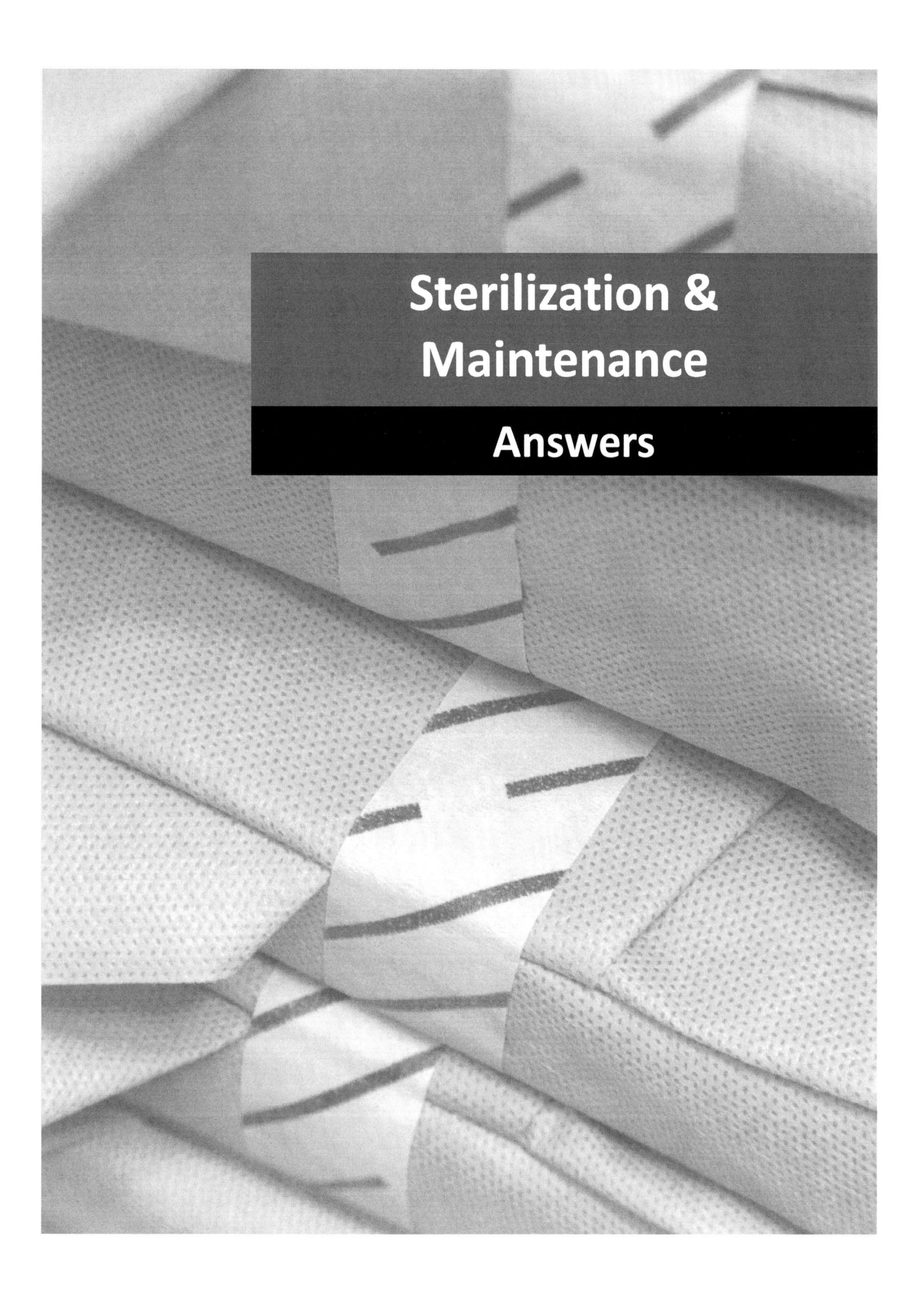
Sterilization &
Maintenance
Answers

1. Which of the following is a common time and temperature for the gravity displacement sterilizer?
C. 15 min.; 250°-254° F - The common parameters for gravity displacement sterilizer are 15 min. at 250°-254° F.

2. What is the common time and temperature for pre-vacuum sterilizer?
B. 4 min.; 270°-276° F - Four minutes at 270°-276° Fahrenheit are the common parameters for the pre-vacuum sterilizer.

3. Where does the air exit in a gravity displacement sterilizer?
D. Air exits from a drain in the bottom of the gravity displacement sterilizer - Air is heavier than steam and will exit the gravity displacement sterilizer from a drain in the bottom front of the unit.

4. Which of the following is not sterilized in a high-speed gravity displacement sterilizer?
B. Power cords - Nonporous and metal items are used in a high speed gravity displacement sterilizer. Power cords will be damaged by the high level temperature.

5. Which of the following uses cavitation for cleaning the instruments?
A. Ultrasonic cleaner - The ultrasonic cleaner uses the cavitation process to clean small particles and soil from the instruments.

6. Who is responsible for presoaking used/dirty instruments once the procedure is completed?
C. STSR - The STSR is responsible for the presoaking of the instruments so organic material does not dry onto the instruments.

7. What motion should be used with the soft bristle brush when cleaning instruments?
D. Back-and-forth motion following the grain of the instrument - Using a back and forth motion following the grain of the instrument prevents the surface of the instrument from being scratched.

8. When should the initial decontamination process begin?
C. At the completion of the surgical procedure - The decontamination process begins immediately following the completion of the surgery.

9. How is the locking mechanism checked on a ratcheted instrument?
A. Tap the instrument lightly in the palm of the hand - Lightly tap the locked instrument in the palm of the hand and if it stays locked it is working properly.

10. What is the lubrication process of instruments called?
C. Milking - 'Milking' is the term used to lubricate the hinges of instruments before they are reassembled and prepared for sterilization.

11. How are surgical scissors tested for sharpness?
B. Cut two 4X4 sponges with little effort - Cutting a 4X4 sponge with little effort is the method used to test the sharpness of surgical scissors.

12. What is the maximum weight for a surgical instrument set?
B. 25 pounds - AAMI recommends instrument sets weigh no more than 25 pounds.

13. Which of the following is the correct method for wrapping items for sterilization?
A. Item is placed diagonally in the center of the wrapper, the corner nearest the worker is placed over the item, the sides are placed over the item, the far corner is placed over the item, indicator tape secures the flaps - The correct method for wrapping items for sterilization: place the item diagonally in the center of the wrapper, the corner nearest the worker is placed over the item, the sides are placed over the item, the far corners placed over the item, and finally the indicator tape or secure the flaps.

14. Which of the following is NOT a performance characteristic of the material used to wrap instruments for the sterilization process?
D. Material should not allow gas and moisture to escape - The material used to wrap instruments for sterilization should be resistant to tears and punctures, allow the air to be completely removed from the package, and cover the contents completely.

15. Which of the following is **NOT** a factor in the steam sterilization process.
D. Type of antiseptic soap - Time, contact, temperature, moisture, and pressure are the five factors of steam sterilization.

16. Before a container is opened to the back table, which of the following do not need to be checked?
B. Weight of the package - Before opening the package\supplies to the back table the package should be completely wrapped, indicator tape turned, and the integrity of the wrapper should be sound.

17. What do chemical indicators in the instrument sets ensure?
C. The instrument has been exposed to the sterilization process - Chemical indicators ensure the item has been exposed to steam in the correct temperature and time. Chemical indicators do not verify sterilization.

18. How often should biologic testing be done on the steam sterilizers?
A. Daily - Biologic testing should be done each day on the first run.

19. Which of the following is used to test for the residual air in the pre-vacuum sterilizer?
D. Bowie-Dick test - The Bowie-Dick test is used to test for residual air in the pre-vacuum sterilizer.

20. Which of the following is **NOT** included in the load control number on items being sterilized?
A. Number of items sterilized in the load - Date of sterilization, sterilizer used and cycle\load number are all included in the load control number on items being sterilized.

21. What is included in the written record that is kept for each sterilization cycle?
A. Sterilizer number, cycle\load number, time and temperature of cycle, date of sterilization, load contents, and initials of the operator - The written record for each sterilization cycle include the sterilizer number, cycle\load number, time and temperature of cycle, date of sterilization, load contents, and initials of the operator.

22. Which of the following refers to a substance that kills or inhibits the growth of microorganisms?
C. Antimicrobial - An antimicrobial substance is a substance that kills or inhibits the growth of microorganisms. A sterilant is used to kill all microorganisms. A disinfectant kills vectors and microorganisms with chemicals.

23. What room will instruments and equipment be cleaned and decontaminated?
B. Decontamination room - The decontamination room is where equipment and instruments are taken to be cleaned and decontaminated prior to being sterilized. The STSR will clean the instruments and equipment in the operating room but not decontaminate them. The sterilization room is where the instruments are assembled and sterilized.

24. Which of the following is a disinfectant and a sterilizing chemical?
C. Glutaraldehyde - Glutaraldehyde is a sterilizing chemical as well as a disinfectant. Sodium Hypochlorite is household bleach. It can be used to disinfect but not to sterilize. Phenol is a chemical used to clean and disinfect. QUAT, quaternary ammonium, is not a sporicide. It is used to clean not sterilize.

25. What is the term used when an instrument is free from all microorganisms but is not sterile?
B. Surgically clean - Surgically clean is the term used when the instruments are free of microorganisms but are not sterile. An ultrasonic cleaner is a machine that is used to remove organic particles and soil from instruments. Chelation is a process that is used so minerals don't bind to the instruments. Sterilized is a process of cleaning where all microorganisms are destroyed.

26. Which machine is used when manual or mechanical cleaning is not adequate to remove minute organic particles from instruments?
C. Ultrasonic washer - The ultrasonic washer is used to remove minute organic particles from instruments.

Administrative & Personnel

Questions

1. What does the CST refer to when checking to see if all supplies, instruments, and equipment have been 'pulled' for the surgery?
A. Computer
B. Circulator
C. Patient
D. Surgeon's preference card

2. What is the surgeon's preference card used for perioperatively?
A. To be sure all instruments, supplies, and equipment have been 'pulled' for the surgery
B. Patient's name and condition
C. To be sure the surgeon has the preferred team in the OR
D. Patient positioning

3. Which of the following are forms of communication between the direct patient care givers and the indirect patient care givers?
A. Verbal communication
B. Medical records
C. Computer records
D. All of the above

4. What are some benefits to having the surgeon's preference card saved on a hospital computer network?
A. It makes it easier to update the card.
B. It makes it easier to retrieve the card perioperatively.
C. It makes it easier for the patient to have access to it.
D. Both A and B

5. In the event of a radiologic or chemical disaster, what is the intial treatment of the patient arriving at the hospital who was exposed to the radiation or chemical?
A. Donning PPE
B. Surgery
C. Remove all clothing
D. none of the above

6. Which of the following are the most likely to be used as biological weapons according to the CDC?
A. Small pox and anthrax
B. Small pox and measles
C. Shingles and anthrax
D. Botulism and measles

7. The acronym 'race' is used by health care facilities to help employees remember what to do in the event of a fire in the operating room. What does 'RACE' stand for?
A. Run, alert by sounding alarm, contain the fire, extinguish and evacuate
B. Remove/rescue, alert by sounding alarm, contain the fire, extinguish and evacuate
C. Remove/.rescue, alert by sounding alarm, cajole the fire, extinguish and evacuate
D. Remove/rescue, alert by sounding alarm, contain the fire, exsanguinate and evacuate

8. Emergency preparedness plans should include all of the following except.
A. Perioperative staff should be able to triage victims
B. There should be a designated area for decontamination
C. Perioperative staff should wear street clothes to the contamination site
D. Equipment that is easy to clean or equipment used on the victims should be disposable

9. Which organization establishes standards for safety in the work place and is committed to protecting the health of workers?
A. National Institute for Occupational Safety and Health
B. Occupational Safety and Health Administration
C. American National Standards Institute
D. National Fire Protection Agency

10. What should be available intraoperatively for the surgical team to use in case of a fire?
A. Sterile water
B. Tap water
C. Oxygen
D. Hydrogen peroxide

11. Appropriate eye protection and high-filtration masks should be worn during which surgery?
A. Bariatric surgery
B. Laparoscopic surgery
C. Laser surgery
D. All surgeries

12. Which of the following is **NOT** a method to control laser or electrosurgical plume?
A. Use an evacuation unit
B. The suction tip should be held 1 cm away from the tissue impact site
C. Surgical team needs to wear gloves, masks, and eye guards
D. STSR should place a wet lap sponge on top of the laser tip

13. The does Aeger Primo mean?
A. "The patient first"
B. "The doctor first"
C. "The family first"
D. "The CRNA first"

14. This is when a health care provider follows through with services for a patient without the patient's proper consent.
A. Defamation
B. Battery
C. Assault
D. Invasion of privacy

15. This is when a health care provider does not perform duties for a patient that a reasonable and prudent person would do in the same circumstances.
A. Malpractice
B. Assault
C. Negligence
D. Defamation

16. The CST is transporting the patient to the OR and realizes he left the patient's chart in the room. The leaves the patient in the hall and quickly returns to the room for the patient's chart. What can the CST can be held liable for?
A. Assault
B. Malpractice
C. Defamation
D. Abandonment

17. When a person grants permission for another to administer care to them it is considered ___.
A. Consent
B. Implied consent
C. Living will
D. Both a and b

18. This is the act that protects patient privacy.
A. NBSTSA
B. HIPAA
C. OSHA
D. HIPA

19. Which of the following surgical team member is responsible for obtaining the surgical consent?
A. Surgical Technologist
B. Patient
C. Surgeon
D. Circulating Nurse

20. Which of the following is not a goal of communication?
A. Provide information
B. File complaint
C. Solve problems
D. Obtain information

21. Which of the following is **NOT** a form of non-verbal communication?
A. Whispering
B. Nodding head
C. Pointing to specimen cup
D. Shrugging shoulders

22. When the CST is unsure of what the surgeon wants, the CST should inquire in the form of a __.
A. Demand- "You should use the Bovi instead of the scalpel."
B. Question- "Are you ready for the Bovi or the scalpel?"
C. Order- "Take the Bovi."
D. None of the above

23. Which of the following lists is **NOT** positive body language communication?
A. Eye contact, leaning toward speaker, smiling
B. Smiling, arms not folded across chest, nodding agreement
C. Leaning toward speaker, eye contact, smiling
D. Frowning, lips pressed tightly together, arms folded tightly across chest

24. Which of the following can influence a patient's health care decisions?
A. Maslow's hierarchy
B. Cultural values and religious values
C. Religious beliefs
D. Maslow's hierarchy and religious beliefs

25. Which of the following organizations has the responsibility to establish fire prevention standards and educating the public on fire safety?
A. NFPA
B. OSHA
C. NIOSH
D. AST

26. What is the practice of sterile technique that includes honesty and morality?
A. Malpractice
B. Negligence
C. Aeger primo
D. Surgical conscience

Administrative & Personnel

Answers

1. What does the CST refer to when checking to see if all supplies, instruments, and equipment have been 'pulled' for the surgery?
D. Surgeon's preference card - The surgeon's preference card has the suture, instruments, and supplies listed on it as well as the surgeon's draping preference. This card is updated frequently.

2. What is the surgeon's preference card used for perioperatively?
A. To be sure all instruments, supplies, and equipment have been 'pulled' for the surgery - The surgeon's preference card has the surgeon's suture, instruments, and supplies listed on it as well as his/her draping preference. This card is updated frequently.

3. Which of the following are forms of communication between the direct patient care givers and the indirect patient care givers?
D. All of the above - Verbal communication, medical records (charts), computer records, requisitions for services, and hospital education sessions are all forms of communication between the different hospital departments.

4. What are some benefits to having the surgeon's preference card saved on a hospital computer network?
D. Both A and B - The doctor's preference card can be easily updated and retrieved when it is on the hospital computer network.

5. In the event of a radiologic or chemical disaster, what is the intial treatment of the patient arriving at the hospital who was exposed to the radiation or chemical?
C. Remove all clothing - The initial treatment for a radiological or chemical injured patient is to remove the patient's clothing.

6. Which of the following are the most likely to be used as biological weapons according to the CDC?
A. Small pox and anthrax - Small pox and anthrax are the two biological agents the CDC had identified as the most likely to be used as bio-weapons.

7. The acronym 'race' is used by health care facilities to help employees remember what to do in the event of a fire in the operating room. What does 'RACE' stand for?
B. Remove/rescue, alert by sounding alarm, contain the fire, extinguish and evacuate - RACE stands for: remove/rescue anyone to a safe area; alert the alarm; contain the fire; extinguish and evacuate

8. Emergency preparedness plans should include all of the following except.
C. Perioperative staff should wear street clothes to the contamination site - An emergency and disaster preparedness plan should include a response to terrorist activity, a response to biological and chemical agent contamination, a perioperative staff that is capable of triaging victims, a designated area for decontamination, and easy to clean or disposable equipment that can be used on victims.

9. Which organization establishes standards for safety in the work place and is committed to protecting the health of workers?
B. Occupational Safety and Health Administration - Occupational Safety and Health Administration sets the standards and these standards are legally enforceable. National Institute for Occupational Safety and Health is an arm of the CDC it sets the limits for chemical vapor and gas exposure. The American National Standards Institute tests equipment and sets the standards for the equipment. The National Fire Protection Agency does research and sets standards for preventing fires as well as puts together fire education for the public.

10. What should be available intraoperatively for the surgical team to use in case of a fire?
A. Sterile water - Sterile water should be used in a sterile environment to put out fires.

11. Appropriate eye protection and high-filtration masks should be worn during which surgery?
C. Laser surgery - Lasers can cause eye damage: the cornea can be burned with CO_2 laser and retina damage and blindness can be caused by Nd:YAG laser.

12. Which of the following is **NOT** a method to control laser or electrosurgical plume?
D. STSR should place a wet lap sponge on top of the laser tip - Controlling electrosurgical and laser plume include: using an evacuation unit, change filter as scheduled, filters should evacuate 0.3µm – 0.1µm size particles, evacuation/suction wand should be 1 cm away from the tissue impact site, wear PPE: gloves, mask, proper eye guard

13. The does Aeger Primo mean?
A. "The patient first" - The AST motto is "the patient rirst" which is translated to Aeger Primo.

14. This is when a health care provider follows through with services for a patient without the patient's proper consent.
B. Battery - Under intentional torts battery is defined as 'the actual act of harmful or unwarranted contact with a person, including contact without proper consent'.

15. This is when a health care provider does not perform duties for a patient that a reasonable and prudent person would do in the same circumstances.
C. Negligence - Negligence is 'defined as an omission (not doing) or commission (doing) of an act that a reasonable and prudent individual would not do under the same conditions'.

16. The CST is transporting the patient to the OR and realizes he left the patient's chart in the room. The leaves the patient in the hall and quickly returns to the room for the patient's chart. What can the CST can be held liable for?
D. Abandonment - Leaving the patient without a caregiver places the patient in harm's way because many patients are under the effects of medication and depend on the caregiver to provide safety to them.

17. When a person grants permission for another to administer care to them it is considered ___.
A. Consent - The definition of 'consent' is a term that refers to permission being given for an action'.

18. This is the act that protects patient privacy.
B. HIPAA - HIPPA is the Health Insurance Portability and Accountability Act that went into effect in April 2003 to protect patient's privacy, insure health insurance coverage, and reduce fraud in the health care community.

19. Which of the following surgical team member is responsible for obtaining the surgical consent?
C. Surgeon - The surgeon is ultimately responsible for obtaining the surgical consent from the patient prior to the surgical procedure.

20. Which of the following is not a goal of communication?
B. File complaint - The goals of communication provide information, solve problems, and obtain information.

21. Which of the following is **NOT** a form of non-verbal communication?
A. Whispering - Nodding the head, pointing, and shrugging shoulders do not require the CST to speak to communicate-this is non-verbal communication. Whispering requires the CST to use her/his voice-this is verbal communication.

22. When the CST is unsure of what the surgeon wants, the CST should inquire in the form of a __.
B. Question- "Are you ready for the Bovi or the scalpel?" - Posing the inquiry in the form of a question allows the CST to find out what the surgeon needs without sounding as though the CST was not paying attention.

23. Which of the following lists is **NOT** positive body language communication?
D. Frowning, lips pressed tightly together, arms folded tightly across chest - Frowning, lips pressed tightly together, and arms folded tightly across the chest are examples of negative body language. Eye contact, smiling, nodding agreement, and leaning toward speaker are examples of positive body language communication methods.

24. Which of the following can influence a patient's health care decisions?
B. Cultural values and religious values - Cultural values and religious values affect the health care decisions patient's make.

25. Which of the following organizations has the responsibility to establish fire prevention standards and educating the public on fire safety?
A. NFPA - National Fire Protection Agency, NFPA, is the organization that establishes fire prevention standards and educates the public on fire safety. OSHA is the Occupational Safety and Health Administration that sets the standards for safety in the workplace. National Institute for Occupational Safety and Health, NIOSH, is the organization that establishes the standards for chemical vapor and gas exposure limits. AST, Association of Surgical Technologists, is the professional membership organization for surgical technologists and Surgical Assistants.

26. What is the practice of sterile technique that includes honesty and morality?
D. Surgical conscience - Surgical conscience is the moral and honest way surgical team members practice sterile technique and conduct themselves in the operating room. Malpractice is when a professional does not follow through with proper behavior and harm takes place to another person. Negligence is when a professional fails to do what a reasonable person would; disregard for the safety of a patient. Aeger primo is the AST's motto: "the patient first".

REFERENCES

Rothrock, Jane C. *Care of the Patient in Surgery, Thirteenth Edition*. St. Louis, Missouri: Mosby Elsevier, 2007.
(Copyright 2007,2003,1999,1987,1983,1978, 1972)

Phillips, Nancymarie and Patricia Kennedy Sedlak *Surgical Instrumentation*. Clifton Park, New York: Delmar Cengage Learning, 2010

Miller-Keane *Encyclopedia and Dictionary of Medicine, Nursing, and Allied Health, Seventh Edition*. Philadelphia, Pennsylvania: Saunders, 2003
(Elsevier)

Chabner, Davi-Ellen *Medical Terminology A short Course, 5th Edition*. St. Louis, Missouri: Saunders Elsevier, 2009
(Copyright 2009,2005,2003,1999,1991)

Herlihy, Barbara *The Human Body in Health and Illness, Third Edition*. St. Louis, Missouri: Saunders Elsevier, 2007
(Copyright 2007,2003,2000)

Colbert, Bruce J., Jeff Ankney, and Karen T. Lee A*natomy and Physiology for Health Professions An Interactive Journey*, Second Edition. Upper Saddle River, New Jersey: Pearson, 2011
(Copyright 2011,2007)

Association of Surgical Technologist, Inc. *Surgical Technology for the Surgical Technologist A Positive Care Approach, Third Edition*. Clifton Park, New York: Delmar Cengage Learning, 2008
(Copyright 2008,2004,2001)

Nemitz, Renee *Surgical Instrumentation An Interactive Approach*. St. Louis, Missouri: Saunders Elsevier, 2010

Association of Surgical Technologists *Surgical Technologist Certifying Exam Study Guide, Second Edition*. Littleton, Colorado: Association of Surgical Technologist, 2007
(Copyright 2004, 2007)

Bergquist, Lois M and Barbara Pogosian *Microbiology Principles and Health Science Applications*. Philadelphia, Pennsylvania: Saunders 2000

Made in the USA
San Bernardino, CA
03 April 2014